STATUS OF THE RED KNOT (*CALIDRIS CANUTUS RUFA*) IN THE WESTERN HEMISPHERE

Lawrence J. Niles, Humphrey P. Sitters, Amanda D. Dey,
Philip W. Atkinson, Allan J. Baker, Karen A. Bennett,
Roberto Carmona, Kathleen E. Clark, Nigel A. Clark, Carmen Espoz,
Patricia M. González, Brian A. Harrington, Daniel E. Hernández,
Kevin S. Kalasz, Richard G. Lathrop, Ricardo N. Matus,
Clive D. T. Minton, R. I. Guy Morrison, Mark K. Peck,
William Pitts, Robert A. Robinson, and Inês L. Serrano

Studies in Avian Biology No. 36

A PUBLICATION OF THE COOPER ORNITHOLOGICAL SOCIETY

Front cover photograph of Red Knots by Irene Hernandez
Rear cover photograph of Red Knot by Lawrence J. Niles

STUDIES IN AVIAN BIOLOGY

Edited by

Carl D. Marti
1310 East Jefferson Street
Boise, ID 83712

Spanish translation by
Carmen Espoz

Studies in Avian Biology is a series of works too long for *The Condor*, published at irregular intervals by the Cooper Ornithological Society. Manuscripts for consideration should be submitted to the editor. Style and format should follow those of previous issues.

Price $20.00. To order, add $2.75 for postage in the US, $9.75 for Canada, and $11.75 for everywhere else. Make checks payable to the Cooper Ornithological Society (in U.S. funds), or pay by MasterCard or Visa. Send orders to Cooper Ornithological Society, c/o John Rotenberry, Department of Biology, University of California, Riverside, CA 92521 USA. Credit card orders may be sent via email to: john.rotenberry@ucr.edu.

ISBN: 978-0-943610-83-2

Library of Congress Control Number: 2008929213

Printed at Cadmus Professional Communications, Ephrata, Pennsylvania 17522

Issued: 15 June 2008

CONTENTS

TABLES

FIGURES

xiii

APPENDICES

LIST OF AUTHORS

PHILIP W. ATKINSON
British Trust for Ornithology
The Nunnery
Thetford, Norfolk IP24 2PU, UK

ALLAN J. BAKER
Royal Ontario Museum
Center for Biodiversity and Conservation Biology
100 Queen's Park
Toronto, Ontario M5S 1C6 Canada

KAREN A. BENNETT
Delaware Department of Natural Resources and
    Environmental Control
Division of Fish and Wildlife
89 Kings Highway
Dover, DE 19901

ROBERTO CARMONA
Departamento de Biologia Marina
University Autónoma de Baja California Sur
Apartado postal 19-B, cp 23000
La Paz, Baja California Sur, Mexico

KATHLEEN E. CLARK
New Jersey Department of Environmental Protection
Division of Fish and Wildlife
Endangered and Nongame Species Program
P.O. Box 400
Trenton, NJ 08625

NIGEL A. CLARK
British Trust for Ornithology
The Nunnery
Thetford, Norfolk IP24 2PU, UK

AMANDA D. DEY
New Jersey Department of Environmental Protection
Division of Fish and Wildlife, Endangered and
    Nongame Species Program
P.O. Box 400
Trenton, NJ 08625

CARMEN ESPOZ
Departamento de Ciencias Basicas
Universidad Santo Tomas
Ejercito 146
Santiago, Chile

PATRICIA M. GONZÁLEZ
Fundacion Inalafquen
Pedro Moron 385
(8520) San Antonio Oeste
Río Negro, Argentina

BRIAN A. HARRINGTON
Manomet Center for Conservation Sciences
81 Stage Road
P.O. Box 1770
Manomet, MA 02345

DANIEL E. HERNÁNDEZ
The Richard Stockton College of New Jersey
Natural Sciences and Mathematics
P.O. Box 195
Pomona, NJ 08240

KEVIN S. KALASZ
Delaware Department of Natural Resources and
    Environmental Control
Division of Fish and Wildlife
4876 Hay Point Landing Road
Smyrna, DE 19977

RICHARD G. LATHROP
Rutgers University
Department of Ecology, Evolution, & Natural
    Resources
School of Environmental and Biological Sciences
14 College Farm Road, Cook Campus
New Brunswick, NJ 08901-8551

RICARDO N. MATUS
Natura Patagonia
Jose Robert 0289
Punta Arenas, Chile

CLIVE D. T. MINTON
Victoria Wader Studies Group
165 Dalgetty Road
Beaumaris, Melbourne, VIC 3193, Australia

R. I. GUY MORRISON
Canadian Wildlife Service
National Wildlife Research Center
Carleton University
Ottawa, Ontario K1A 0H3 Canada

LAWRENCE J. NILES
Conserve Wildlife Foundation
516 Farnsworth Avenue.
Bordentown, NJ 08505

MARK K. PECK
Royal Ontario Museum
Center for Biodiversity and Conservation Biology
100 Queen's Park
Toronto, Ontario M5S 1C6 Canada

WILLIAM PITTS
Endangered and Nongame Species Program
New Jersey Division of Fish and Wildlife
Assunpink Wildlife Management Area
1 Eldridge Road (Upper Freehold Twp.)
Robbinsville, NJ 08691-3476

ROBERT A. ROBINSON
British Trust for Ornithology
The Nunnery
Thetford, Norfolk IP24 2PU, UK

INÊS L.SERRANO
Instituto Brasileiro do Meio Ambiente e dos Recursos
  Naturais Renováveis
C. Postal 102,
João Pessoa-PB, CEP 58.440-970 Brazil

HUMPHREY P. SITTERS
Editor
International Wader Study Group Bulletin
Limosa, Old Ebford Lane
Ebford, Exeter EX3 0QR, UK

Studies in Avian Biology No. 36:1–185

STATUS OF THE RED KNOT (*CALIDRIS CANUTUS RUFA*) IN THE WESTERN HEMISPHERE

Lawrence J. Niles, Humphrey P. Sitters, Amanda D. Dey, Philip W. Atkinson, Allan J. Baker, Karen A. Bennett, Roberto Carmona, Kathleen E. Clark, Nigel A. Clark, Carmen Espoz, Patricia M. González, Brian A. Harrington, Daniel E. Hernández, Kevin S. Kalasz, Richard G. Lathrop, Ricardo N. Matus, Clive D. T. Minton, R. I. Guy Morrison, Mark K. Peck, William Pitts, Robert A. Robinson, and Inês L. Serrano

Abstract. The population of the *rufa* subspecies of the Red Knot (*Calidris canutus*), which breeds in the central Canadian Arctic and mainly winters in Tierra del Fuego, has declined dramatically over the past 20 yr. Previously estimated at 100,000–150,000, the population now numbers 18,000–33,000 (18,000 if just the Tierra del Fuego birds are *C. c. rufa*, more if the Red Knots of uncertain subspecific status that winter in northern Brazil (7,500) or Florida (7,500) are also *C. c. rufa*). Counts show that the main Tierra del Fuego wintering population dropped from 67,546 in 1985 to 51,255 in 2000, 29,271 in 2002, 31,568 in 2004, but only 17,653 in 2005 and 17,211 in 2006.

Demographic studies covering 1994–2002 showed that the population decline over that period was related to a drop in annual adult survival from 85% during 1994–1998 to 56% during 1999–2001. Population models showed that if adult survival remained low, *C. c. rufa* would go extinct within about 10 yr. After 2002, the population held up in 2003–2004, but plunged again by nearly 50% in 2005 increasing the likelihood of extinction within the next decade. Despite intensive studies, the reasons for the population decline and reduced adult survival are imperfectly known.

During northward migration, most *C. c. rufa* stopover in Delaware Bay where they feed mainly on the eggs of horseshoe crabs (*Limulus polyphemus*) and lay down fat and protein reserves both to fuel the 3,000 km flight to the arctic breeding grounds and ensure their survival after they arrive at a time when food availability is often low. The crucial importance of Delaware Bay is demonstrated by studies that show that Red Knots with lower mass in Delaware Bay have lower survival than heavier birds and that from 1998–2002 the proportion of birds there at the end of May weighing more than the estimated departure mass of 180 g declined by >60%. This might be the result of the progressive failure of the food supply in Delaware Bay and/or a trend for birds to arrive there later and/or in poorer condition. In years when Red Knots experience reduced food availability and arrive late, the result may be an exacerbation of the effects of each of these deleterious factors.

The main identified threat to the *C. c. rufa* population is the reduced availability of horseshoe crabs eggs in Delaware Bay arising from elevated harvest of adult crabs for bait in the conch and eel fishing industries. Since 1990 the crab population has declined substantially. Although significant uncertainty regarding the extent of the decline of the horseshoe crab population remains, there is general agreement that horseshoe crab stocks have declined to a level where increased management of the fishery is necessary and appropriate. The decline in crabs has led to a decrease in the density of eggs available to shorebirds. Because of the crab's delayed maturity, demographic models indicate that even if further exploitation of crabs ceases immediately, it will be some years before the horseshoe crab population recovers to its former level. Although clear evidence, as in 2003 and 2005, shows that the reduced availability of eggs is already having an impact in some years on the Red Knots ability to gain mass in Delaware Bay, it is likely that other threats to *C. c. rufa* exist and that these are the cause of some birds arriving in the bay late and/or in poor condition. It is not known what these are, but they could be related to Bahia Lomas, the main wintering site in Tierra del Fuego (because the largest reduction in recent years has occurred there and because northward migration from Bahia Lomas along the Atlantic coast of Argentina has taken place 1–2 wk later since year 2000).

If it is proved that something leads Red Knots to arrive late in Delaware Bay and/or in poor condition, this does not diminish the importance of the Delaware Bay food resource. If anything, it is increased because it is of critical importance in enabling the birds to recover quickly and reach the breeding grounds on time and in good reproductive condition.

Actions being taken to improve feeding conditions for Red Knots and other shorebirds in Delaware Bay include beach closures to prevent disturbance and exclosures to reduce competition from gulls. However, although these measures help, they are no substitute for a recovered horseshoe crab population. Actions to conserve horseshoe crabs have included reduced harvest quotas, more efficient use of crabs as bait, closure of the harvest in certain seasons and places and the designation of a sanctuary off the mouth of Delaware Bay. The latest information indicates that the crab population may have stabilized, but there is no evidence of recovery.

Another Red Knot subspecies, *C. c. roselaari*, breeds in Alaska and is presumed to include those Red Knots that winter on the Pacific coast of the United States and Mexico. Two other Red Knot wintering populations are of uncertain subspecific status—one in the southeastern U.S. (mainly Florida) of about 7,500 and one on the north coast of Brazil also of about 7,500. These populations have not been the subject of regular systematic surveys, but it is not thought that either has suffered the same catastrophic decline as the *C. c. rufa* that winter in Tierra del Fuego. Substantial proportions of both pass through Delaware Bay during northward migration, but banding shows that these are distinct populations without interchange with the Tierra del Fuego birds. Moreover, genetic studies show that no exchange of genes has occurred between the southeastern U.S. and the Tierra del Fuego birds for at least 1,200 yr.

Some progress has been made toward understanding why the Tierra del Fuego population has suffered a major decline, but the northern wintering birds have apparently remained more stable. It appears that physiological constraints mean that the southern birds, which mostly make a long, non-stop flight to Delaware Bay from at least northern Brazil, are more reliant on soft, easily-digested horseshoe crab eggs in Delaware Bay than the northern winterers, many of which feed on blue mussel (*Mytilus edulis*) spat or surf clams (*Donax variablis*) on the Atlantic coast of New Jersey. Evidence from Patagonia suggests that, for a reason that remains obscure, northward migration of Tierra del Fuego birds has become 1–2 wk later since the year 2000 and this has probably led to more Red Knots arriving late in Delaware Bay. Late arriving birds have been shown to have the ability to make up lost time by increasing their mass at a higher rate than usual provided they have sufficient food resources. However, late-arriving Red Knots failed to do this in 2003 and 2005 when egg availability was low.

Although *C. c. rufa* Red Knots are spread thinly across a large area of the Canadian Arctic during the breeding season, for the rest of the year they occur mainly in large flocks at a limited number of key coastal wintering and staging sites. This review describes each of these sites and the threats the birds face ranging from oil pollution to disturbance and reclamation for development.

Overall the goal of conservation activities throughout the flyway should be to increase the *C. c. rufa* population to at least the number of 25 yr ago—100,000–150,000 by 2015. Given the uncertain genetic relationships between the three main wintering populations we suggest the following population increases: (1) Tierra del Fuego wintering population to 70,000–80,000 birds, (2) Brazilian wintering population to 20,000–25,000, (3) Florida wintering population to 20,000–25,000, and (4) other sites to 15,000–20,000.

The means whereby such population increases might be achieved include: (1) recovery and maintenance of Delaware Bay horseshoe crab egg densities to levels sufficient to sustain stopover populations of all shorebirds including 100,000 Red Knots, (2) control impact of disturbance at all stopovers and wintering areas, particularly in high-importance, high-disturbance areas like Delaware Bay and the west coast of Florida, (3) by 2008, develop a system for the yearly determination of population demographic status based on counts, capture data, and resightings of banded individuals, (4) by 2008, determine the genetic and breeding status of the three main wintering populations (Tierra del Fuego, Maranhão, and Florida), (5) by 2008, identify all important breeding locations in Canada and recommend protection needs and designations for the most important sites, (6) by 2009, complete site assessments and management plans for all important wintering areas and stopovers in the flyway, (7) by 2009, delineate and propose protection measures for key habitats within the main wintering areas of Maranhão, Tierra del Fuego, and Florida, and develop management plans to guide protection, (8) by 2009, determine key southbound and northbound stopovers that account for at least 80% of stopover areas supporting at least 100 Red Knots, and develop coast-wide surveillance of birds as they migrate, and (9) by 2011, create a hemisphere-wide system of protected areas for each significant wintering, stopover, and breeding area.

Also crucial to *C. c. rufa*'s recovery is adequate funding to support the conservation actions and research needed. Despite the fact that much of the research, survey, monitoring, and conservation work has been carried out by volunteers and has been supported financially by state, federal government and non-government agencies, present funding levels are inadequate to sustain the work required.

Key words: breeding, *Calidris canutus rufa*, conservation, Delaware Bay, non-breeding, population, Red Knot, status, stopover.

ESTATUS DEL PLAYERO CANUTO (*CALIDRIS CANUTUS RUFA*) EN EL HEMISFERIO OESTE

Resumen. La población del playero ártico (*Calidris canutus*) subespecie *rufa*, la cual anida en el ártico central canadiense y mayoritariamente inverna en Tierra del Fuego, ha declinado dramáticamente en los últimos 20 años. Previamente estimada en 100,000–150,000 individuos, la población bordea actualmente los 18,000–33,000 individuos (18,000 si todas las aves de Tierra del Fuego son *C.c. rufa* y más, si los playeros árticos con asignación subespecífica incierta que invernan en el norte de Brasil (7,500) o Florida (7,500) son también *C. c. rufa*). Los conteos indican que la población principal que inverna en Tierra del Fuego ha decaído de 67,546 en 1985 a 51,255 en el 2000, 29,271 en el 2002, 31,568 en el 2004, sólo 17,653 en el 2005 y 17,211 en el 2006.

Estudios demográficos realizados entre 1994 y 2002 han mostrado que el decrecimiento poblacional en este período se relaciona con una caída en la sobrevivencia anual de adultos la cual va desde 85% en el período 1994–1998 hasta 56% en 1999–2001. Modelos poblacionales muestran que si la sobrevivencia de adultos permanece baja, *C. c. rufa* podría extinguirse dentro de los siguientes 10 años. Después de 2002, la población aumentó en 2003–2004, pero decayó nuevamente cercano al 50% en 2005 incrementando así la probabilidad de extinción dentro de la siguiente década. A pesar de los intensos estudios realizados, las razones para el decrecimiento poblacional y la reducida sobrevivencia adulta aún se desconocen.

Durante la migración hacia el norte, la mayoría de la población de *C. c. rufa* se detiene en Bahía Delaware donde se alimenta principalmente de los huevos de cangrejos cacerola (*Limulus polyphemus*), obteniendo así grasas y proteínas necesarias para realizar el vuelo de 3,000 km hacia los sitios de reproducción en el Ártico y también para asegurar su sobrevivencia después que llegan, en un período en que frecuentemente el alimento es escaso. La importancia de Bahía Delaware es señalada en estudios que muestran que en esta Bahía los playeros árticos con menor masa corporal tienen menor probabilidad de sobrevivencia, y que desde 1998–2002 la proporción de aves que están hasta fines de mayo pesando más del peso ideal de 180 g, estimado como peso de partida, ha declinado en más de 67%. Lo anterior puede ser el resultado de una falla progresiva en la disponibilidad de alimento en Bahía Delaware y/o una tendencia de las aves a llegar más tarde o en peores condiciones.

La mayor amenaza identificada para la población de *C. c. rufa* es la reducida disponibilidad de huevos de cangrejos cacerola en Bahía Delaware, producto del incremento en la extracción de adultos los que son utilizados como cebo en la industria pesquera de anguila y caracol. Desde 1990 la población de estos cangrejos ha disminuido sustancialmente. A pesar que aún existe cierta incertidumbre respecto de la extensión del decrecimiento de la población de cangrejos, hay consenso en que los stocks han disminuido a un nivel en que urge el manejo de la pesquería. La disminución de cangrejos ha producido un decrecimiento en la densidad de huevos disponible para las aves costeras. Debido a la madurez retrasada de los cangrejos, modelos demográficos han mostrado que aun cuando la explotación de éstos cese inmediatamente se requerirán algunos años antes que la población se recupere a su nivel original. Si bien la evidencia muestra, tal como en 2003 y 2005, que la reducida disponibilidad de huevos tiene un impacto en la habilidad de los playeros árticos para ganar masa corporal, existen otras amenazas para la población de *C. c. rufa* pudiendo ser éstas las causas que expliquen la llegada tardía a la bahía y/o las malas condiciones en que llegan. No se sabe cuáles son exactamente las causas pero éstas pueden estar relacionadas con Bahía Lomas, principal sitio de invernada en Tierra del Fuego. Esto, debido a que la mayor reducción en los últimos años ha ocurrido allí y también porque desde el año 2000 la migración desde Bahía Lomas hacia el norte ha tomado lugar una o dos semanas más tarde.

Si se prueba que algo hace que los playeros árticos lleguen tarde a Bahía Delaware y/o en malas condiciones, esto no limita la importancia que tiene el recurso alimento en esta bahía. Por el contrario, ésta aumenta debido a la importancia crítica que tiene para las aves tanto para recuperarse rápidamente como para alcanzar los sitios reproductivos a tiempo y en buenas condiciones.

Se deben emprender acciones para mejorar las condiciones de alimentación de los playeros árticos y otras aves costeras en Bahía Delaware incluyendo cierres de playas para prevenir las perturbaciones y exclusiones para reducir la competencia con las gaviotas. Si bien estas medidas ayudan, no hay substitutos para la recuperación de la población de cangrejos cacerola. Acciones para conservar a los cangrejos han incluido reducción de la extracción en ciertas estaciones del año y sitios, y la designación de un santuario fuera de la boca de Bahía Delaware. La información reciente indica que la población de cangrejos puede haberse estabilizado sin que exista evidencia de una recuperación.

Otra subespecie de *Calidris canutus*, *C. c. roselaari*, se reproduce en Alaska y se presume incluye a aquellos playeros árticos que invernan en la costa Pacífico de los Estados Unidos y México. Otras dos poblaciones de playeros árticos con estatus subespecífico incierto invernan una en el sur de EUA (mayoritariamente en Florida) con cerca de 7,500 individuos y la otra en la costa norte de Brasil también con aproximadamente 7,500 individuos. Aun cuando estas poblaciones no han sido objeto de estudios sistemáticos, se piensa que no han sufrido las mismas reducciones catastróficas de la población de *C. c. rufa* que inverna en Tierra del Fuego. Una proporción sustancial de las poblaciones antes mencionadas pasa por Bahía Delaware durante la migración hacia el norte, pero estudios de marcaje muestran que éstas son poblaciones distintas sin que exista intercambio con las aves de Tierra del Fuego. Más aun, estudios genéticos indican que no ha ocurrido intercambio de genes entre las aves del sureste de EUA y las de Tierra del Fuego por al menos 1,200 años.

Algunos progresos se han hecho para entender el por qué la población de Tierra del Fuego ha sufrido una reducción mayor, mientras las aves que invernan más al norte han permanecido más estables. Pareciera que las restricciones fisiológicas de las aves del sur, las que hacen un largo vuelo sin detención desde al menos el norte de Brasil hasta Bahía Delaware, son más dependientes de lo blando y digerible de los huevos de cangrejos cacerola en Bahía Delaware que las restricciones de las aves que invernan en el norte, muchas de las cuales se alimentan del mitílido (*Mytilus edulis*) o semillas de almejas (*Donax variabilis*) en la costa Atlántica de Nueva Jersey.

La evidencia de la Patagonia sugiere que, por una razón que aun no está clara, la migración hacia el norte de las aves de Tierra del Fuego se ha atrasado 1–2 semanas desde el año 2000 y que probablemente esto hace que los playeros lleguen tarde a Bahía Delaware. Las aves que llegan tarde han mostrado tener la habilidad de recuperar el tiempo perdido al incrementar su masa a una tasa mayor que la usual. Esto con los suficientes recursos alimentarios. No obstante lo anterior, los playeros fallaron en hacer esto en 2003 y 2005 cuando la disponibilidad de huevos fue baja.

Si bien *C. c. rufa* está distribuida en un área amplia del ártico canadiense durante la época reproductiva, el resto del año ellas ocurren mayoritariamente en grandes bandadas en un número limitado de sitios costeros claves de invernada y parada. La presente revisión describe cada uno de estos sitios y las amenazas que enfrentan las aves, desde la contaminación hasta los disturbios causados por el desarrollo.

Globalmente, la meta de las actividades de conservación a lo largo de la ruta migratoria debe ser el incremento de la población de *C. c. rufa* hacia los tamaños poblacionales que se registraban hace 25 años atrás (i.e., 100,000–150,000 individuos hacia el 2015). Dadas las relaciones genéticas inciertas entre las tres mayores poblaciones invernantes se sugieren los siguientes incrementos poblacionales: (1) para la población invernante de Tierra del Fuego 70,000-80,000 aves, (2) para la población invernante de Brasil a 20,000-25,000 aves, (3) para la población invernante de Florida a 20,000–25,000 individuos, y (4) otros sitios hacia 15,000-20,000 aves.

Entre las razones por las cuales estas poblaciones pudieran incrementar están: (1) recuperación y mantención de las densidades de huevos de cangrejos cacerolas en Bahía Delaware a niveles tales que soporten todas las poblaciones de aves costeras que paran en el lugar incluidos los playeros árticos, (2) control del impacto de los disturbios en todas las áreas de parada e invernada, particularmente aquellas de importancia alta como Bahía Delaware y la costa oeste de Florida, (3) hacia el 2008, desarrollo de un sistema para la determinación anual del estatus poblacional demográfico basado en conteos, datos de captura y observación de individuos marcados, (4) hacia el 2008, determinar el estado genético y reproductivo de las tres mayores poblaciones invernantes (Tierra del Fuego, Maranhao y Florida), (5) hacia el 2008, identificar todos los sitios reproductivos importantes en Canadá y recomendar las necesidades de protección y manejo para los sitios más importantes, (6) hacia el 2009, completar las evaluaciones y planes de manejo para todas las áreas importantes de invernada y parada, (7) hacia el 2009, delinear y proponer medidas de protección de hábitats claves dentro de las mayores áreas de Maranhao, Tierra del Fuego y Florida, y desarrollar planes de manejo para guiar la protección, (8) hacia el 2009 determinar las paradas claves de los límites sur y norte las que dan cuenta de al menos el 80% de las áreas de parada que soportan al menos 100 playeros árticos, y desarrollar un monitoreo costero amplio de aves a medida que migran, y (9) hacia el 2011 crear un sistema hemisférico de áreas protegidas para cada sitio de invernada y reproducción significante.

También crucial para la recuperación de *C. c. rufa* es el adecuado financiamiento para apoyar las acciones de conservación e investigación que se necesiten. Aparte del hecho que mucho del trabajo de investigación, muestreo, monitoreo y conservación ha sido llevado a cabo por voluntarios y ha sido apoyado financieramente por el estado, gobierno federal y agencias no gubernamentales, en el presente los niveles de financiamiento son inadecuados para sostener el trabajo requerido.

The Red Knot (*Calidris canutus*) is a worldwide species with a total population of approximately 1,050,000 (Wetlands International 2006; C. D. T. Minton, unpubl. data; this review). Breeding in the Arctic and wintering as far south as New Zealand, Australia, South Africa and Tierra del Fuego, the Red Knot is one of nature's most prodigious travelers exciting the interest of scientists and conservationists around the world. The Red Knot is also one of the most extensively studied of the world's 221 species of shorebird (Table 1). Central to this research effort is a team led by Theunis Piersma on Texel in the Netherlands where the Royal Netherlands Institute for Sea Research has a laboratory, the size of an aircraft hangar, for studying Red Knots under precisely controlled conditions.

Six subspecies of the Red Knot together have a circumpolar arctic breeding distribution though each breed in a distinct area and winters separately. Except as otherwise noted, this status assessment focuses on the New World Red Knot subspecies *Calidris canutus rufa*.

Building on earlier work led by the Manomet Center for Conservation Science, *C. c. rufa* has been the subject of intensive studies throughout the western Atlantic shorebird flyway since 1997. These studies were originally instigated and have since been sustained by concern that the Patagonian population has fallen from 100,000–150,000 in the early 1980s to

TABLE 1. NUMBER OF CITATIONS OF THE MOST EXTENSIVELY STUDIED SHOREBIRDS IN THE WORLD (THOMAS ET AL. 2003).

Species	Number of citations in title only	Number of citations in text
Eurasian Oystercatcher (*Haematopus ostralegus*)	112	292
Dunlin (*Calidris alpina*)	58	137
Northern Lapwing (*Vanellus vanellus*)	51	125
Red Knot (*Calidris canutus*)	36	132
Redshank (*Tringa totanus*)	29	88
Ruff (*Philomachus pugnax*)	22	57
Eurasian Curlew (*Numenius arquata*)	20	43
Black-bellied Plover (*Pluvialis squatarola*)	18	73

around 17,200 in 2006. The work has involved a diverse selection of people and organizations, government and non-government from Argentina, Chile, Brazil, and Canada as well as all East Coast states of the U.S. from Florida to Massachusetts and the U.S. Fish and Wildlife Service (USFWS). From the beginning, shorebird ecologists from outside the Americas have also been involved, especially from the United Kingdom, The Netherlands, and Australia, several of whom have contributed to this review.

Studies of *C. c. rufa* have focused on determining the cause of the population decline and whether anything can be done to reverse the situation. With limited resources, they have sought to cover the whole of *C. c. rufa*'s latitudinal range of over 120° from Tierra del Fuego (54° S) to King William Island (68° N) and the whole of its annual cycle from one arctic breeding season to the next. More specifically, a large proportion of the effort has been directed at measuring demographic rates and identifying where in the annual cycle the problems lie. All this has proved very challenging and we do not yet know all the answers. Nevertheless, considerable progress has been made, due in no small part to the use of modern and sometimes innovative techniques as well as much hard work and the support of many people and organizations.

Worldwide, the main organization concerned with research and conservation science in relation to the world's 221 species of shorebird is the International Wader Study Group, which organized a workshop attended by 132 specialists from 20 countries in 2003 to determine if shorebird populations worldwide are

in decline. The conclusions show that of those shorebirds whose population trend is known, 48% are declining and only 16% increasing (International Wader Study Group 2003). Many of the declining populations were found to be those of long-distance migrants and *C. c. rufa* was cited as a prime example. Problems identified as common to several long-distance migrants were their high dependency on a very limited number of key stopover sites making them particularly vulnerable to habitat loss (as in the Yellow Sea where huge areas of intertidal habitat have been lost to reclamation) and declining food resources at stopover sites arising from the unsustainable exploitation of natural resources. In the latter case, the prime examples worldwide were considered to be unsustainable shell-fish harvesting in the Dutch Wadden Sea and the exploitation of horseshoe crabs (*Limulus polyphemus*) in Delaware Bay.

As a result of *C. c. rufa*'s decline, in November 2005 the parties to the Convention on the Conservation of Migratory Species of Wild Animals, also known as the Bonn Convention (which include Argentina and Chile, but not the U.S., Brazil, or Canada), determined that *C. c. rufa* was endangered and as such added it to appendix 1 of the convention which commits the parties to strive towards protection of the species and the conservation of its habitat. In April 2007, the Canadian government's Committee on the Status of Endangered Wildlife in Canada determined that *C. c. rufa* was endangered following completion of a status review. In Brazil the Red Knot is being proposed for listing as endangered.

A problem arising from the continuous nature of the *C. c. rufa* studies over the past nine years has been a lack of time and resources to write up and publish results. All too often, data have been analyzed and partly written up only to be overtaken by the accumulation of more data. We therefore greatly welcome the opportunity that this status review affords to take stock and set out a full account of our current knowledge. We describe *C. c. rufa* in the context of worldwide Red Knot populations and assess its status, its general natural history, its habitat, its breeding system, its migrations, and its feeding ecology. We address especially the threats it faces and the conservation actions that may lead to its recovery.

TAXONOMY

Red Knots are currently classified into six subspecies, each with distinctive morphological traits, migration routes, and annual cycles. Available evidence from long-term banding

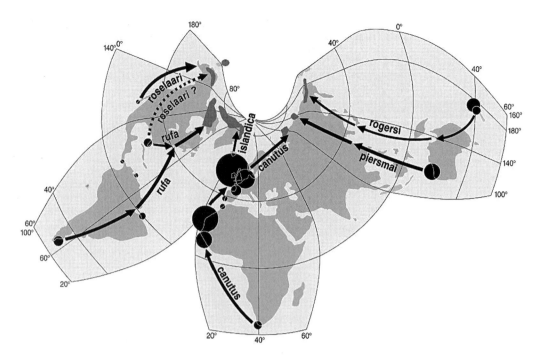

FIGURE 1. Worldwide distribution of the six recognized subspecies of the Red Knot. All breeding areas (dark gray shading) are on high-arctic tundra where the adults spend June–July. After their long-distance migrations (arrows), they spend the non-breeding season (August–May) mainly in intertidal soft-sediment habitats (dots, which are scaled according to population size). This map was prepared in 2003 and revised according to recent studies described in this review. Note that it is uncertain whether the Red Knots that winter in Northern Brazil and/or Florida are *Calidris canutus roselaari*, but some birds presumed to be *C. c. roselaari* winter on the coast of California and Baja California (map drawn by Dick Visser, provided by Jan van Gils, and reproduced with their permission).

programs indicates that distinct flyways exist (Piersma and Davidson 1992) and six separate breeding areas are known to host different populations, all of which are now formally recognized as subspecies based on body size and plumage characteristics (Tomkovich 1992, Piersma and Baker 2000, Tomkovich 2001; Fig. 1; Table 2). *C. c. roselaari* is thought to breed in northwest Alaska and Wrangel Island. Its wintering areas are unknown, but museum skins studies by Tomkovich (1992) indicate that this subspecies may migrate down the Pacific coast of North America and winter in the Gulf of Mexico. Because Red Knots wintering in Florida, Georgia, and South Carolina have a different molt schedule, and they do not migrate to southern South America, they have been referred to *C. c. roselaari*. The breeding grounds of the southeastern U.S. wintering Red Knots have not been confirmed. *C. c. rufa* breeds in the central Canadian Arctic and winters in southern Patagonia and Tierra del Fuego. Another group wintering in northern Brazil and possibly Venezuela is presumed to belong to this subspecies. *C. c. rogersi* breeds on the Chukotski Peninsula in eastern Russia and winters in

TABLE 2. POPULATION ESTIMATES OF THE SIX SUBSPECIES OF THE RED KNOT (*CALIDRIS CANUTUS*).

Subspecies	Estimated population size	Source
C. c. canutus	400,000	Wetlands International (2006)
C. c. islandica	450,000	Wetlands International (2006)
C. c. rogersi	90,000	C. D. T Minton (unpubl. data)
C. c. piersmai	50,000	C. D. T Minton (unpubl. data)
C. c. roselaari	35,000–50,000[a]	Wetlands International (2006)
C. c. rufa	18,000–35,000	This review

[a] As discussed elsewhere in this review, *C. c. roselaari* almost certainly has a much smaller population than that suggested by Wetlands International (2006).

southeast Australia and New Zealand. *C. c. piersmai* breeds on the New Siberian Islands in northcentral Russia and winters in northwest Australia, and *C. c. islandica* breeds in northern Greenland and northeast Canada and winters in northwest Europe. The nominate subspecies *C. c. canutus* breeds on the Taymyr Peninsula in western Siberia and winters in west and southwest Africa. Earlier work failed to distinguish geographically isolated groups indicating apparent panmixia caused by a late Pleistocene bottleneck (Baker et al. 1994, Piersma 1994). This analysis, however, was limited by an extreme lack of genetic variability making it difficult to distinguish between genetic variation inherited from a common ancestral stock following a recent bottleneck and current gene flow between current populations.

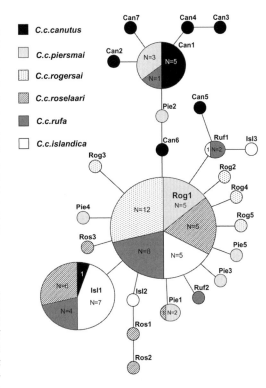

FIGURE 2. Minimum spanning network showing the relationships between haplotypes from the mitochondrial control region of Red Knots. Ovals represent haplotypes and connecting lines represent a single base pair change between haplotypes. Small open circles on lines represent multiple base pair changes between haplotypes.

GENETIC EVIDENCE FOR RED KNOT SUBSPECIES

To detect possible genetic differences among Red Knot subspecies, Buehler and Baker (2005) assayed genetic variation by sequencing 675 base pairs of the fast-evolving control region of the mtDNA molecule in 91 individuals sampled worldwide. Most haplotypes in the Red Knot network differ by a single base change, producing a star-like pattern characteristic of a species that has undergone a recent bottleneck with subsequent expansion (Fig. 2). Despite the apparent lack of sorting of haplotypes into discrete genetic lineages in each subspecies, Red Knots showed low but significant population differentiation using both conventional F-statistics and exact tests. Four genetically distinct groups were found corresponding to *C. c. canutus*, *C. c. piersmai*, *C. c. rogersi*, and a North American group containing *C. c. roselaari*, *C. c. rufa*, and *C. c. islandica* (see Table 3 for FST summary; pooled exact test, P < 0.001).

Genetic differences between subspecies are also apparent in nuclear DNA. A genomic scan of 836 loci using amplified fragment length polymorphisms (AFLP) detected different frequencies of these dominant markers at 129 loci, and showed significant genetic differentiation among subspecies ($F_{st} = 0.089$). The genetic distance between *C. c. roselaari* and *C. c. rufa* is small (0.1) but similar to the genetic distance between *C. c. rogersi* (southeastern Australia and New Zealand) and *C. c. canutus* (Eurasia).

The demographic history of Red Knot populations can be deduced from the genetic signature in the control-region sequences, providing they are selectively neutral (which appears to be the case in Red Knots) and can be done by computing the number of mutational differences

TABLE 3. ESTIMATES OF F_{ST} FOR POPULATION DIFFERENTIATION IN RED KNOTS (BELOW DIAGONAL) CALCULATED USING mtDNA CONTROL REGION SEQUENCES.

	C. c. canutus	C. c. islandica	C. c. piersmai	C. c. rogersi	C. c. roselaari	C. c. rufa
C. c. canutus	0	+	+	+	+	+
C. c. islandica	0.19	0	+	+	-	-
C. c. piersmai	0.07	0.12	0	+	-	-
C. c. rogersi	0.27	0.20	0.07	0	+	-
C. c. roselaari	0.17	−0.04	0.08	0.15	0	-
C. c. rufa	0.23	0.005	0.07	0.05	0.002	0

Note: Above the diagonal + indicates the relationship was significant (P = 0.01) and - indicates not significant (P > 0.01).

between each pair of sequences in individual birds. These pair-wise differences in Red Knot subspecies have a single peak pattern expected when a population expands after a recent bottleneck (i.e., most birds have haplotypes that differ by only one–three mutations; Fig. 3).

Coalescent modeling of the sequence variation using a rate of molecular evolution calibrated for shorebirds estimated that divergence times of populations representing all six subspecies of Red Knots occurred within the last 20,000 yr (95% CI: 5,600–58,000 yr ago), thus corresponding to the Last Glacial Maximum 18,000–22,000 yr ago. This basal split separated *C. c. canutus* in central Siberia that migrated to western Africa from a lineage that expanded into eastern Siberia and began to migrate to Australia (the ancestor of *C. c. rogersi* and *C. c. piersmai*).

As the ice retreated the latter lineage eventually expanded across Beringia into Alaska and established the North American lineage about 12,000 yr ago (95% CI: 3,300–40,000). At this time an ice-free corridor had opened between the ice sheets covering the Rocky Mountains to the west and the Great Plains to the east, which served as a dispersal route for an assortment of organisms including humans, other mammals, and probably birds. This corridor was oriented northwest–southeast, and thus may have guided the evolution of a new migratory pathway between Alaska or the western

Canadian Arctic and the southeastern U.S. As the ice sheets retreated further eastward across the high Arctic of Canada the ancestral population was fragmented sequentially within the last 5,500 yr into three breeding populations, corresponding today to *C. c. roselaari, C. c. rufa* and *C. c. islandica*. If this is correct, then the present wintering flocks in the southeastern U.S. are properly attributed to *C. c. roselaari* and we would predict that they return annually to their ancestral breeding grounds in arctic northwestern North America. Furthermore, the migration pathways of *C. c. rufa* and *C. c. islandica* are newly evolved responses to the eastward expansion of their breeding ranges. The divergence of *C. c. piersmai* and *C. c. rogersi* was estimated to have occurred about 6,500 yr ago (95% CI = 1,000–23,000), probably as a consequence of their isolated breeding ranges in the New Siberian Islands and the Chukotski Peninsula in Russia.

Given the recency of these divergence times, it is not surprising that the level of genetic differentiation in these neutral mtDNA sequences and nuclear AFLP is small. Time has not been sufficient for mutations to accumulate in these DNA regions to track evolutionary changes operating in the more immediate scale of ecological time. In such cases, conservation geneticists have cautioned that these apparent small genetic differences in neutral DNA sequences should not be misinterpreted in defining subspecies (Avise

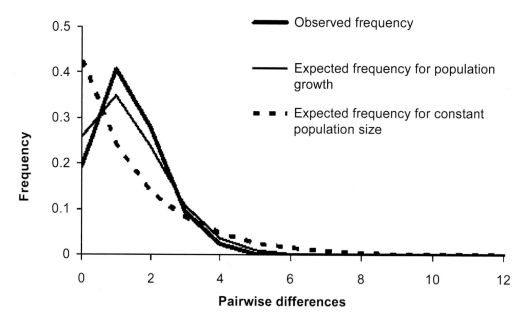

FIGURE 3. Observed and expected mismatch distributions of mitochondrial control region sequences in Red Knots. Red Knots closely match the pattern expected under population growth in the recent past.

1989). Instead, more emphasis should be placed on morphological and ecological differences because they likely track more immediate adaptive changes that are much more rapid responses to positive natural selection.

Despite the lack of fixed genetic differences among subspecies, the population divergence time of the Red Knots that winter in the southeastern U.S. (presumed to be *C. c. roselaari*) and those that winter in Tierra del Fuego (*C. c. rufa*) is estimated to be about 1,200 yr ago (Buehler and Baker 2005). Therefore, these populations have not been exchanging a significant number of individuals per generation for a long time, and clearly are independent units for conservation. This conclusion is supported by other biological information such as different primary molt schedules and, as described below, the lack of exchange of color-marked individuals.

ECOLOGICAL AND MORPHOLOGICAL EVIDENCE FOR SUBSPECIES IN NORTH AMERICA

Because *C. c. islandica* has a completely separate breeding range in northeastern Canada and Greenland, winters in western Europe, and has brighter breeding plumage and considerably shorter average bill length than other Nearctic-breeding Red Knots, it clearly warrants subspecies status (Roselaar 1983). Knots attributed to *C. c. rufa* and *C. c. roselaari* are much paler by comparison and have much longer average bill length. To our knowledge no one has adequately compared morphological variation in *C. c. rufa* and *C. c. roselaari* populations. To address this inadequacy, bill length and body weight were measured in samples of Red Knots from Bahía Lomas in Chile (the Tierra del Fuego population [TDF]), Maranhão in northern Brazil (MA population) and Florida (southeastern U.S. population). The samples were selected because all specimens were sexed molecularly (Baker et al. 1999a.), and thus the sexes could be analyzed separately. Additionally, they were taken in January or February which reduces variation in body weight due to different periods of the annual cycle. As in all Red Knots, sexual dimorphism in both bill length and body weight is apparent, with females having longer bills (Fig. 4a) and higher body mass (Fig. 4b) on average than males in all three populations. Comparisons among localities for each sex separately showed highly significant geographic variation. Analysis of variance followed by HSD post hoc tests for unequal sample sizes revealed that average bill length is significantly longer in Red Knots from both Florida and Maranhão in northern Brazil than from Bahía Lomas in Tierra del Fuego (females,

$P < 0.001$; males, $P < 0.01$) indicating that these populations are discrete (but no significant difference was found between the bill lengths of birds from Florida and Maranhão). Conversely, controlling for differences in mass related to sex, size (using bill length), and whether a bird is in primary molt, Red Knots wintering in Bahía Lomas have significantly lower mass than those wintering in Florida ($P < 0.001$), and knots wintering in Maranhão have significantly lower mass than knots wintering in the other two sites ($P < 0.01$) (Niles et al. 2006; Fig. 4b). However, lower body weight in more tropical wintering populations of Red Knots is also demonstrated in Australia (C. D. T. Minton, unpubl. data).

In addition to the significant differences in these ecologically important biometrical variables, a small but apparently diagnostic difference occurs in winter plumage in Florida Red Knots. All 26 collected specimens from western Florida have more heavily marked flanks and throats, and have more pronounced brown flecks and vermiculations extending further distally on the background white plumage of the breast and belly. Knots from Maranhão closely resemble the ventral plumage of the Tierra del Fuego population.

EVIDENCE FOR DISCRETE WINTERING POPULATIONS

In addition to these morphological and ecological differences, discrete wintering populations are evident. Color-banding studies have been conducted where individuals are banded with color-marked flags based on the wintering grounds where they were captured. Based on re-capture and resighting data, individuals from the two northernmost populations in Florida and Maranhão have not been recaptured or re-sighted in Tierra del Fuego, and vice versa. Moreover, extensive searches of the Maranhão flocks in the austral summers of 2004 and 2005 failed to find any Red Knots marked from Tierra del Fuego, or any birds with southeastern U.S. color combinations, indicating that they are a completely separate population (Baker et al. 2005a). However, 15 of the 46 Red Knots marked in Maranhão with individually inscribed blue flags were resighted in Delaware Bay in May–June 2005, showing that at least some of these birds pass through the bay each spring.

One possibility is that both the Maranhão and southeastern U.S. Red Knots are *C. c. roselaari*, in which case the risk of extinction of this subspecies and *C. c. rufa* will be significant, because both have winter range census populations of only 15,000–20,000 (Baker et al. 2005a, B. A. Harrington, unpubl. data; B. Winn, pers.

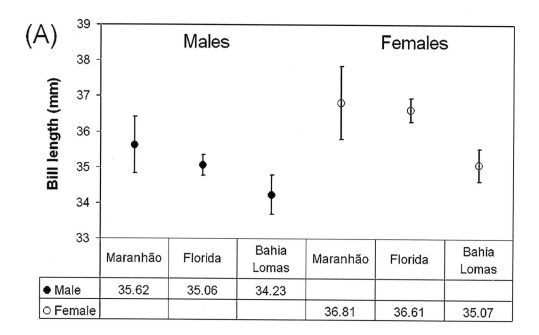

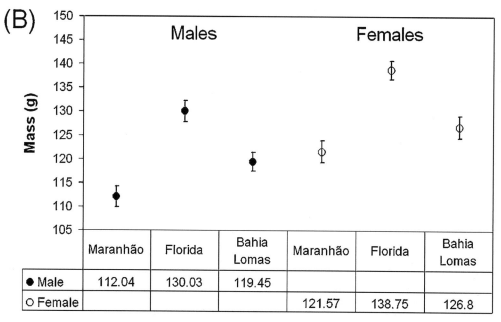

FIGURE 4. Biometrical variation of male and female Red Knots in the wintering populations of Maranhão (Brazil), Florida, and Bahia Lomas (Tierra del Fuego) indicated by (A) bill length and (B) body mass (mean ± 95% confidence intervals (data are from Baker et al. 2005a and Niles et al. 2006).

comm.). Based on genetic data, the effective population size of either subspecies is probably in the order of 1,000–2,000 adult breeders, as the effective number of breeders can be as low as about 10% of the adult population (Whitlock 2000). At this threshold of effective population size, both theoretical modeling and empirical estimates of population genetic parameters predict a much greater risk of extinction both from mutation accumulation in the long term and from the immediate ecological threats to small populations (Whitlock 2000).

Alternatively, the Maranhão population could be an easternmost part of the *C. c. roselaari* population which is also speculated to winter in Mexico. If that is true the southeastern U.S. population would have a census population size of about 7,500 birds, based on counts in winter in western Florida, Georgia, and South Carolina in 2005 implying that the effective size of the southeastern U.S. population is approaching the critical population size for persistence in the longer term and is in danger of extinction from the perspective of stochastic ecological risk factors in the near future. These ecological risk factors caused the severe decline in the Tierra del Fuego population (Baker et al. 2004).

The third possibility is that all three Red Knot populations (Tierra del Fuego, Maranhão and southeastern U.S.) really belong to one subspecies (*C. c. rufa*). This seems implausible biologically, because the aggregate evidence from genetic, ecological, morphological, and banding data clearly document differences among these populations. Furthermore, these differences equate with those used to recognize the other four subspecies of Red Knots worldwide (Tomkovich 1992, 2001). Risk-averse management should take as the absolutely minimum position that each of these three populations are distinctive population fragments of *Calidris canutus*, and that two subspecies are probably represented.

In summary, clarification of the taxonomic status of these populations will require further genetic research using a larger battery of high-resolution microsatellites and AFLPs. Additionally, we need to better understand their migration pathways, breeding ranges, and population vital rates. The status of the Red Knots seen staging in South Carolina and Georgia and wintering in Florida and the Caribbean cannot be assumed to be *C. c. roselaari* until their breeding range is discovered and further genetic studies are completed. Of the six currently recognized subspecies of Red Knots in the world, three breed in the U.S. and Canadian Arctic (*rufa*, *roselaari*, and *islandica*) and only the first two will be discussed throughout this document except where studies of other subspecies apply to Red Knots worldwide. Within the Americas taxonomic uncertainty exists about small population segments in Maranhão in northern Brazil and on the Pacific coast of Mexico. These segments along with the southeastern U.S. wintering population are each less than 10,000 birds and are apparently in decline, but by far the most alarming decline is in the long-distance migrant population in Tierra del Fuego which has fallen from 67,000 in the 1980s to about 17,200 in 2006.

PHYSICAL DESCRIPTION

Essentially, the plumage of all Red Knots is mainly chestnut-red or salmon-colored during the breeding season and white and gray for the remainder of the year. The differences between the subspecies are largely confined to breeding plumage and size. In the detailed account of the subspecies below, we concentrate on male plumages because they show the most pronounced differences. We also focus on *C. c. rufa* and the critical difference (for some of the issues discussed in this review) between *C. c. rufa* and *roselaari*. In addition, we outline the plumages of the other subspecies to give an idea of the general nature of subspecific variation in the species. We also present biometric data from Harrington (2001) covering wing-chord and culmen length (Table 4) and mass (Table 5), although differences noted by these data may possibly be attributed to phenotypic plasticity rather than inter-subspecific ones.

The upperparts (crown, mantle, tail, and scapulars) are plain ash gray, with light fringes (when newly molted) on the scapulars and median wing coverts. The underparts are dull white. The underwing, rump, lower back and axillary feathers are light gray to dirty white with dark subterminal chevrons. The upper breast is dirty white with faint, suffused, dark or gray to brown, fine vertical streaking, which may extend laterally to the flanks. The head has dull patterning: the crown, chin, throat, hindneck, and neck sides are plain to light gray with an indistinct whitish supercillium. The greater upperwing coverts and inner primary coverts have white tips, which appear as a white wing-line when in flight. The primaries are dark brown to black on the outer webs, more pale on the inner webs, and white at the base. The proximal primaries have light borders on the outer webs. The distal primary coverts and alula are dark brown-black. The secondaries and tertials and remaining greater and lesser wing coverts are ash gray, broadly tipped with white. The rectrices are gray with narrow white fringes; the outer rectrices often have a dark subterminal band. The feather rachises are dark (Hayman et al. 1986, Harrington 2001).

First Basic Plumage

This is similar to the definitive basic plumage, except for retained back to upper tail coverts, some rectrices, and a few tertials or median upper wing coverts, all of which may occasionally be replaced. Birds wintering in South America may also replace primaries (Harrington 2001).

TABLE 4. MEAN WING CHORD AND CULMEN MEASUREMENTS FROM MUSEUM SPECIMENS OF RED KNOTS TAKEN FROM WESTERN HEMISPHERE LOCATIONS.

Source	Wing-chord length (mm)	Culmen length (BAH)
Adults		
Females	164[a] ± 22 (78)	36.3[b] ± 3.1 (78)
West[c]	167[e] ± 21 (11)	37.0[f] ± 6.0 (11)
Northeast[d]	161[e] ± 23 (29)	35.9[f] ± 2.8 (29)
Males	161[a] ± 17 (97)	34.9[b] ± 2.2 (97)
West[c]	162[g] ± 23 (18)	35.8[h] ± 1.8 (18)
Northeast[d]	160[g] ± 19 (35)	34.9[h] ± 2.6 (35)
Juveniles		
Females	160[a] ± 16 (35)	34.4[b] ± 4.9 (35)
West[c]	161[e] ± 15 (13)	36.0[f] ± 4.7 (13)
Northeast[d]	159[e] ± 15 (13)	33.4[f] ± 2.6 (22)
Males	154[a] ± 27 (37)	32.6[b] ± 5.6 (37)
West[c]	158[g] ± 13 (9)	33.7 ± 6.8 (9)
Northeast[d]	159[g] ± 15 (22)	32.2 ± 4.9 (28)

[a] Not significantly different between sexes (adults, F = 1.32, P = 0.10, juveniles, F = 1.65, P > 0.05).
[b] Significantly different between sexes in adults (F = 1.45, P < 0.05) but not in juveniles (F = 1.15, P > 0.05).
[c] West includes Alaska, Alberta, British Columbia, and California.
[d] Northeast coast includes North Carolina and coastal points north and east.
[e] West and northeast wing lengths were significantly different (adults: t = 3.52, P < 0.001; juveniles: t = 2.06, P < 0.05).
[f] West and northeast bill lengths were significantly different (adults: t = 1.67, P < 0.05; juveniles: t = 4.01, P < 0.001).
[g] West and northeast wing lengths were not significantly different among adults (t = 1.27, P > 0.05), but were significantly different in juveniles (t = 1.96, P < 0.05).
[h] West and northeast were not significantly different (t = 1.57, P > 0.05) among adults but were significantly different among juveniles (t = 1.96, P < 0.05).
Note: Data given as mean ± SD (N); adult Red Knots measured between April and June, juvenile Red Knots during fall migration; taken from Harrington (2001).

TABLE 5. BODY MASS OF WESTERN HEMISPHERE RED KNOTS AT DIFFERENT STAGES OF NORTH AND SOUTH MIGRATION.

Location	Date[a]	Body mass (grams)	Significance[b]
Winter			
Sarasota, FL	283	124.9 ± 7.1 (103–140, 101)	G
	6	136.5 ± 8.9 (112–158, 120)	F
	10	139.7 ± 9.1 (123–160, 25)	F
North migration			
Punta Rasa, Argentina[c]	98	138.9 ± 16.6 (105–167, 30)	F
Península Valdés, Argentina[c]	101	151.3 ± 13.1 (114–182, 102)	E
	110	148.2 ± 17.0 (104–185, 162)	E
Lagoa do Peixe, Brazil[c]	119	199.9 ± 17.6 (135–246, 139)	A
	123	204.4 ± 21.6 (150–289, 141)	A
Delaware Bay, NJ	133	159.2 ± 12.7 (129–198, 221)	CD
	138	153.6 ± 16.8 (91–205, 385)	DE
	143	175.4 ± 18.1 (107–210, 278)	B
	148	162.4 ± 24.1 (105–198, 24)	C
South migration			
Scituate, MA	209	148.4 ± 19.2 (101–206, 608)	E
	215	169.3 ± 18.7 (135–205, 23)	B
	220	172.4 ± 20.2 (103–225, 659)	B
	232	168.9 ± 20.2 (128–207, 32)	B
Plymouth, MA	235	124.2 ± 16.1 (90–149, 18)	G

[a] Dates are Julian dates.
[b] Means sharing the same letter were not statistically different (P > 0.05) according to a general linear means model (SAS PROC GLM) and a Duncan's multiple range test (SAS Institute, 1985).
[c] Samples do not include birds recorded as in basic plumage. Definitive basic (non-breeding, or winter plumage).
Notes: From Manomet Center for Conservation Sciences (unpubl. data) given as mean ± SD (range, N). Taken from Harrington (2001).

DEFINITIVE ALTERNATE PLUMAGE

In definitive alternate plumage the face and underparts are variable chestnut-red, with variable amounts of white and brown on the rear belly and white flecks on the front belly. The lower rump and uppertail are whitish gray. The mantle, scapulars, and tertials have blackish centers, and are edged with rufous and tipped with pale gray. The wing coverts are grayish with white (Hayman et al. 1986).

ALTERNATE PLUMAGE

Alternate or breeding, plumages vary by subspecies and by sex (Harrington 2001). In alternate plumage, *C. c. rufa* is distinguished by its characteristic pale rufous color on the breast, neck and head (Sibley 2000). Back feathers and scapulars have dark brown-black centers edged with faded rufous. Scapulars and tertials are unevenly colored with broad, dark, irregular-shaped centers, widely edged in notched patterns to variable degrees, some with faded rufous and others with bright salmon-red color. Post-breeding adults have a worn mantle and scapulars, which become extensively blackish, rendering the different subspecies indistinguishable (Hayman et al. 1986).

FEMALES

Females are similar to males, though rufous colors are typically less intense with more buff or light gray coloration in the dorsal parts. Females of all subspecies have less evenly and less brightly colored underparts than males and may have scattered white feathers. Females also have more extensive white on the lower belly and may have scattered breast and/or flank feathers with wavy, dark marks at the tips. The supercillium is less pronounced than in males, and may be indistinct from the crown and eye-line. The hindneck is more buff than cinnamon.

MALES — *CALIDRIS CANUTUS RUFA*

Of all races, *C. c. rufa* males have the palest chestnut underparts with more extensive white on the rear belly and a duller underwing area (Hayman et al. 1986). They have a nearly white vent, lower flanks, and under tail coverts (Harrington 2001). Crown and nape are streaked with black and gray and/or salmon. Other features include prominent brick red or salmon red superciliary stripe, auricular region and lores colored as in crown but with finer streaks; chin, throat, breast, flanks, and belly brick red or salmon red, sometimes with a few scattered

light feathers mixed in; undertail white, often including scattered brick-red or salmon-red feathers marked with dark, terminal chevrons laterally. Back feathers and scapulars have dark brown-black centers edged with faded salmon. Scapulars and tertials are unevenly colored with broad, dark, irregular-shaped centers widely edged in notched patterns to variable degrees, some with faded salmon and others with bright salmon-red color. Lower back and upper tail-coverts are barred black and white, with scattered rufous (Paulson 1993). Remiges, rectrices, and about half of the wing coverts are retained from basic plumage. Primaries are dark brown to black, secondaries and remiges gray, and there is a narrow wingbar. Putative younger males tend to be less brightly colored dorsally (Harrington 2001) and have greater numbers of light feathers scattered among ventral feathering (Hobson 1972). Adults passing through James Bay during southward migration show molt of body feathers as well as scapulars (Hope and Shortt 1944). Southward-migrating individuals in Massachusetts during July and early August (mostly *C. c. rufa* bound for austral wintering grounds) show molt of ventral and dorsal body feathers, but do not show any flight-feather molt. Body-feather molt appears to become arrested before departure in mid-August (Harrington 2001). In contrast, data from adults captured later than August in New England and many caught in the southeastern U.S show advanced prebasic molt of primaries, secondaries, and rectrices, suggesting that these individuals may, in fact, be *C. c. roselaari*. This flight-feather molt appears to be virtually completed before *C. c. roselaari* move to Florida winter locations during October and November (Harrington 2001).

MALES — *CALIDRIS CANUTUS CANUTUS*

This subspecies has deep chestnut underparts and dark chestnut fringes on the upper body (Hayman et al. 1986). The vent and under tail coverts are deep rufous (Harrington 2001). The black marks on the upperparts are heavy, with rufous marks small and deeply colored, rounded on tips of scapulars (Harrington 2001).

MALES — *CALIDRIS CANUTUS ROGERSI*

Subspecies *rogersi* appears paler in color than the nominate subspecies (*C. c. canutus*), and the lower belly typically has more white (Hayman et al. 1986). This subspecies also has more coloration on lower belly and under tail-covert region and appears less grayish and slightly more rufous above than *C. c. rufa* (Harrington 2001). The vent and lower belly, however, are similarly light colored as on *C. c. rufa*, but may be marked with black (Harrington 2001).

MALES — *CALIDRIS CANUTUS ISLANDICA*

Subspecies *C. c. islandica* is similar in appearance to *C. c. rogersi*, but with yellowish fringes on the mantle and has medium-chestnut underparts (Hayman et al. 1986). Coloration of this subspecies is also similar to that of *C. c. canutus*, but with less intense rufous on the underparts, more yellow on the hindneck with more narrow black marks and paired squarish dots of rufous on the tips of the scapulars (Harrington 2001). This subspecies also appears more richly colored than *C. c. rufa* (Harrington 2001).

MALES — *CALIDRIS CANUTUS ROSELAARI*

The coloration of the dorsal plumage of *roselaari* is similar to that of *canutus*, but darker and with more variegated pattern. Ventral coloration is similar to *C. c. rufa*, particularly with respect to the amount of white plumage on the lower belly and vent. Some evidence shows that this subspecies, in the southeastern Atlantic U.S, shows prebasic molt of ventral and dorsal body feathers, as well as actively molting primaries and rectrices during August and September in contrast to other subspecies in the northeastern U.S. Based on analysis of museum specimens, this subspecies is also longer winged than other subspecies (Harrington 2001).

FIRST ALTERNATE PLUMAGE

This is extremely variable among both individuals and subspecies. Individuals that molt few feathers may appear as basic-plumaged birds, but with worn and frayed primaries. Individuals that undergo a more extensive molt may appear as intermediates between definitive basic and definitive alternate plumages.

JUVENILE PLUMAGE

Juvenile plumage is similar to definitive basic plumage, and no difference occurs between the sexes (Harrington 2001). The mantle, scapular and covert feathers have boldly pencilled sub-marginal lines and white fringes which give a characteristic scaly appearance (Hayman et al. 1986). The upper breast is suffused in buff with fine brown streaks and dots (Harrington 2001). The underparts appear suffused in olive to gray ash, slightly darker than in definitive basic plumage (Harrington 2001).

HATCHLINGS

Hatchlings have downy plumage with dull, blackish brown underparts speckled with rows of white or cinnamon hourglass-shaped dots. The plumage lightens on the sides and underparts with a buffy-grayish wash on the breast. The crown is dark with some stripes below the eye, the supercillium, cheek and auriculars are mottled and the chin is white. The bill is blue-gray with a dusky tip; the legs are grayish yellow with dusky spots. (Harrington 2001).

DISTRIBUTION IN TIME AND SPACE

THE ANNUAL CYCLE

The diagrammatic representation of the annual cycle of a Red Knot wintering in Tierra del Fuego (Fig. 5) is based on the approximate dates that Red Knots occur at different sites as more fully set out elsewhere in this review and is merely intended to assist the reader. It is not suggested that any individual Red Knots make exactly the movements shown.

Soon after the chicks hatch in mid-July, the females leave the breeding grounds and start moving south. Thereafter, parental care is provided solely by the males, but about 25 d later (around 10 August) they also abandon the newly fledged juveniles and move south. Not long after, they are followed by the juveniles, which start to appear along the northeast coast of the U.S. in the second half of August. Throughout the flyway, the adults generally precede the juveniles as they move south from stopover to stopover. At each, the adults gradually replace their red breeding plumage with white and gray, but do not molt their flight or tail feathers until they reach their winter quarters.

During southward migration and in some parts of the winter quarters, the number of juveniles gives a good indication of breeding success which tends to show some correlation with predator-prey cycles and weather conditions on the arctic breeding grounds. In some years, when there are many arctic predators and few prey (mainly lemmings *Lemmus* and *Dicrostonyx*), and/or when there is unseasonably cold weather, breeding success may be extremely low and many adults may abandon their breeding territories and move south earlier than usual (van de Kam et al. 2004). In other years, good breeding conditions may mean that substantial proportions of all Red Knots in the flyway are juveniles. However, it seems that although some juveniles of the Tierra del Fuego wintering population migrate all the way to Tierra del Fuego, others

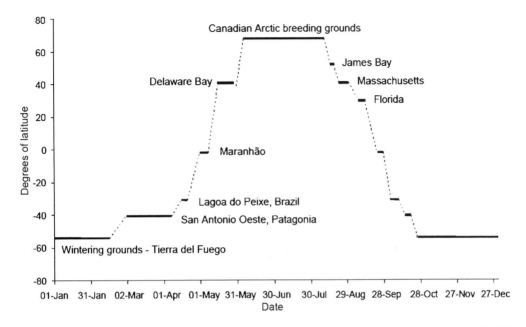

FIGURE 5. Diagrammatic representation of the annual cycle of a typical Tierra del Fuego wintering Red Knot (*Calidris canutus rufa*) in terms of latitudinal location and date. Horizontal lines represent periods when birds stay on the breeding or wintering grounds or stopover while on migration; dotted lines represent largely non-stop migratory flights.

winter farther north in South America (P. M. González, unpubl. data).

Arrival in Tierra del Fuego is from late September through October. As soon as they arrive, the adults start their annual molt of flight and tail feathers which they finish in January. Although a few may depart before the end of January, the main movement north is not until February. At each stopover as they move north along the coast of South America they molt into breeding plumage with most of the change from white/gray to red taking place during March and early April. From Maranhão in northern Brazil, most probably fly directly to Delaware Bay or to the southeastern coast of the U.S. In Delaware Bay, they feed heavily on horseshoe crab eggs, and in an average of 10–14 d, almost double their weight and depart at the end of May on the 3,000 km flight to their arctic breeding grounds (S. Gillings et al., unpubl. data). This stopover duration is much shorter than final stopovers by other populations of Red Knots (21–28 d) and reflects the rapid mass gains possible when feeding on *Limulus* eggs (4.9 g/d) compared with other prey (2.7–3.0 g/d; S. Gillings et al., unpubl. data; Piersma et al. 2005).

It is thought that most or all of the juveniles of the Tierra del Fuego population remain in South America during their first year of life.

Those that have spent the austral summer in Tierra del Fuego move farther north, while others that have wintered in the mid- or northern latitudes of the continent may move relatively little. Eventually, in about September, these birds move to Tierra del Fuego in advance of most of the returning adults and commence their first molt of flight and tail feathers. After spending the austral summer in Tierra del Fuego, these immatures migrate with the rest of the adults to the Arctic where they breed for the first time at 2 yr of age.

BREEDING RANGE

Morrison and Harrington (1992) considered that the breeding range of *C. c. rufa* extended across the central Canadian Arctic from Southampton Island to Victoria Island, but pointed out that uncertainty existed as to whether it occurred in all parts of this range owing to lack of coverage. In May 1999, biologists from the New Jersey Department of Environmental Protection Division of Fish and Wildlife (NJDFW) and the Royal Ontario Museum (ROM) attached radio transmitters to 65 Red Knots passing through Delaware Bay on their way to the breeding grounds. In July 1999, aerial radio tracking was carried out on Southampton Island where eight birds were relocated. Six were found in the barren tundra uplands characteristic of most of the island, but two were found in the coastal wetlands. In a subsequent ground search, the nest of one radio-tagged *C. c. rufa* was located.

Using land cover characteristics at the sites where the eight Red Knots were relocated in 1999, biologists with the NJDFW, ROM and Rutgers University Center for Remote Sensing and Spatial Analysis (CRSSA) developed a simple model based on three main characteristics: elevation, amount of vegetation cover, and distance to ocean coast. Using land cover images of the entire eastern Arctic the team created a map

predicting the location of Red Knot habitat (Fig. 6). Additional refinements to the habitat predictive model were added based on results from the radio-tracking work.

Over the next 3 yr, 200 more transmitters were attached to birds which were tracked throughout the Canadian Arctic as far west as Victoria Island, east to Baffin Island, north to Prince of Wales Island and south to Coats and Mansel Islands. In all, 20 birds were relocated, all within areas predicted to be Red Knot habitat. Additional refinements to the habitat predictive model were added based on the new relocated birds.

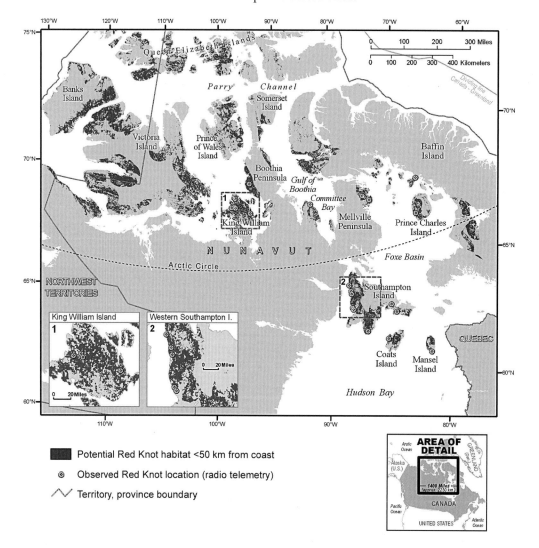

■ Potential Red Knot habitat <50 km from coast

◎ Observed Red Knot location (radio telemetry)

∧ Territory, province boundary

FIGURE 6. Predicted Red Knot nesting habitats based on land cover types in the Canadian Arctic and point locations of Red Knots obtained by radio telemetry (Red Knot data from New Jersey Department of Environmental Protection Endangered and Nongame Species Program; potential Red Knot habitat data from Grant F. Walton Center for Remote Sensing and Spatial Analysis (CRSSA) Rutgers University; boundary data from GeoCratis Canada).

In summary, our knowledge of the breeding range of *C. c. rufa* is sparse and we can only be sure that it extends to those places where birds have been found as shown in Fig. 6. There are no data to indicate whether the range or distribution has changed over time.

WINTER (NON-BREEDING) RANGE

After breeding, all Red Knot populations migrate south to spend the northern winter in large flocks at a relatively small number of key intertidal wetlands. These invariably provide hard-shelled bivalves as the Red Knots' main food resource. These are swallowed whole, the shells being crushed in the gut and excreted by defecation.

Red Knots that are or might be of the *C. c. rufa* subspecies winter in four distinct coastal areas of the Western Hemisphere (Fig. 7): (1) the southeastern U.S. (mainly Florida and Georgia, with smaller numbers in South Carolina), (2) Texas, (3) Maranhão in northern Brazil, and (4) Tierra del Fuego (mainly Bahía Lomas in Chile and Bahía San Sebastián and Río Grande in Argentina with smaller numbers northwards along the coast of Patagonia). Other Red Knots, presumed to be *C. c. roselaari* winter on the Pacific coast of California and Baja California, parts of the Pacific northwest coast of Mexico in

the Gulf of California, and probably also farther south (Morrison and Ross 1989; Morrison et al.1992, 2004; Page et al. 1997, 1999; Baker et al. 2005a, 2005b).

In the 1982–1985 survey of South America (Morrison and Ross 1989), Red Knots were found wintering along the coast of Patagonia from Tierra del Fuego north to Buenos Aires Province in Argentina. However, because the southern wintering population has declined, only extremely low numbers of Red Knots have been observed in Patagonia north of Tierra del Fuego, with no birds found in some years (Morrison et al. 2004).

In the southernern U.S., the wintering Red Knot population is believed to be distributed variably from year-to-year between Florida, Georgia, and South Carolina (Fig. 8), depending on invertebrate prey abundance (B. A. Harrington and Winn, unpubl. data).

The number of wintering Red Knots in Georgia varies between and within years. Results of an annual winter ground survey of the entire Georgia coast since 1996 during the last 2 wk of January into early February show the minimum number of Red Knots to be in the hundreds and the highest to be nearly 5,000. The distribution of wintering Red Knots is generally unpredictable and dispersed over much of the barrier coast and appears to be linked

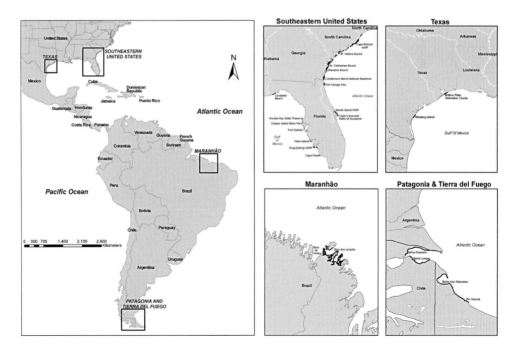

FIGURE 7. Red Knot wintering areas in the Western Hemisphere. Each area boxed in the left map is shown in greater detail and delineated in black.

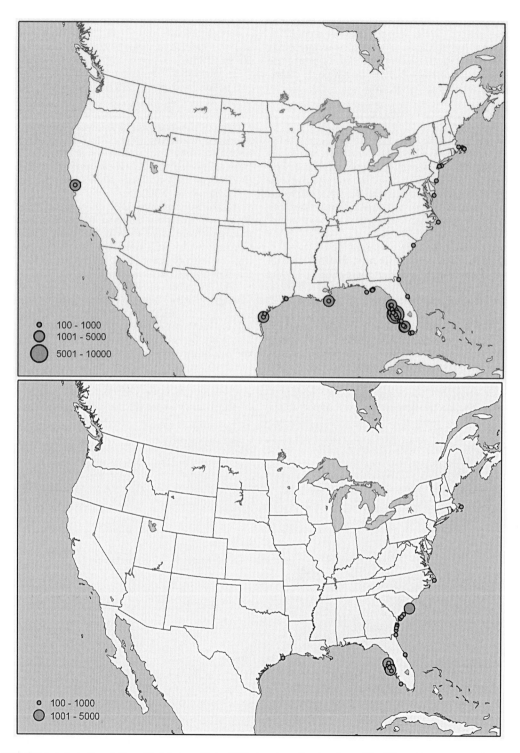

FIGURE 8. International Shorebird Survey Data (ISS) showing distribution of Red Knots in winter in the U.S. before year 2000 (upper) and during 2000–2004 (lower). The level of ISS survey effort declined after 2000; therefore, the differences in numbers before and since 2000 may partly represent reduced survey effort (Brian Harrington, pers. comm.).

closely with the abundance and availability of dwarf surf clams (*Mulinia lateralis*). The Red Knots feed primarily on dwarf surf clams and secondarily on coquina clams (*Donax variablis*).

In Florida, frequent beach replenishment in areas such as Fort Myers and Estero Island (N. Douglass, pers. comm.) may cause the loss of invertebrate prey populations and displace wintering Red Knots to more productive foraging areas elsewhere in Florida and Georgia.

In Texas, the wintering population was of the order of 3,000 during 1985–1996 with the largest numbers occurring on the Bolivar flats (Skagen et al. 1999). However, this population seems to have declined. The only recent count of any size is of 300 in January 2003 (B. A. Harrington, unpubl. data).

MIGRATORY RANGE AND MAJOR STOPOVER AREAS

While migrating, all Red Knot populations are dependent on a limited number of stopover sites that provide adequate food resources. These act like stepping stones in that if one is lost because the food supply fails, a whole population of Red Knots may be jeopardized. For the subspecies *C. c. rufa*, Delaware Bay is a particularly vital link in its migration between Tierra del Fuego and the Canadian Arctic, since it is at this final stopover that the birds need to be able to accumulate both fuel for the journey and additional body stores to enable them to survive and attain good breeding condition after arrival in the Arctic.

The southbound 15,000 km migratory journey of *C. c. rufa* begins in August and takes it from its breeding grounds in the central Canadian Arctic through Hudson Bay and James Bay, through some parts of eastern Canada, such as the Mingan Islands in the Gulf of St Lawrence, and through most of the east coast states of the U.S. (Fig. 9). At this time, they tend to use northern sites in Massachusetts, Connecticut, and Rhode Island more than they do in spring. After a final U.S. stopover, they fly to northern Brazil and then on through Argentina to Tierra del Fuego. The majority of the population winters on the main island of Tierra del Fuego, where in one bay in the Chilean sector, Bahía Lomas, most of the population can be found from November to February (Morrison and Ross 1989, Morrison et al. 2004). Other Red Knot populations begin their migration from the Arctic about the same time as the Tierra del Fuego birds, but stop to over-winter in the southeastern U.S. (mainly Florida) and Maranhão, Brazil (Morrison and Ross 1989, Baker et al. 2005b). As discussed in the taxonomy section of this volume, the subspecific status of these populations is uncertain.

In comparison with the southward migration, the northbound flight to the Arctic is more time-constrained and demanding, especially in the northern parts of the route, because it is important for successful breeding and survival that the adults arrive on their arctic breeding grounds at the right time and in good condition for breeding, and with sufficient resources to sustain themselves while arctic food is in short supply.

After departing Tierra del Fuego, major stopover sites are found at Río Gallegos, Península Valdés, San Antonio Oeste, and Punta Rasa in Argentina and Lagoa do Peixe in southern Brazil. From there, the birds fly across Amazonia to a possible last feeding stop in South America in the Maranhão region of northern Brazil (Fig. 10). From Maranhão, the majority fly directly to Delaware Bay, with a smaller proportion making landfall farther south along the U.S. East Coast, anywhere from Florida to Virginia (Fig. 11). The Red Knots that have wintered in Maranhão are also thought to fly directly to the East Coast of the U.S., but it is not known whether they migrate with or at the same time as the birds from Tierra del Fuego. The evidence is sparse, but it is possibile that at least some Tierra del Fuego birds migrate directly from Lagoa do Peixe to Delaware Bay, a distance of 8,000 km, which is around the limit of a Red Knot's potential flight range (Harrington and Flowers 1996). Most important stopover sites are depicted in Fig. 12.

Some birds arrive in Delaware Bay in a greatly depleted condition, weighing as much as 30% below their normal fat-free mass. There they spend about 2 wk feeding on horseshoe crab eggs and virtually double their mass. Some of the birds that have spent the winter in Florida pass through Delaware Bay, but it seems that many migrate northward along the Atlantic coast of the U.S. feeding on bivalves (mainly *Donax*. and blue mussel spat) and bypass Delaware Bay altogether (P. Atkinson et al., unpubl. data; S. Karpanty, pers. comm.). At the end of May, *C. c. rufa* depart on the last leg of their flight to the Arctic. In the final days before departure, the birds almost cease feeding and undergo physiological changes to prepare for migration including reducing their digestive organs and increasing flight muscle size (Piersma and Gill 1998, Piersma et al. 1999). They leave Delaware Bay heading inland north-northwest toward their breeding grounds. This route takes them across the vast boreal forest and low tundra of Canada, which in late May to early June can be a hostile environment to shorebirds. Many pass through and along the coasts of James Bay and Hudson Bay, although

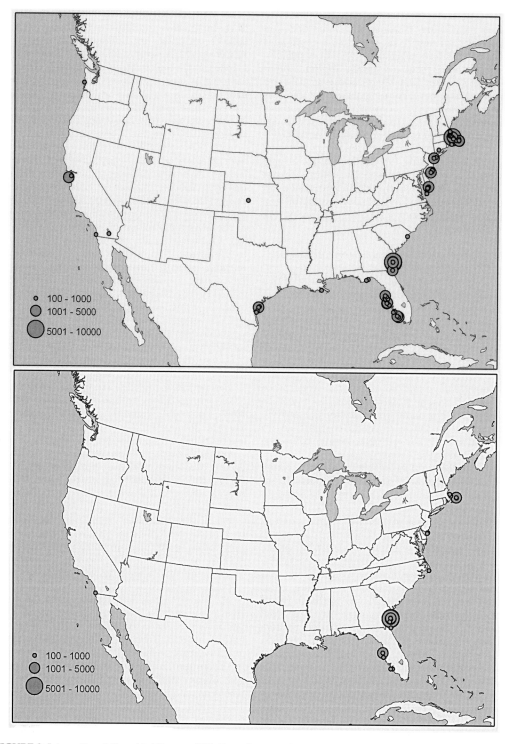

FIGURE 9. International Shorebird Survey (ISS) Data showing distribution of Red Knots during fall migration in the U.S. before year 2000 (upper) and during 2000–2004 (lower). The level of ISS survey effort declined after 2000; therefore, the differences in numbers before and since 2000 may partly represent reduced survey effort (Brian Harrington, pers. comm.).

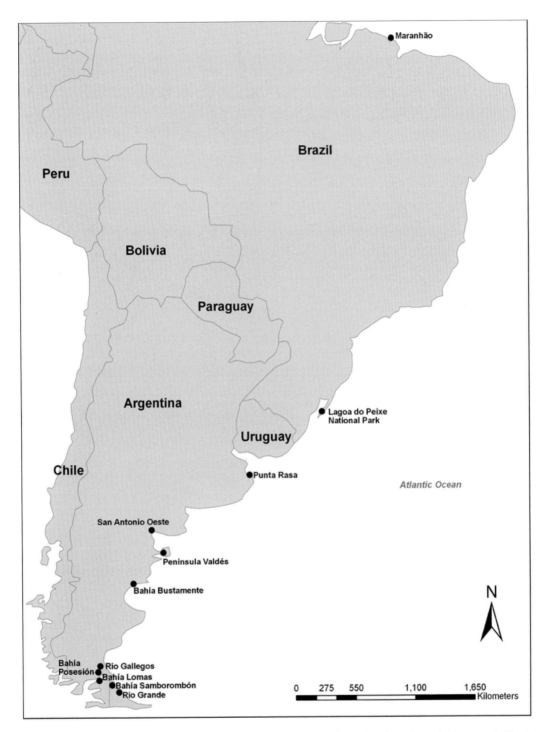

FIGURE 10. Critical stopover sites used by Red Knots during northward and southward migration in South America.

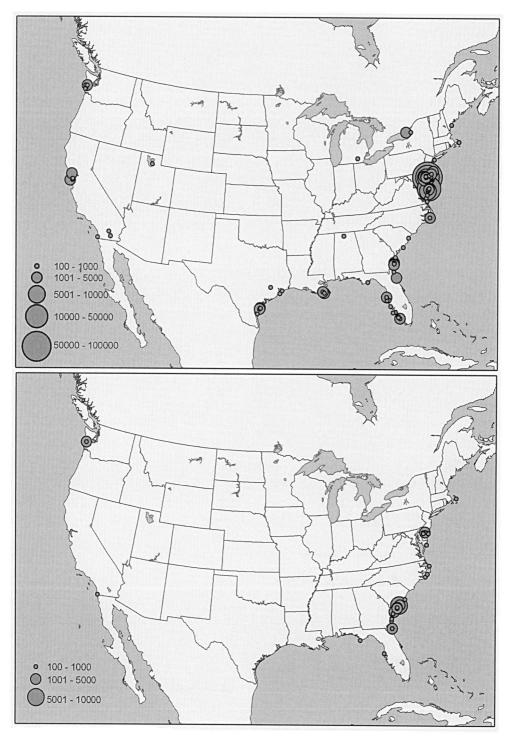

FIGURE 11. International Shorebird Survey (ISS) Data showing distribution of Red Knots during spring migration in the U.S. before 2000 (upper) and during 2000–2004 (lower). The level of ISS survey effort declined after 2000; therefore, the differences in numbers before and since 2000 may partly represent reduced survey effort (Brian Harrington, pers. comm.).

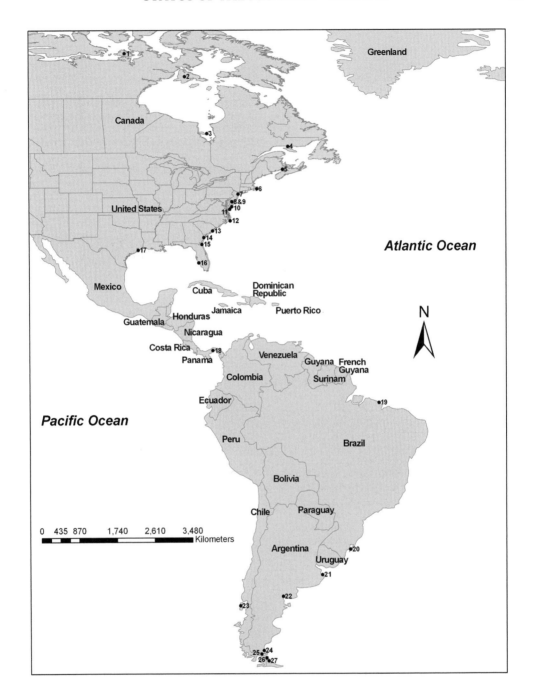

FIGURE 12. Critical breeding, migration stopover, and wintering habitat for the Red Knot *Calidris canutus rufa*. Numbers on the map correspond with the numbers in Table 6.

they are not believed to stop in these areas for any significant period (R. I. G. Morrison, unpubl. data; M. Peck, unpubl. data).

Once they arrive on their breeding grounds, their digestive systems are restored, but often little food is available. Therefore their survival and their ability to attain good breeding condition may depend on surplus fat resources brought to the breeding grounds (Morrison et al. 2005) from Delaware Bay. This in turn may be affected by weather and feeding conditions further south because if Red Knots arrive in Delaware Bay late and/or in poor condition they may have insufficient time to store the resources they require. In this way any problems further south may result in a cascade effect that jeopardizes their ability to survive and reproduce.

Of all the sites visited by the *C. c. rufa*, Delaware Bay is one of the most critical (Harrington and Flowers 1996, Harrington 2001). Without the ability to obtain sufficient resources in Delaware Bay, both the survival of the adult birds and their productivity may decline (Baker et al. 2004). As early as 1986, the importance of Delaware Bay to Red Knots and at least five other shorebird species was recognized when it became the first Western Hemisphere Shorebird Reserve. This recognition was also part of the impetus for the development of shorebird reserves throughout the western hemisphere (Myers et al. 1987).

The number of shorebirds stopping over in Delaware Bay has declined dramatically in the last 10 yr. In the 1980s and early 1990s, horseshoe crabs covered the beaches and, along much of the bayshore, the eggs within reach of a Red Knot's bill in the top 5 cm of sand exceeded 50,000 m^{-2} at a number of sites around Delaware Bay. In the 1980s, the combined peak counts of the three shorebird species that feed almost entirely on horseshoe crabs' eggs (Red Knot, Sanderling [*Calidris alba*], and Ruddy Turnstone [*Arenaria interpres*]) averaged 163,000. Now, egg densities at many sites are <4,000 eggs m^{-2} and peak shorebird aerial census numbers for 2003–2005 were down to 66,500 with Red Knots showing the greatest drop from 1980s maxima of 95,000–15,000 in 2005 (Clark et al. 1993; K. Clark, unpubl. data). Although the Red Knots from northern wintering populations exploit other food resources in the vicinity of Delaware Bay (such as blue mussels and surf clams on the Atlantic coast of New Jersey), horseshoe crab eggs are crucially important for the long-distance migrants from Tierra del Fuego. As explained in the habitats section of this review, a combination of physiological and time constraints means that they cannot utilize the alternative foods and rely on the more easily digested eggs.

The harvest of horseshoe crabs along the northeast coast of the U.S., and the associated reduced availability of their eggs as a food resource for migrating shorebirds, was first identified as a serious threat in the mid-1990s. Until 1993, the crab harvest, mainly for eel and minnow bait, was minimal and accounted for no more than about 400,000 per year, which were mostly taken by hand or as by-catch. However, in 1993, collapsing fisheries in New England and elsewhere led commercial fishermen to the profitable conch fishery, for which horseshoe crabs are the preferred bait. This brought commercial fishermen to Delaware Bay, where the harvest increased dramatically as the conch fishery expanded in the mid-Atlantic coast. By 1996, the annual harvest from Virginia to New York, both mechanical and manual, exceeded 2,000,000 crabs (Fig. 13). According to a Delaware Department of Natural Resources and Environmental Control, Division of Fish and Wildlife (DDFW) survey, the population of crabs fell by about 85% between 1990 and 1998 (S. Michels, pers. comm.). While minor restrictions were imposed, the intensive harvest of horseshoe crabs continued (Fig. 13). By 2000, egg densities had fallen from an average of well over 10,000 to <4,000 eggs m^{-2}. Only a few places favored by crabs, such as Mispillion Harbor, held significantly greater densities.

The greatest risk of the declining availability of horseshoe crab eggs in Delaware Bay to Red Knots is that it jeopardizes their ability to achieve the mass required to reach the Arctic and attain good breeding condition. Between 1998 and 2002, the proportion of Red Knots that had attained an estimated threshold departure mass of 180 g around the normal departure date (28 May) declined by >60% (Baker et al. 2004). This decline may be the result of arriving late in Delaware Bay and/or in poor condition as well as an inadequate supply of crabs' eggs (Robinson et al. 2003, Clark et al. 2004). Moreover these factors could interact and exacerbate the birds' predicament. Birds might arrive late or in poor condition and find an inadequate supply of eggs. Bala et al. (2005, pers. comm.) and M. Hernández (unpubl. data) report that northward passage of Red Knots through Peninsula Valdés, Patagonia, Argentina has become 1–2 wk later since year 2000. There is some evidence that this has been reflected by later arrival into Delaware Bay, in 2000, 2001, and especially in 2003 (Baker et al. 2004; K. Clark, unpubl. data).

Baker et al. (2004) found a decline in the Red Knot's annual survival rate from an

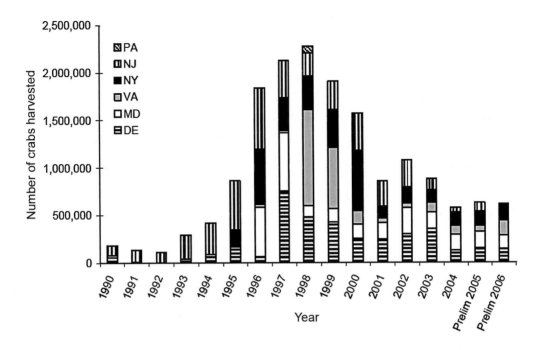

FIGURE 13. Annual landings of horseshoe crabs in Virginia, Maryland, Pennsylvania, Delaware, New Jersey, and New York, 1990–2006 (Morrison et al. 2004). Most states had mandatory reporting by 1996 and all did by 1998, so landings data prior to 1998 may be underrepresented.

average of 85% during 1994–1998 to 56% during 1998–2001. They further showed that over the years 1997–2002, birds caught in Delaware Bay at a lower mass were less likely to survive than heavier birds and that there had been a significant increase in the proportion of poorly conditioned, low-weight birds at the end of May. This was postulated to be the result of a trend for birds to arrive later and/or in poor condition and/or an inadequate food supply. This change in survival coupled with almost zero recruitment of juveniles to the adult population (P. Atkinson, unpubl. data) lies behind the decrease in the Tierra del Fuego wintering population from over 50,000 in 2000 to 30,000 in 2002–2004. Baker et al. (2004) predicted that if annual survival of the Tierra del Fuego population remained stable at 56%, the population could approach extinction by 2010. It is not possible to predict future survival, but the most recent count of 17,221 in January 2006 shows that the trend is following this worst-case scenario trajectory and the risk of extinction is high.

BIOLOGY AND NATURAL HISTORY

Except as otherwise indicated, this account of the biology and natural history of *C. c. rufa*

and the following account of its habitat is based on the Red Knot species text in Harrington (2001). This source is founded on an extensive review of the literature and the works cited in it are not repeated here. Some of the information from Harrington (2001) is quoted verbatim.

REPRODUCTION

Red Knots are thought to have a monogamous mating system in which single pairs mate and nest in territories. Pair bonds form soon after arrival on breeding grounds and remain intact until shortly after the eggs hatch (L. J. Niles et al., unpubl. data) when the females leave their broods. Thereafter, the males look after the chicks until they fledge at about 25 d when they too abandon them. Little information is available for *C. c. rufa* on mate fidelity, though many Red Knots return to the same area to breed from year to year (Morrison et al. 2005; R. I. G Morrison, unpubl. data).

The breeding chronology of *C. c. rufa* is poorly known. Other races may be paired or unpaired on arrival in breeding areas in late May–early June; start of breeding varies with snowmelt conditions. Simultaneous arrival of male and female *C. c. islandica* has been noted in late May–early June, though males tend to predominate amongst early arrivals (Morrison et al. 2005), followed by movement into inland nesting habitats within a few days.

No published information is available for *C. c. rufa* on mate fidelity between years or duration of courtship between reunited mates versus new mates. On a 9.15 km² study site on Southampton Island, Nunavut, Canada, we observed only limited evidence of site fidelity despite the fact that studies of other subspecies suggest that breeding site fidelity is high, especially in males. In 5 yr of monitoring breeding densities, we observed one male return to his territory of the previous year and only one female return to the study site but to a different territory (L. J. Niles et al., unpubl. data). In some instances, Red Knots have been thought to arrive on breeding grounds in pairs. Flocks sometimes arrive at breeding latitudes before snow-free ground is available in breeding habitats. Upon arrival or as soon as favorable conditions exist, males and females occupy breeding habitat and territorial displays begin.

Age of first breeding is uncertain but for most birds is probably 2 yr (Harrington 2001). All juveniles of the Tierra del Fuego wintering population are thought to remain in the Southern Hemisphere during their first northern summer though their distribution is largely unknown (P. M. González, unpubl. data). Some basic-plumaged Red Knots arrive in Delaware Bay in May and can constitute a considerable proportion of the individuals remaining at the end of the stopover. It would seem likely that these are 1-yr-old birds from northern wintering populations that will remain in the vicinity of Delaware Bay throughout the breeding season, but this has yet to be proved.

Mating displays

During early breeding stages, Red Knots show a variety of behaviors associated with area defense and advertisement which may begin on the day of arrival. Most agonistic behaviors involve territorial males. Fighting, though uncommon, is mostly seen between males. Song flights, performed only by males, occur as soon as males return to breeding grounds and evidently continue into the incubation period. Song flights usually begin and end in the territory, though they may extend well beyond its boundaries. Other aerial displays include the v-wing flight, which resembles a simple, low song flight originating and ending in territories, and aerial chases which are initiated by territorial males and are the most frequently seen agonistic behaviors.

Ground displays include the two-wing lift, ground singing, and horizontal point. The two-wing lift involves a standing bird, usually a male, and is often given after a song flight or a v-wing flight, but often immediately before flying or when one member of a pair lands near its mate, or by males landing near their chicks. Another display, ground singing, is most commonly performed by a standing male on territory when other males are singing overhead, performing v-wing flights, or singing from the ground nearby. Horizontal point displays are performed by males in response to another male singing, at territorial borders, at a neighbor ground-singing male and is also given as a precursor to attacking intruders, when it is typically accompanied by singing.

The tail-up display is a common behavior seen in varied contexts, typically presented by a male to the receiver laterally or posteriorly. This display is most often seen during courtship or as prelude to copulation. It is also occasionally observed in pairs reuniting after a separation, in activity after roosting, during a nest-scrape ceremony, or after fights with intruding females. This display is not seen after the egg clutch has been completed.

The tail-drop fan display is given by a male as a prelude to nest-scrape advertisement, by a stationary male when his mate comes close, during a fight with an intruding female when the male walks away from his mate, and by a male after copulation. Males in the nest give the nest-scrape advertisement display, after arrival of females. Once the female settles in the scrape, the male assumes a ground point display.

Sexual behavior

The behaviors leading up to copulation are variable though more predictable prior to mounting. A male typically follows behind a female in a tail-up display. Meanwhile, he begins the rapid, high-pitched copulation call while pecking rapidly at the female's back. If the female is receptive, the male flies up on to her back to begin copulation while continuing to flutter his wings.

The rate of male calling increases prior to cloacal contact. Meanwhile, the female drops her wings slightly to expose the back and rump. The female's tail is then raised, the male bends his tail under it, and cloacal contact is made. Coition lasts roughly 1 min. Following contact, the male falls off the female's back and holds her head, neck, or nape feathers in his bill for 1–30 sec.

Copulation attempts are evidently initiated by the male, and take place throughout the day.

In one pair, copulation was seen within 1–2 hr after arrival of the female; in another pair it was not seen for the first 36 hr. In three pairs, copulation was first noted 3, 5, and 8 d before the first egg is laid.

No data are available on the occurrence of extra-pair copulation; however, they appear to be unlikely given the apparent monogamous mating system and the vigorous territorial defense shown by males.

Nest sites

Nests are cup-shaped depressions, often with well-defined rims, lined with dried leaves, grasses, and sometimes lichens, averaging 11.9 cm across, 11.1 cm wide, and 4.4 cm deep. The lichens, which Red Knots use for nest lining are species that form hollow tubes thus providing an excellent insulating layer above the cold ground. On Southampton Island, nest cups were most often lined with the small leaves of mountain avens (*Dryas octopetala*) and rarely lined with lichen; nest cups averaged 11.1 cm wide and 5.7 cm deep (L. J. Niles et al., unpubl. data).

Males prepare three–five nest scrapes in their territory before females arrive. Vegetation is removed by pulling with the bill and by sitting in the nest depression and pivoting on the breast while kicking backwards with the feet. Once in the nest, the female removes vegetation from under her breast, placing it at her side or tossing over her back while kicking backwards with her feet.

Red Knot nests may be scraped into the main body or edges of mountain avens patches or in low, spreading vegetation on hummocky ground containing lichens, leaves, and moss. Selection of nest sites may vary with snow or other conditions when individuals arrive in breeding areas. Knots generally use nest sites on dry, slightly elevated tundra locations often on wind-swept ridges or slopes with little vegetation. Isolated patches of stunted willow (*Salix* spp.) and/or mountain avens often dominate the vegetation in the area. The majority of nests found on Southampton Island were within 300 m of wetlands >2 ha in area, which allows suitable foraging habitat for parents and young after the eggs hatch (L. J. Niles et al., unpubl. data).

On Southampton Island, nests were most often found on small patches (~0.5 m dia.) of mountain avens. Nests were located in exposed areas of glacial, shattered rocks, and mudboils. The amount of vegetative cover averaged 33% within 1 m of the nest and 25% within 10 m of the nest (L. J. Niles et al., unpubl. data).

Red Knot nests are located principally at elevations <150 m, often in damp habitats, though they may nest in drier sites, but not far from damp areas. Nest sites are often on higher ground where little winter snow accumulates and/or where spring snowmelt is earliest. Twenty-one nests on Southampton Island were found, on average, to be within 360 m of a glacial ridge/esker and within 200 m of a wetland (L. J. Niles et al., unpubl. data). Red Knot nests also tend to be widely separated, located between 0.75 km and 1.5–15 km apart. Nests evidently are located within the display flight areas.

Number of broods

Red Knots lay only one clutch per season and, so far as is known, do not lay a replacement clutch if the first is lost.

Clutch size

The usual clutch size is four eggs, though three-egg clutches have been recorded. It is estimated that the clutch of four eggs is laid over 4–6 d. The average egg size measured on Southampton Island (N = 90) had a length of 42 mm (range = 37.8–44.5 mm) and a width of 29 mm (range = 26.6–31.3; L. J Niles et al., unpubl. data) and is similar to other Red Knot studies (Harrington 2001). Fresh egg mass is estimated to be 18–19 g on Southampton Island (M. Peck, unpubl. data).

Incubation period

The incubation period lasts approximately 22 d from the last egg laid to the last egg hatched. Both sexes participate equally in egg incubation.

Nestling period

Hatching occurs within the first half of July and within clutches is apparently quite synchronous, occurring within the same day. The fledgling period is estimated to be 18 d.

Young birds leave the nest within 24 hr of hatching. Broods have been observed to move 300 m within 24 hr of leaving the nest. No published measures of growth and development exist, in part because broods are extremely cryptic, recognize and respond to parental alarm calls by freezing, and are difficult to follow.

After hatching, families quickly move away from high nesting terrain to lower, wetland habitats. Although information conflicts, typically only the male parent stays with the brood once the chicks leave the nest. Male parents brood and defend the young. No information is available on how long young require brooding. Young forage for themselves and are not fed by their parents.

Nesting success

Annual variation of hatching success is unknown. It probably varies in parallel with snow-cover conditions at nest sites in spring, particularly the timing of snowmelt.

MORTALITY

Despite little information from the breeding grounds, the Long-tailed Jaeger (*Stercorarius longicaudus*) is prominently mentioned as a predator of chicks in most accounts. Also mentioned are Parasitic Jaeger (*S. parasiticus*) and arctic fox (*Alopex lagopus*), and it is likely that other arctic predators, including Pomarine Jaegers (*S. pomarinus*) commonly take chicks and eggs. Herring Gulls (*Larus argentatus*) and Glaucous Gulls (*L. hyperboreus*) may also be predators of chicks.

Away from the breeding grounds, the most common predators of Red Knots are Peregrine Falcons (*Falco peregrinus*), harriers (*Circus* spp.), accipiters, Merlins (*Falco columbarius*), Short-eared Owls (*Asio flammeus*), and Great Black-backed Gulls (*Larus marinus*). Knots' selection of high-tide resting areas on the coast appears to be strongly influenced by raptor predation, something well demonstrated in other shorebirds.

A full account of diseases and parasitic infections recorded in *C. c. rufa* is presented in the Threats section of this review.

LONGEVITY

To our knowledge, the oldest Red Knot ever recorded worldwide was one that was originally banded on The Wash, southeastern England, in August 1968 as an adult and recaptured there in September 1992 (Wash Wader Ringing Group 2004). Given that it could not have been hatched later than July 1967, it was at least 25 yr old when it was recaptured. The oldest recorded *C. c. rufa* was banded as a juvenile at Punta Rasa, Argentina, in October 1987 and recaptured on the wintering grounds at Bahía Lomas, Tierra del Fuego, in February 2003, making it 16 yr old (L. J. Niles et al., unpubl. data). Although these records demonstrate that the potential lifespan of a Red Knot is considerable, most live much shorter lives. Annual adult survival in stable populations has been estimated at around 80% and the survival of juveniles is about half that (Boyd and Piersma 2001). Therefore, very few Red Knots live for more than about 7 yr.

SITE FIDELITY

Red Knots, especially males, appear to exhibit high breeding site fidelity. They are also very faithful to specific migration and wintering staging sites. Banding studies indicate that no mixing occurs between Red Knots wintering in Florida and those wintering in Argentina, suggesting that Red Knots are also faithful to wintering sites.

MIGRATION

Red Knots are long-distance migrants and have one of the longest-distance migrations in the animal kingdom. Those that breed in the Western Hemisphere, migrate from breeding grounds in the middle- and high-Arctic to wintering sites on the eastern and western Atlantic coasts, including southernmost South America. Knots are jump migrants, flying many thousands of kilometers without stopping. In between these jumps, high proportions of entire populations may use a single migration stopover site. In some Red Knot populations, including *C. c. rufa*, a substantial number of birds remain south of the breeding grounds throughout the breeding season, many but not all of which are 1-yr-old birds.

Red Knots tend to migrate in single-species flocks, largely because of species-specific migration habits. Departures tend to occur in the few hours before twilight on sunny days. Size of the departing flocks tends to be large (>50 birds). Configuration of departing flocks may vary from v-formations to echelons, clusters or bunches.

As Red Knots prepare to depart on long migratory flights, they usually have a mean body mass 50–55% greater than estimated fat-free mass. At stopover sites, mass varies greatly from very light birds that have just arrived to very heavy birds that are just about to depart. In Delaware Bay, for example, some arrive as light as 89 g (32% below fat free weight), whereas near departure a few exceed 240 g (85% above fat free weight) (L.J. Niles et al., unpubl. data). In addition to acquiring fat, Red Knots undergo physiological changes on arrival and shortly before departure including substantial changes in metabolic rates, organ size, and muscle mass. Before departure, these changes include substantial decreases in mass and size of the gizzard, liver, kidneys, and guts, and increases in flight muscle and fat mass (Piersma and Gill 1998).

Red Knots arriving from lengthy migrations are not able to feed maximally until their digestive systems regenerate, a process that may take several days (Piersma et al. 1999). This exacerbates the situation of time-constrained migrants and underscores the need for stopovers that are rich in easily digested food resources.

C. c. rufa undergoes a lengthy migration, with wintering grounds on the southern coasts of the Chilean and Argentinian sectors of Tierra del Fuego (Fig. 14) Two other populations are of uncertain subspecific status, but which might be *C. c. rufa*. One winters in the southeastern U.S. (mainly the western and northeastern coasts of Florida, but also the coasts of Georgia and South Carolina), the other in the Maranhão region of northern Brazil. Generally, northward migration begins in February for birds wintering in Tierra del Fuego, though a few leave before the end of January. They reach Brazil in April and depart in early May. Relatively few individuals were thought to use the southeastern Atlantic coasts of the U.S. during migration. However, recent spring surveys on the Atlantic coasts of northern Florida, Georgia, South Carolina, North Carolina, and Virginia indicate that Red Knots stopover in these states in May and early June with numbers ranging from tens to >9,000 (P. Leary, pers. comm.; B. Watts, pers. comm.; B. Truitt, pers. comm.). The length of stopover at these locations is generally believed to be brief and reliant on ephemeral food resources such as mussel spat (B. Truitt, pers. comm.) and small clams (*Donax spp.*; B. Winn, pers. comm.). *C. c.*

rufa becomes abundant in the northeastern U.S. in early May, especially on Delaware Bay where the highest numbers occur. Some Red Knots use the interior flyway from Texas–Louisiana via Saskatchewan to the Arctic during spring and to a lesser extent during autumn migration (Skagen et al. 1999). Although up to 2,500 Red Knots were recorded in both Texas and Saskatchewan in spring during 1980–1996, we do not know of any more recent record of substantial numbers using this flyway. Nevertheless recent observations of a Red Knot on the Texas coast color marked in Argentina in May 2004 and a Red Knot color marked on Delaware Bay in August 2005 indicate that the flyway is still being used.

During southbound migration, *C. c. rufa* begin to stage in mid-July on Hudson and James Bays and on the Atlantic coast of the U.S., especially at sites in Massachusetts and New Jersey. Several studies suggest that adults fly directly to South America from the eastern seaboard of North America, departing U.S. staging areas and arriving in northern South America in August. Passage continues across Amazonia, towards wintering (non-breeding) areas in southern Argentina and Chile. Recent observations show that Red Knots banded in South America (mainly Argentina and Chile) start to move through Georgia in July and are gone by November (B. A. Harrington, unpubl. data; B. Winn, pers. comm.). This suggests that some portion of the Red Knot population migrates down the Atlantic coast of the U.S. and departs to South America from southern U.S. staging areas. Most adult Red Knots pass through Suriname during the latter half of August and first half of September (Spaans 1978). Knots wintering in southern Argentina and Chile generally arrive by late September through October (Baker et al. 2005a). *C. c. rufa* are uncommon on the western coasts of the North and South American continents.

Another subspecies, *C. c. roselaari*, breeds in Alaska and Wrangel Island. At least some of these birds winter in California and Baja California, others probably winter farther south, but, as discussed in the population size and trends section of this document, known winter numbers are far less than those thought to occur in Alaska in late spring.

FEEDING HABITS

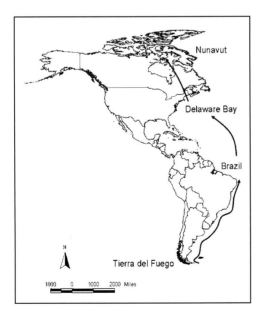

FIGURE 14. Migration route of *Calidris canutus rufa* between its wintering grounds on Tierra del Fuego, South America, stopover areas along the Patagonian Coast of Argentina, and in the northeastern United States, and breeding grounds in the Canadian Arctic.

Knots use three main foraging methods: pecking, plowing, and probing. Pecking is generally used when foraging on epifauna, such as horseshoe crab eggs, small snails, and mussels. Probing and plowing may be involved in detecting buried bivalve prey. On the breeding grounds, the diet of Red Knots consists mostly of terrestrial invertebrates, though they will also eat plant material especially early in the season. During the rest of the year, at stopover sites and on their wintering grounds in Tierra del Fuego, Chile, Maranhão, Brazil, and the southeastern U.S., they feed almost exclusively in intertidal habitats, particularly on mudflats and beaches and, on the coast of Argentina, on restingas (broad, wave-cut platforms extending across the intertidal zone) where they specialize on bivalves which are swallowed whole. Common bivalves consumed include *Mytilus*, *Mulinea*, *Donax*, *Macoma*, *Tellina*, *Myadora*, *Nucula*, and possibly *Gemma*. They will also take gastropods, such as *Hydrobia*, *Littorina*, and *Heleobia*, amphipods, and occasionally polychaetes.

When stopping over in Delaware Bay, they feed almost exclusively on the eggs of horseshoe crabs. Feeding on horseshoe crab eggs on Delaware Bay, however, is a major departure from the prey usually taken.

HABITAT

Red Knots use very different habitats for breeding and wintering and migration. Breeding habitats are located inland, but close to arctic coasts. Wintering and migration habitats are similar—generally coastal with large areas of intertidal sediments.

Preferred Microhabitats

Selection of preferred microhabitats on breeding grounds may vary depending on the amount of snow cover individuals encounter when they arrive. Nests are usually located on sparsely vegetated, dry, sunny, elevated, wind-swept ridges or slopes. Nest locations are also usually located near wetlands and lake edges, which then become the preferred microhabitat after hatching.

Preferred wintering and migration microhabitats are muddy or sandy coastal areas, more specifically, the mouths of bays and estuaries, unimproved tidal inlets and tidal flats (Table 6; Fig. 12).

Breeding Habitat

As described above, Red Knot breeding habitat is principally at elevations of <150 m and includes small wetlands where the chicks can feed. At the landscape scale, a model of potential breeding habitat was developed by New Jersey Department of Environmental Protection Division of Fish and Wildlife Endangered and Nongame Species Program (NJENSP) and Rutgers University using remotely-sensed land-cover characteristics. The model showed that Red Knot breeding habitat is generally found at elevations <150 m above sea level, <50 km from the coast and where vegetation cover is <5%. Red Knots and their chicks and fledglings forage in shallow sedge meadows and on sparsely vegetated lake edges proximate to nest sites.

Migration and Stopover Habitat—Canada

The critical staging areas for Red Knots during spring and fall migration in Canada are along sandy beaches and tidal mudflats in James Bay and tidal mudflats and salt marshes in the northern Bay of Fundy (R. I. G. Morrison, unpubl. data; M. Peck, unpubl. data; K. Ross, pers. comm.). In the Bay of Fundy, Red Knot migrants are rare in spring, but relatively common in the fall (Hicklin 1987).

Migration and Stopover Habitat—Northeastern U.S.

It is not believed that large numbers of Red Knots occur during migration in Maine (L. Tudor, pers. comm.), New Hampshire (C. Raithel, pers. comm.), Connecticut, and Rhode Island (J. Dickson, pers. comm.; D. Varza, pers. comm.). In the northeastern U.S. (New Jersey–Maine), the principal Red Knot staging areas are along the New Jersey, New York, and Massachusetts coastlines. In Massachusetts, Red Knots use sandy beaches and tidal mudflats during fall migration near Scituate, Duxbury, and Plymouth Beach, and along the shoreline in Cape Cod south to Monomoy (B. A. Harrington, unpubl. data). New York's Jamaica Bay Wildlife Refuge has a concentration of migratory Red Knots during spring and fall along sandy beaches and most commonly within the impoundment (K. Tripp, pers. comm.). Along the Atlantic coast of New Jersey, Red Knots utilize sandy beaches during spring and fall migration for foraging (K. Clark, unpubl. data; D. Hernández, unpubl. data; L. J. Niles, unpubl. data; H. P. Sitters, unpubl. data).

Migration and Stopover Habitat—Delaware Bay, U.S.

Delaware Bay is the most important staging area during northbound migration and is normally used by the whole or a large proportion of the *C. c. rufa* population which spends 2–3 wk staging there in the latter half of May. Beaches typical of the Delaware Bay shore are a mixture of sand and smooth gravel, and shorebirds

TABLE 6. HABITAT TYPES UTILIZED BY FORAGING RED KNOTS ON BREEDING GROUNDS (B), SPRING MIGRATION (S), FALL MIGRATION (F), AND WINTERING GROUNDS (W).

#[a]	Location	Sandy beach	Tidal mud-flat	Peat bank	Restinga/inter-tidal rocky flat	Salt marsh	Mangrove	Brackish lagoon/impoundment	Rocky barrens	Source
1	King William Island, Canada								B	R. I. G. Morrison (unpubl. data), M. Peck (unpubl. data), R. K. Ross (pers. comm.)
2	Southampton Island, Canada								B	R. I. G. Morrison (unpubl. data), M. Peck (unpubl. data); R. K. Ross (pers. comm.)
3	James Bay, Canada	S, F								R. I. G. Morrison (unpubl. data), R. K. Ross (pers. comm.)
4	Mingan Archipelago, Canada				F					Y. Aubry (pers. comm.)
5	Northern Bay of Fundy, Canada		S, F			S, F				Hicklin (1987), R.I.G. Morrison and M. Peck (unpubl. data)
6	Massachusetts, U.S.	F	F							B. A. Harrington (unpubl. data)
7	New York, U.S.	S, F						S, F		B. A. Harrington (unpubl. data), K. Tripp (pers. comm.)
8	Atlantic coast New Jersey, U.S.	S, F								K. Clark (unpubl. data), D. Hernández (unpubl. data), L. J. Niles, (unpubl. data), H. P. Sitters (unpubl. data)
9	Delaware Bay, U.S.	S, F				S				K. Bennett (unpubl. data), K. Clark (unpubl. data), K. Kalasz (unpubl. data), H. P. Sitters (unpubl. data)
10	Maryland, U.S.	S, F	S, F							G. Therres (pers. comm.)
11	Virginia, U.S.	S, F	S, F	S, F						S. Rice (pers. comm.), B. Truitt (pers. comm.), B. Watts (pers. comm.)
12	North Carolina, U.S.	S, F	S, F							S. Cameron (pers. comm.)
13	South Carolina, U.S.	S, F W?								F. Sanders (pers. comm.)
14	Georgia, U.S.	S, F W?		S, F W?						B. Winn (pers. comm.)
15	North Florida, U.S.	S, F W	S, F W			S, F W		S, F W		N. Douglass (pers. comm.), P. Leary (pers. comm.), Sprandel et al. (1997)
16	South Florida, U.S.	S, F W	S, F W				S, F W	S, F W		N. Douglass (pers. comm.), P. Leary (pers. comm.), Sprandel et al. (1997)

TABLE 6. CONTINUED.

#[a]	Location	Sandy beach	Tidal mud-flat	Peat bank	Restinga/inter-tidal rocky flat	Salt marsh	Man-grove	Brackish lagoon/impound-ment	Rocky barrens	Source
17	Texas, U.S.	S, F; W	S, F; W			S, F; W				J. Arvin (pers. comm.) W. Burkett (pers. comm.) B. Ortego (pers. comm.)
18	Panama Bay, Panama	S	S, W				S			Buehler (2002)
19	Maranhão, Brazil	S, F; W	S, F; W				S, F; W			I. Serrano (unpubl. data)
20	Lagoa do Peixe, Brazil	S, F; W						S, F; W		I. Serrano (unpubl. data)
21	Punta Rasa, Argentina	S, F								P. M. González (unpubl. data)
22	San Antonio Oeste, Argentina	S, F	S, F		S, F					P. M. González (unpubl. data)
23	Chiloé Island, Chile	S								L. A. Espinosa (pers. comm.)
24	Río Gallegos, Argentina	S, F	S, F		S, F					P. M. González (unpubl. data)
25	Bahía Lomas, Chile		W							C. Espoz (unpubl. data)
26	Bahía San Sebastián, Argentina		W							R. Matus (unpubl. data) P. M. González (unpubl. data)
27	Río Grande, Argentina	W	W		W					P. M. González (unpubl. data)

[a] The numbers correspond to those on Fig. 12.

are distributed on Delaware Bay relative to availability of horseshoe crab eggs. One of the most critical issues for the conservation of the Red Knot population is its dependence on huge quantities of eggs produced by the mass spawning of the largest known population of Atlantic horseshoe crabs (Shuster and Botton 1985). Crab eggs are especially important to Red Knots because of time constraints in completing their 15,000 km trans-hemispheric migration from Tierra del Fuego to the Canadian Arctic (Morrison and Harrington 1992, Harrington 2001). To stay on schedule and ensure breeding opportunities, Red Knots must increase body mass in Delaware Bay by 50–100% in 2–3 wk (Baker et al. 2004), one of the most rapid fattening events in birds. Some Red Knots may arrive at or below normal lean body mass of 110 g and depart at 180–220 g. Food quality, quantity and availability as well as the time constraints associated with nutrient acquisition (foraging, food processing, and assimilation) are critically linked in achieving this unique anabolic event.

Habitats important for Red Knots in Delaware Bay

Most horseshoe crabs spawn on sandy beaches around high tide, burying their eggs close to the high-tide line. Spawning activity usually peaks during the latter half of May to early June, which coincides with the main Red Knot stopover (Botton et al. 1994). The most important habitats in Delaware Bay for spawning crabs are the sandy beaches along the New Jersey shore mainly from Town Bank to Gandys Beach and along the Delaware shore mainly from Slaughter Beach to Port Mahon (Fig. 15). In New Jersey, Red Knots also make extensive use of the Atlantic coast, particularly the sand-spits and sandbanks around Stone Harbor Point and Hereford Inlet for roosting and occasionally for foraging on surf clams. They also forage on spat of the blue mussel in the protected intertidal marshes behind the Atlantic coast. In Delaware, Red Knots sometimes roost day and night in an area of relatively unvegetated marsh about 1.7 km inland from the bayshore and 500 m north of the Mispillion River. So far as we can determine, this is the only place in the world where Red Knots have been recorded roosting inland at night. In 2004 and 2005, this site became flooded and many Red Knots regularly commuted from the Delaware shore, where they fed by day, to roost at Hereford Inlet on the Atlantic coast of New Jersey at night, a round trip of 94 km (H. P. Sitters, unpubl. data).

Extensive coastal marshes and mudflats that are typically fronted by a sandy barrier beach fringe Delaware Bay. These sandy beaches mainly overlay marsh sediments (generally a fibrous peat formed by the root mat of the marsh plants) and vary in thickness from a thin veneer to about 2 m (Phillips 1986a). The back beaches, above normal high tide, form a low dune and are often colonized by common reed (*Phragmites australis*; Phillips 1987). The intertidal portions of the sandy beaches are of special significance as these are the focus of horseshoe crab spawning activity and of Red Knots' foraging. Horseshoe crabs prefer beaches dominated by coarse sandy sediments and avoid beaches that have a high amount of peaty sediments or are adjacent to exposed peat banks (Botton et al. 1988). These factors were used by Botton et al. (1988) to develop a classification scheme that ranked beaches as either preferred or avoided habitat for horseshoe crab spawning. Horseshoe crabs deposit most of their eggs 10–20 cm deep in sandy beach sediments (Botton et al. 1992); eggs are then redistributed to shallower depths or the surface and become available to foraging shorebirds by subsequent spawning and wave action. Although it is widely thought that the major process that brings eggs to the surface is the action of female crabs digging up earlier nests as they spawn, the way this works is poorly understood. Possibly there is some critical density of spawning crabs below which few eggs come to the surface and above which many do. If so, it would be valuable to determine what that density is as an aid to establishing the size of the crab population that is needed to support the shorebird stopover.

Starting in 1999, systematic surveys were conducted to count intertidal (i.e., spawning) horseshoe crabs throughout Delaware Bay (Smith et al. 2002a, 2002b). Various short-term studies of egg density preceded systematic surveys that were started on the New Jersey shore in 1996 and on the Delaware shore in 1997 (M. L. Botton, pers. comm.; R. E. Loveland, pers. comm.; NJDFW, unpubl. data; Weber 2003). These used different methods making it difficult to determine how egg densities varied between the two states and it was not until 2005 that the two projects were combined into a single bay-wide survey using the same methodology. All these surveys show that egg densities vary by several orders of magnitude, sometimes exceeding 10^6/m of shoreline (Smith et al., 2002b). Smith et al. (2002b) found that beach morphology and wave energy interact with the density of spawning females to explain much of the variation in the density and distribution of eggs and larvae between the study beaches. Horseshoe crabs showed a preference for spawning on low-energy (i.e., wave-protected) sandy beaches. While the surveys

FIGURE 15. Map of the Delaware Bay (New Jersey and Delaware) showing some of the most important refueling sites for Red Knots.

only sampled bay-front beaches, beaches along tidal creeks were also noted as being potential hotspots for crab spawning and shorebird foraging. At a broader, bay-wide scale, the use of intertidal beaches as horseshoe crab spawning habitat is limited in the north by low salinity (Sea Breeze in New Jersey and Woodland Beach in Delaware) and by ocean-generated energy in the south (North Cape May, New Jersey and Broadkill, Delaware).

Not surprisingly, migratory shorebird abundance is spatially variable within the Delaware Bay estuary as a consequence of these larger bay-wide patterns of horseshoe crab abundance and spawning activity. Migratory shorebirds

in Delaware Bay showed a strong preference for beaches with higher numbers of crab eggs although shorebird abundance also depends on other factors such as competition, disturbance, and risk of predation (Botton et al. (1994). Shorebirds were recorded to aggregate near shoreline discontinuities, such as salt marsh creek deltas and jetties, which acted as concentration mechanisms for passively drifting eggs. Human disturbance can greatly reduce the value of foraging habitat for Red Knots. The various studies outlined above show that a complex array of factors determine the value of Delaware Bay beaches as horseshoe crab spawning and shorebird foraging habitat.

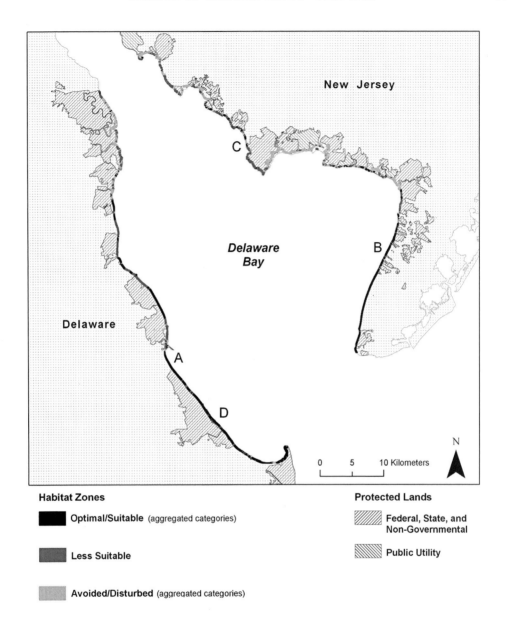

FIGURE 16. Map of horseshoe crab spawning habitat suitability with location of protected conservation lands. Several key locations have been annotated: (A) Slaughter Beach, (B) Cape May NWR, (C) Fortescue, and, (D) Broadkill Beach. Protected Lands GIS Data Sources: NJDEP, NJ Green Acres, TNC-NJ Chapter, DE Parks and Recreation.

A large portion of Delaware Bay shore has some form of conservation protection (Fig. 16). The New Jersey shore includes state-owned lands at Dennis Creek, Heislerville and Egg Island Wildlife Management Areas; USFWS-owned land (Cape May National Wildlife Refuge [NWR]); The Nature Conservancy (TNC) land; and the Public Service Electric and Gas Company land managed by TNC. The Delaware shore includes large areas in USFWS ownership at Bombay Hook and Prime Hook NWRs, state-owned land (Little Creek, Ted Harvey, and Milford Neck Wildlife Areas and Cape Henlopen State Park), and a significant amount of conservation land owned by TNC and Delaware Wildlands. However, in both states, large areas of shoreline are in private ownership and subject to habitat disturbance and loss. In New Jersey, while the intertidal beach is considered publicly owned, key beaches lie immediately adjacent to residential development including Villas, Reed's Beach, and Fortescue. In Delaware, private property ownership generally extends to mean low water. Similar to New Jersey, residential development in Delaware is adjacent to key beaches including Pickering, Kitts Hummock, Bowers, and Slaughter beaches. Port Mahon and Mispillion Inlet are different in that commercial use and bulkheading threaten critical Red Knot habitat. Regardless of residential proximity where the bayfront is accessible by car, human disturbance is a threat that can reduce the value of habitat for Red Knots.

Red Knot feeding ecology in Delaware Bay

The strong reliance of Red Knots on horseshoe crab eggs has been confirmed by stomach content analyses (Tsipoura and Burger 1999) and stable-isotope, diet-tracking studies, which show that horseshoe crab eggs are the main constituent of the Red Knots' diet during their stopover in Delaware Bay (Haramis et al. 2007). Other studies (Castro et al. 1989, Castro and Myers 1993) have estimated the daily requirement of shorebirds for horseshoe crab eggs based on the birds' energetic requirements. These show that Sanderlings would need 8,300 and Red Knots 30,000 eggs per day (Castro et al. 1989, Castro and Myers 1993, Hernández 2005). A more recent study using pen trials estimated that Red Knots need 13,000 eggs per day to maintain body weight and 24,000 eggs per day when fattening optimally (Haramis et al. 2007).

A key question, however, is not just how many eggs are required or consumed, but how important are horseshoe crab eggs to migratory fattening and to what extent alternative foods in the Delaware Bay environment are utilized. Haramis et al. (2007) conducted research in Delaware Bay from 2000–2004 that considered the trophic link between Red Knots and crab eggs using stable-isotope diet tracking and pen-feeding trials. He measured stable isotopes (SI, $\delta^{15}N$ signal) in the plasma of captive Red Knots that were fed exclusively on horseshoe crab eggs and compared these signals to free-ranging Red Knots. The close consistency in SI pattern of response and convergence of diet asymptotes between free-ranging and captive birds confirm the importance of crab eggs in the diet of Red Knots during stopover in Delaware Bay.

Throughout their worldwide range, Red Knots generally feed wholly or mainly on bivalves which are swallowed whole (Alerstam

et al. 1992, Dekinga and Piersma 1993, Piersma et al. 1993, González et al. 1996). Therefore, the most likely alternative prey in the Delaware Bay system would be blue mussels, coquina clams, or ribbed mussels (*Modiolus demissus*). As filter feeders, bivalves are low in the food chain and have SI values that can be discriminated easily from crab eggs. This enabled Haramis et al. (2007) to show that while some Red Knots may consume bivalves, they do not form a significant part of the diet of most birds in Delaware Bay in spring. However, in most years a significant minority of birds (<30%) has been observed foraging on these alternative food resources. These tend to occur on the Atlantic coast of New Jersey and the majority of these birds are short-distance migrants (possibly *C. c. roselaari*) from wintering areas in the southeastern states of the U.S. (P. W. Atkinson et al., unpubl. data). It is hypothesized that these short-distance migrants are either able to arrive in Delaware Bay earlier than birds from South America and regrow their digestive apparatus to deal with the hard-shelled prey, or do not undergo the major physiological changes of gut size reduction that the long-distance migrants have to undertake to migrate in such long hops (P. W. Atkinson et al., unpubl. data). However, for long-distance migrants, particularly the birds from Tierra del Fuego, crab eggs are crucial to successful fattening and these birds are therefore likely to be more vulnerable to a decline in the availability of eggs than those that have not come so far.

Hernández (2005) analyzed prey-attack patterns (peck and probe rates), locomotion patterns (step rates), and the interactions between these patterns as a measure of foraging efficiency relative to egg density and patchiness. However, because he was not able to tell whether or not a peck or probe was successful, he could not determine the relationship between intake rate (eggs per second) and egg density, which is essential for measuring the critical egg densities that affect overall foraging success. Atkinson et al. (2003) describe the use of feeding pans containing known numbers of eggs, either on the surface or buried in the top 5 cm of sand, and placed these in foraging flocks of Red Knots in the field and recorded feeding rates and depletion. Knowing the relationship between egg density and egg-intake rate, and the daily egg requirements from the Haramis et al. (2007) study, it is possible to estimate the number of hours of feeding required for a given density of eggs.

From these experiments, Atkinson et al. (2003) determined that the number of eggs consumed per peck (i.e., success rate of pecks) increased asymptotically with egg density (Gillings et al. 2007). Whether present on the surface or buried in the sand, eggs consumed per second increase asymptotically with egg density (Fig. 17). Higher intake rates are achieved from pecking eggs off the sand surface and, even at very low surface egg densities, it is significantly more profitable to peck than probe (Fig. 18).

Daylight during staging is around 15 hr and crab eggs are laid near the high tide mark so birds theoretically could feed for most of daylight hours. Then, the required daily egg intake could be achieved by feeding on surface eggs at a density of only 360 eggs m^{-2}, or buried eggs at a density of 19,200 eggs m^{-2} (Table 7). However, the availability of eggs on the sand

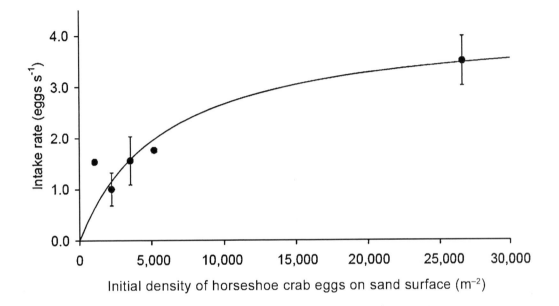

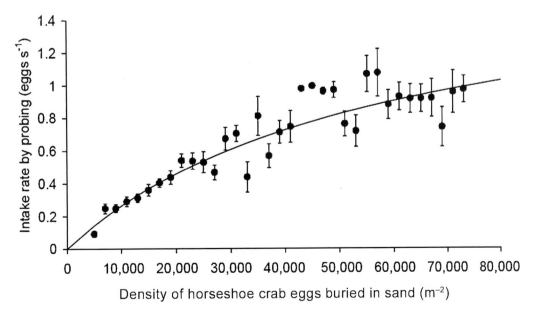

FIGURE 17. Functional responses relating the intake rate (eggs s^{-1}) achieved by Red Knots to the density of (upper) eggs present on sand surface and (lower) eggs buried and mixed in the top 5 cm of sand.

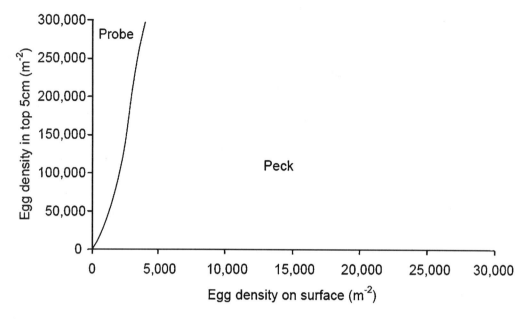

FIGURE 18. Density of eggs on the sand surface or buried and mixed in the sediment (down to 5 cm) will determine whether it is most profitable to peck or probe.

surface, and buried in the top 5 cm of sand are likely to vary through the tidal cycle with density of spawning crabs, wave action, and depletion by shorebirds and gulls. Furthermore, eggs remaining on the sand surface rapidly dry out (within an hour of deposition on hot windy days) and become hardened. During 10 yr of observations Red Knot have never been seen consuming these dessicated eggs and the Semipalmated Sandpiper (*Calidris pusilla*) is the only species having been seen consuming dessicated eggs and that only on one day (S. Gillings, pers. comm.; N. Clark, unpubl. data). These processes mean that optimal feeding is constrained to bouts of consumption of eggs freshly deposited on the sand surface by the falling tide and/or consumption of buried eggs where they are present at sufficiently high density.

Based on field studies in Delaware Bay between 2003 and 2004, Hernández (2005) predicted that a minimum density of at least 300,000 eggs m^{-2} was needed for Red Knots to completely maximize foraging efficiency on buried eggs. This fits well with predictions in Table 7. So far as we know, Red Knots do not feed on horseshoe crab eggs at night in Delaware Bay and cannot feed continuously

TABLE 7. THE AMOUNT OF TIME (HR) NEEDED TO ACHIEVE THE DAILY HORSESHOE CRAB EGG CONSUMPTION OF 24,000 FRESH EGGS (HARAMIS ET AL. 2007) IN RELATION TO EGG AVAILABILITY (EGGS M^{-2}) DEPENDENT ON WHETHER EGGS ARE: (A) FREELY AVAILABLE ON THE SAND SURFACE OR (B) BURIED WITHIN THE TOP 5 CM OF SAND.

(A) Surface egg density	Required feeding time	(B) Buried egg density	Required feeding time
360	15.0	19,200	15.0
500	11.3	50,000	8.1
1,000	6.7	100,000	6.0
2,000	4.3	200,000	4.9
3,000	3.6	300,000	4.5
4,000	3.2		
5,000	2.9		
10,000	2.5		
20,000	2.2		
30,000	2.2		

Notes: These calculations are based on intake rates from experimentally measured functional responses (Atkinson et al. 2003, Gillings et al. 2007). For reference, the density of eggs yielding a 15-hr foraging time (day length) is shown.

throughout the day as they need to spend time on other behaviors such as vigilance and preening. Moreover feeding areas are not available when the tide covers them, neither are surface eggs if they are subject to rapid desiccation at low tide on hot days. The foraging models also suggest that Red Knot foraging efficiency is adversely affected by decreased egg density and increased egg patchiness.

Studies by Haramis et al. (2007) and Hernández (2005) describe the importance of horseshoe crab eggs to Red Knots and the lack of alternative foods being used during stopover. Data from NJENSP indicate average egg densities in New Jersey in 2004 of around 3,200 eggs m^{-2} in the top 5 cm. If these were all on the surface they would theoretically be sufficient. However, in reality many of these will have been buried and those on the surface may have desiccated on hot days. Therefore, Red Knots may not be able to meet their energetic requirements during stopover due to insufficient numbers of eggs. In conclusion, low egg densities constitute a direct threat to migratory fattening in *C. c. rufa*. Moreover it has been demonstrated that low weight birds in Delaware Bay subsequently have a lower resighting rate in the flyway, implying lower adult survival (Baker et al. 2004).

Studies of Red Knots trapped twice during a single spring stopover show that the mean rate of mass gain of birds that arrive in mid May is around 4 g/d, but that late-arriving birds can achieve gains two–three times higher. This indicates that if there is sufficient food they have some flexibility and are able to make up for lost time (though it is likely that this comes at some physiological cost). This relationship broke down in 2003 and 2005 and late-arriving birds were apparently unable to achieve higher rates of mass gain because of inadequate food supplies (Atkinson et al. 2007).

In summary, feeding studies in Delaware Bay appear to go some way toward explaining why Tierra del Fuego wintering Red Knots have shown a sharp decline, but northern wintering populations have apparently been more stable. The southern birds are more reliant on horseshoe crab eggs, the availability of which has declined. Migration has become later in Patagonia and some evidence shows later arrival into Delaware Bay (Baker et al. 2004, Bala et al. 2005; K. Clark, unpubl. data). Late arrivals do not have the ability to recover lost time if egg numbers are not sufficient. In contrast, northern-wintering birds have shown no change in migration phenology and are less reliant on crab eggs. Therefore, if factors lead Red Knots to arrive late in Delaware Bay and/or in poor condition, it does not diminish the importance of the Delaware Bay food resource. If anything, it is increased because it is of critical importance in enabling the birds to recover quickly and reach the breeding grounds on time and in good reproductive condition.

Mapping horseshoe crab spawning habitat suitability

Lathrop and Allen (2005) used visual interpretation of high-spatial-resolution color-infrared digital orthophotography to provide the first comprehensive inventory and characterization of the Delaware Bay shoreline. Several categories of information were mapped that are relevant to the bayshore's value as horseshoe crab spawning habitat: (1) shoreline type and width, (2) presence of near-shore development, and (3) shoreline stabilization structures on both the fore-shore and back-beach. Sand beach dominates the foreshore of the Delaware side of the bay, while organic beach composed of either eroding peat banks or salt marsh dominates the New Jersey side (Table 8). Overall, about 54% of Delaware Bay's shoreline represents the horseshoe crab's preferred spawning habitat of sand beach (Fig. 16). These sand beaches are generally narrow in width, averaging only 10.9 m on the Delaware side and 5.9 m on the New Jersey side of the bay. Some of the widest beaches (some nearly 100 m in width) are found along the central and southern portions of Cape May in New Jersey and the central sections of the Delaware coast.

TABLE 8. CHARACTERIZATION AND LENGTHS OF THE DELAWARE BAY SHORELINE.

Shoreline type	Delaware		New Jersey	
	Kilometers	(%)	Kilometers	(%)
Sand	67.50	(74.3%)	61.86	(41.7%)
Armor (fore-shore)	3.66	(4.0%)	8.35	(5.6%)
Organic	19.68	(21.7%)	78.10	(52.7%)
Total shoreline	90.84	(100%)	148.30	(100%)
Armor (back)[a]	2.67	(2.9%)	5.06	(3.4%)
Development	13.35	(14.7%)	5.72	(3.8%)

[a] Back-beach armor and developed area measurement are separate from the total shoreline measurement.

Beach stabilization structures (e.g., armoring practices such as bulkheading or riprap) account for 4.0% of the Delaware shoreline and 5.6% of the New Jersey side (Table 8). An additional 2.9% and 3.4% of the Delaware and New Jersey shorelines, respectively, also had some form of armoring in the back beach (Table 8), which may come into play as beaches erode and shorelines recede, exposing these structures in the future. About 8.0% of the Delaware Bayshore is subject to near-shore development. While some beaches in New Jersey and Delaware have had development removed (e.g., Thompson's Beach, New Jersey, and Big Stone Beach, Delaware), Lathrop and Allen's ground truthing surveys observed construction of new development and redevelopment on the Delaware side of the bay.

Using the mapped shoreline geographic information system (GIS) data, Lathrop and Allen (2005) classified the Delaware Bay shoreline into five categories of horseshoe crab spawning suitability based on criteria proposed by Botton et al. (1988). These were:

1. Optimal—undisturbed sand beach.
2. Suitable—sand beach with only small areas of peat and/or backed by development.
3. Less suitable habitat—exposed peat in the lower and middle intertidal zone and sand present in the upper intertidal.
4. Avoided habitat—exposed peat or active salt marsh fringing the shoreline, no sand present.
5. Disturbed—beach fill, riprap, or bulkheading.

Based on this more refined mapping assessment, about a quarter (23.9%) of Delaware Bay's shoreline was classified as optimal spawning habitat (34.5% of Delaware and 17.4% of New Jersey bayshore; Table 9). Only an additional 6.6% of shoreline came in the next, suitable, category (11.6% Delaware, 3.4% New Jersey). Most of the optimal and suitable spawning habitat is located in the lower parts the bay; the bay becomes more fragmented farther up

(Fig. 19). Lathrop and Allen's map should be regarded as only a provisional assessment of spawning habitat suitability because it does not include site-specific consideration of beach morphology or wave energy characteristics that may also be important. Thus the map probably overestimates the amount of optimal habitat. For example, the lowest section of the Delaware shoreline (15 km south from Broadkill) and the southern third of the Cape May Peninsula (8.5 km) on the New Jersey side were mapped affording optimal or suitable habitat. However, Smith et al. (2002b) did not record high levels of horseshoe crab spawning on these beaches, presumably due to their greater exposure to the ocean leading to higher wave energies and less suitable beach morphology. It should be noted that in a few areas classified as disturbed, groins have resulted in low energy sandy beaches which are ideal for spawning horseshoe crabs. An example of this is Mispillion Harbor, which has the highest reported density of crab eggs in the whole of Delaware Bay.

Of the optimal spawning habitat, 39.5% has some form of conservation protection (i.e., federal, state, public utility, or non-governmental organization—41% Delaware, 37% New Jersey; Table 10). Therefore, while significant stretches of optimal habitat are protected, key sections have no formal protection (Fig. 16), though that does not necessarily mean that they are threatened. On the Delaware side, Slaughter Beach is one of the longest stretches of optimal habitat that is largely unprotected. Similarly several pockets of optimal or suitable habitat exist along the northern New Jersey bayshore (e.g., Fortescue and Gandy's Beaches) that are largely unprotected. Although a long section of optimal or suitable habitat would appear to be protected by the Prime Hook NWR (Fig. 16), this is only partially true because some stretches of the barrier beach are in private ownership and developed (e.g., Broadkill Beach) and only the back-bay marshes and adjacent uplands are in refuge protection.

TABLE 9. LENGTH OF SHORELINE IN DELAWARE AND NEW JERSEY ACCORDING TO SUITABILITY FOR HORSESHOE CRAB SPAWNING.

Habitat suitability	Delaware		New Jersey	
	Kilometers	(%)	Kilometers	(%)
Optimal	31.28	(34.5%)	25.69	(17.4%)
Suitable	10.56	(11.6%)	5.07	(3.4%)
Less suitable	28.98	(32.0%)	48.88	(33.1%)
Avoided	16.78	(18.5%)	58.84	(39.8%)
Disturbed	3.08	(3.4%)	8.31	(5.6%)
Total shoreline[a]	90.68		147.79	

[a] The five categories are adapted from Botton et al. (1988). Due to differences in GIS processing, the total shoreline lengths are slightly different compared with Table 8.

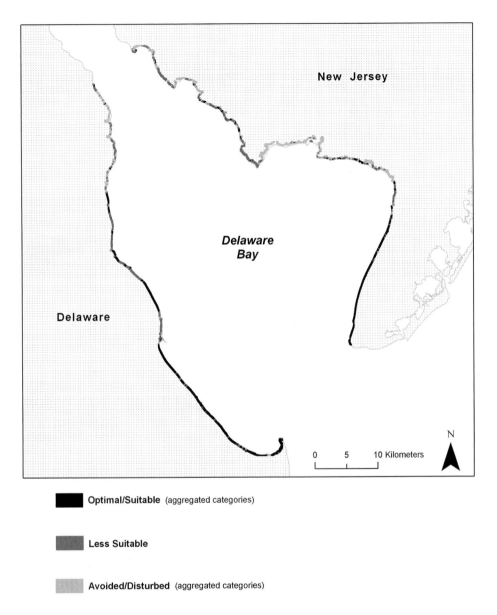

FIGURE 19. Map of horseshoe crab spawning habitat suitability on Delaware Bay based on beach sediment and development characteristics (Lathrop and Allen 2005). Note that this mapping does not include consideration of beach morphology or wave energy characteristics that may be also be important in determining the suitability of the beach as horseshoe crab spawning habitat or other human disturbance or habitat factors that might influence bird usage.

Mapping critical Red Knot habitat

During 1986–2005, weekly aerial shorebird surveys were carried out along the Delaware Bay shore over the 6-wk period of the spring stopover from the beginning of May to early June (Clark et al. 1993; K. Clark, unpubl. data). These data have been examined to determine which Delaware Bay beaches are most important for Red Knots. For the survey, the bayshore was divided into 81 segments of about 3 km each (48 in New Jersey and 33 in Delaware), which were geo-referenced to permit mapping. The survey data have been summarized for 5-yr periods. For each period, the aggregate number of Red Knots counted in each segment was

TABLE 10. LENGTH AND PERCENTAGE OF EACH SPAWNING HABITAT SUITABILITY CATEGORY IN CONSERVATION OWNERSHIP.

| | In conservation ownership | | | |
| | Delaware | | New Jersey | |
Habitat suitability	Kilometers	(%)	Kilometers	(%)
Optimal	12.87	(41.1%)	9.62	(37.4%)
Suitable	0.74	(7.0%)	0.13	(2.6%)
Less suitable	18.57	(64.1%)	33.56	(68.6%)
Avoided	11.55	(68.8%)	48.87	(83.0%)
Disturbed	0.99	(32.1%)	0.53	(6.4%)

Notes: Conservation ownership may include federal, state, public utility, or non-governmental organization land that is primarily held for the conservation of wildlife or other natural resources. The percentages are based on the shoreline lengths shown in Table 8.

expressed as a percentage of the total aggregate number summed (across the whole study area for the entire 5-yr period). The survey data were analyzed as percentages to examine the spatial distribution of beach use on a relative, rather than absolute basis.

Comparison of the maps for the first and last 5-yr periods suggests that the spatial distribution of Red Knot use has changed (Fig. 20; K. Clark, unpubl. data). During 1986–1990, Red Knots were relatively evenly distributed along the New Jersey shore from Reeds Beach to Ben Davis Point. However, during 2001–2005, a greater concentration occurred from Norbury's Landing to Reed's Beach and from Egg Island Point to Gandy's Beach. During 1986–1990, the Red Knots were relatively evenly distributed along Delaware shore from Bowers Beach through Bombay Hook NWR with a major concentration in the Slaughter Beach-Mispillion Harbor area. During 2001–2005, however, a much greater concentration occurred around Slaughter Beach-Mispillion Harbor and around Bowers Beach. Mispillion Harbor consistently supports high concentrations of Red Knots, sometimes more than 20% of the entire bay population.

Other areas of the Bayshore were little used by Red Knots; for example, in New Jersey the Cape May Peninsula south of Norbury's Landing, and in Delaware the central and lowest sections (Big Stone Beach and Broadkill Beach to Cape Henlopen). These low Red Knot-use sections coincide with areas of low horseshoe crab spawning activity as recorded by Smith et al. (2002b). Lathrop and Allen (2005) classified other parts of the bayshore as less suitable and even as avoided as crab-spawning habitat in 2002, that were recorded as having medium-high Red Knot use in 1986–1990. In many cases, Red Knot use of these beaches had diminished by 2001–2005; for example the Bombay Hook NWR in Delaware and the Maurice River area in New Jersey (Fig. 20). Whether these changes are due to beach erosion and/or reduced

numbers of horseshoe crabs or spawning activity is unknown.

In addition to the aerial surveys, ground surveys have been conducted by NJENSP to identify other high use areas for Red Knots during both spring and autumn stopover. In particular, large numbers of Red Knots have been recorded using the Hereford Inlet area on the Atlantic coast of Cape May and the adjacent marshes in spring. Fall ground surveys have also recorded significant numbers of Red Knots in the Hereford Inlet area. Stone Harbor Point and the nearby Nummy, Champagne, and Humphrey Islands include undeveloped sand beach, sandbar, mudflat, and salt-marsh habitats which afford critically important roosting areas, especially on spring high tides and at night. This area is also important for supplementary foraging by Red Knots in spring and as a main foraging area in autumn when surf clams and mussel spat are available.

In addition to the Delaware beaches identified from aerial surveys, International Shorebird Surveys (ISS) conducted in Delaware during the 1992–1997 spring migrations suggest that managed impoundments along Delaware Bay may also provide important habitat for Red Knots. Each year from 1993–1996, 1,200–5,300 Red Knots were recorded in an impoundment at the Ted Harvey Wildlife Area. Managed impoundments in Delaware may represent critical habitat for high-tide and nighttime roosts if conditions are suitable.

Maps showing the distribution of horseshoe crab spawning habitat and Red Knot use in Delaware Bay (Figs. 16, 19, and 20) identify the main areas that should be considered as critical habitat to support the Red Knot's spring stopover. Knot use is probably the better criterion because it not only reflects areas of high egg density but also the birds' other requirements, such as safety from predators and suitable and safe high water and nighttime roost sites. For example, coastal areas of Egg Island modeled as less suitable or avoided by spawning crabs, are

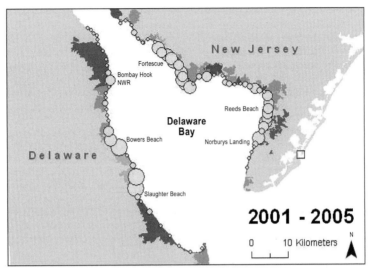

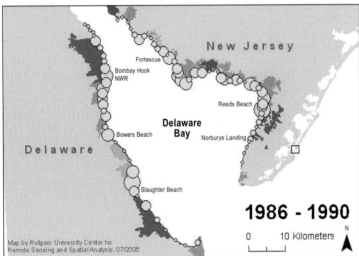

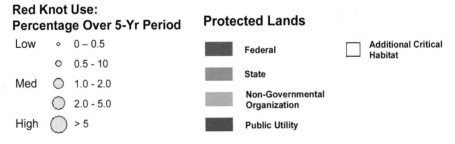

FIGURE 20. Map of percent Red Knot use for spring stop over between 1986–1990 and 2001–2005. Survey data summed across the 5-yr period and percent of total calculated for each beach segment (K. Clark, unpubl. data).

nevertheless valuable Red Knot habitat because they are used for roosting during day and night high tides. Their attraction is that they are protected by water channels from ground predators and are free from human disturbance.

On the basis of the most recent as well as the 1980s data, the Delaware Bay shore in New Jersey from Norbury's Landing to Dennis Creek should be considered critical Red Knot habitat. This portion of the Cape May Peninsula has been the focus of land conservation acquisition as part of the Cape May NWR. However, the significant gaps that still exist in the existing refuge boundaries (Fig. 16) should be a high priority for future acquisition or conservation management. Likewise, important stretches of shoreline in the Fortescue and Gandys Beach areas should be considered critical Red Knot habitat and prioritized for protection. The Hereford Inlet area, between Stone Harbor and Wildwood, and Stone Harbor Point should also be considered critical habitat due to its importance during both spring and fall migration.

The survey data suggest that some parts of the New Jersey shore between East Point and Moores Beach had higher relative use by Red Knots during 1986–1990 than more recently. This area has experienced considerable beach erosion and some stretches have a history of development and beach armoring. Therefore, it would seem possible that beach restoration might be feasible in this area (e.g., at Thompson's Beach). The most southerly portion of the Cape May Peninsula (south of Villas), while mapped as optimal/suitable horseshoe crab spawning habitat (and appearing as major gaps in conservation protection in Fig. 16), probably need not be considered as important Red Knot habitat due to its lower usage by spawning crabs and foraging Red Knots.

In Delaware, the shores in the vicinity of Bower's Beach and Slaughter Beach-Mispillion Harbor were recorded as critically important for Red Knots, but they are significantly lacking in protection due to private land ownership and density of residential development. These areas should be given priority for conservation acquisition or management in future. The area of Slaughter Beach-Mispillion Harbor should receive special consideration due to its outstanding concentrations of Red Knots (Fig. 20). The lowest section of the Delaware shore (south of Broadkill Beach), while mapped as optimal/suitable horseshoe crab spawning habitat (and appearing as major gaps in conservation protection, Fig. 16), probably should not be considered as critical Red Knot habitat due to its lower usage by spawning crabs and foraging shorebirds.

While it is the intertidal beaches that comprise the most important Red Knot habitat in Delaware Bay, Burger et al. (1997) have shown that migrant shorebirds, including Red Knots, move actively between the bay's habitats using them for foraging, resting, and other behaviors according to the state of the tide, date, and time of day. Though the beaches are of critical importance, during high tides (especially spring) the birds would be restricted to areas without sufficient food for profitable foraging and too close to vegetation and structures that could harbor predators. Therefore, Red Knots often go elsewhere, including nearby salt marshes, sand spits, and islands. On some occasions, Red Knots fly all the way across the Cape May Peninsula to use the extensive sandy beach, mud flats, and salt marshes in the vicinity of Stone Harbor for both foraging and roosting.

Evidence of decline in both the population of horseshoe crabs and the availability of their eggs for Red Knots

Currently, several surveys monitor the horseshoe crab population, the total density of eggs in the beaches, and the proportion of eggs in the upper 5 cm of sand that are potentially available to the shorebirds. Only two surveys, however, have been running long enough (and using consistent methods) to show how crab and egg numbers have changed over the period of increased horseshoe crab harvest which started in 1996. These are the DDFW trawl survey of crabs in Delaware Bay, which has focused on the in-bay population of crabs, and egg density surveys on the New Jersey bay shore since 1985. The egg density survey began in 1985–1986 by K. Williams, a contractor under NJDFW, and was continued by Rutgers University (M. L. Botton and R. E. Loveland) in 1990. Botton and Loveland analyzed the data collected by K. Williams in 1985–1986 in their subsequent study, using conversion factors derived from side-by-side sampling (M. L. Botton and R. E. Loveland, unpubl. data). The egg density survey has been carried out since 2000 by NJENSP. The Delaware Bay trawl survey shows a highly significant decline in the number of adult crabs in Delaware Bay (Fig. 21) and the New Jersey egg density survey shows a highly significant decline in the density of eggs in the upper 5 cm of sand in New Jersey (Fig. 22). In respect of both parameters, the main decline took place in the 1990s, before the Delaware Bay horseshoe crab spawning activity survey began in 1999 (Michels and Smith 2006) and before the horseshoe crab benthic trawl survey began in 2001 (Hata 2006). Both of these new and thorough

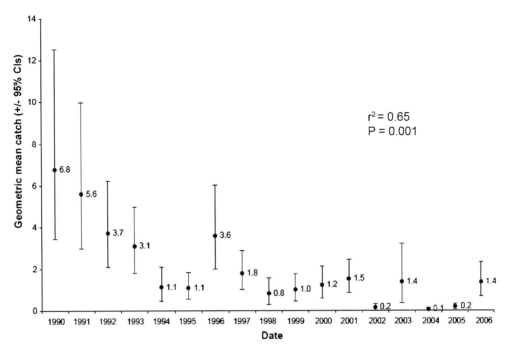

FIGURE 21. Number of horseshoe crabs in 30-foot trawls in Delaware Bay during May 1990–2006 (S. Michels, pers. comm.). The declining trend is highly significant (r² = 0.65, P < 0.001).

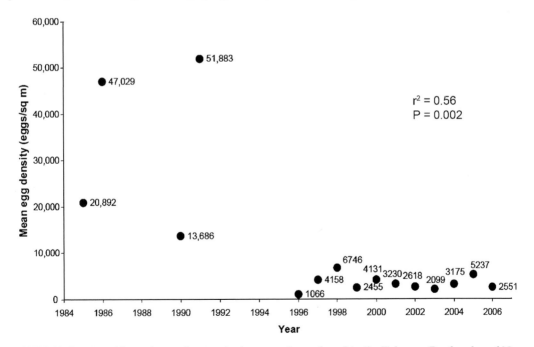

FIGURE 22. Density of horseshoe crabs eggs in the upper 5 cm of sand in the Delaware Bay beaches of New Jersey during late May 1985–2006. The declining trend is highly significant (r² = 0.56, P = 0.002). Source: 1985–1999 (M. L. Botton, pers. comm.; R. E. Loveland, pers. comm.); 2000–2006 (NJENSP, unpubl. data). Confidence intervals are not plotted because the raw data are not available for the earlier period and for the later period they are very small in relation to the scale. All data points relate to 2–6 sampling dates spread over May and early June and to core samples taken along transects between the high and low tide lines at 3-m intervals.

surveys indicated no major change in the size of the horseshoe crab population since they were instigated. The spawning activity survey shows that in 2003 and 2005 spawning was later than usual, probably on account of cold weather, and was much reduced in May. This led to a reduction in the availability of eggs during the peak Red Knot stopover and late-arriving birds in particular were unable to make the mass gains they needed (Atkinson et al. 2007). The confidence limits associated with the crab data preclude precise estimation of the scale of the decline, but it would seem to be of the order of 80% (based on geometric mean; Fig. 21). Similarly there is uncertainty about the scale of the decline in available eggs, but the data suggest somewhere in the range of 80–97% (Fig. 22).

Horseshoe crab spawning is greatly reduced by heavy on-shore wave action (M. L. Botton and R. E. Loveland, pers. comm.), and in some years long periods of winds from a particular direction lead to more crab spawning on one side of the bay than the other (the sheltered side, where the wind is offshore). For example, in 1997 persistent westerly winds led to far more spawning in Delaware than in New Jersey, but the reverse occurred in 2003 (L. J. Niles, unpubl. data). However, the fact that more Red Knots fed in New Jersey than Delaware every May from 2002–2005 (Fig. 23), including 2003 when winds were off-shore in New Jersey, indicates that on-shore winds alone are not responsible for the decreased densities of eggs on the New Jersey shore shown in Fig. 22.

Occasionally, (as on the Delaware shore in May 2003 [N. Clark, unpubl. data]) a storm will deposit large quantities of new sand on exposed beaches so that eggs already laid become buried so deeply that they are completely inaccessible to the shorebirds. Storms and wave action, as well as variation in the quality of different beaches as spawning habitat and depletion of eggs by foraging shorebirds and gulls mean that in any season considerable spatial and temporal variation occurs in the availability of eggs to Red Knots. The birds show a preference for foraging on beaches with high densities of available eggs; they also avoid concentrations of, and competition with, large numbers of gulls (Botton et al. 1994).

Studies of horseshoe crab spawning phenology show variation associated with seawater temperature; for example spawning was delayed by about 2 wk in 2003 when water temperatures averaged 2.8°C lower than the 1997–2002 mean (Weber 2003). This could have negative implications for the shorebird stopover if global warming results in a change in local seawater temperatures as a result of which the peak of spawning and the stopover do not coincide.

Egg-density sampling has not been carried out in Delaware for as long as in New Jersey and differences in methodology make comparison of trends between states virtually impossible. Therefore, no such comparisons are presented here. However, sampling in Delaware has demonstrated that one site, Mispillion Harbor, which is very well sheltered by long groins, is by far the most important horseshoe crab spawning location in the entire bay and often has eggs densities that are an order of magnitude greater than any other site sampled (Fig. 24).

The peak in the harvest of horseshoe crabs took place during 1996–1999 after which

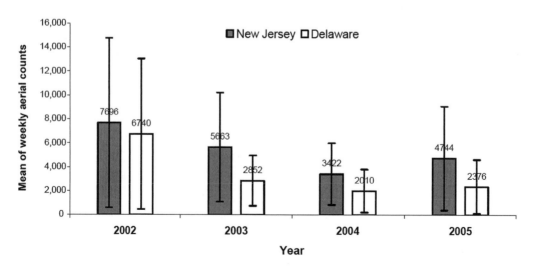

FIGURE 23. Mean of weekly aerial counts of Red Knots in New Jersey and Delaware in May 2002–2005.

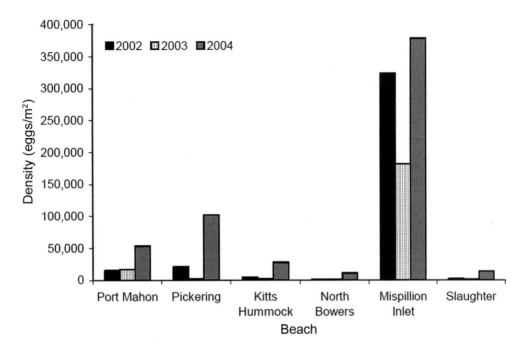

FIGURE 24. Mean densities of horseshoe crab eggs in the upper 5 cm of sand from beach transects sampled once in late May and once in early June at six sites on the Delaware shore of Delaware Bay during 2002–2004 ordered from north (Port Mahon) to south (Slaughter Beach) (Weber 2003, 2004). At each site on each sampling date, 20 core samples were taken along each of two transects covering 83% of the distance between the nocturnal high tide line and the tidal flat. Only the means for both transects are given by Weber so confidence intervals are not available.

harvest restrictions and management actions appear to have resulted in a more or less stable crab population, albeit at a relatively low level (Figs. 13, 21; Morrison et al. 2004). Crabs do not breed until 9–11 yr of age (Shuster et al. 2003), and thus measures already taken or even a complete cessation of all further harvest, may not be reflected by an increase in the breeding population of horseshoe crabs for several years.

MIGRATION AND STOPOVER HABITAT — SOUTHEASTERN UNITED STATES

In the southeastern U.S., Red Knots forage along sandy beaches during spring and fall migration from Maryland through Florida, and in Texas. During migration, Red Knots also use the tidal mudflats in Assateague Island National Seashore in Maryland and along the barrier islands in North Carolina (S. Cameron, pers. comm.; G. Therres, pers. comm.). In addition to the sandy beaches, Red Knots forage along peat banks for mussel spat in Virginia (S. Rice, pers. comm.; B. Truitt, pers. comm.; B. Watts, pers. comm.), and along small pockets of peat banks where the beach is eroding in Georgia (B. Winn, pers. comm.). Red Knots in Florida

also utilize salt marshes, brackish lagoons, and tidal mudflats, in addition to mangroves in southern Florida (N. Douglass, pers. comm.; P. Leary, pers. comm.; Sprandel et al. 1997). In Texas, migratory Red Knots concentrate at the Bolivar Flats in Galveston County with smaller numbers on the outer beaches utilizing the tidal mudflats and salt marshes (W. Burkett, pers. comm.; B. Ortego, pers. comm.).

In Virginia, an invertebrate study was conducted in May 2000 (Truitt and Brown 2000). Nineteen days were spent in the field on Metompkin (12 d in peat bank habitat), Parramore (6 d in sandy beach habitat), and Fisherman Islands (1 d in sandy beach habitat); 105 core samples were collected for invertebrate analysis and counts were made of migratory Red Knots. The peat banks of Metompkin Island had both the highest density and diversity of invertebrate species (Table 11). The blue mussel was by far the most abundant invertebrate with densities ranging from 33,000 m^{-2} to 181,000 m^{-2}. Observations confirmed that the Red Knots were feeding on these mussels which covered the peat banks in dense mats. Other species noted in the core samples included six polychaetes, five amphipods, and

TABLE 11. TOTAL NUMBERS OF ALL BENTHIC INVERTEBRATES COLLECTED DURING TRANSECT SAMPLING ON METOMPKIN (MET), PARRAMORE (PARR), AND FISHERMAN ISLANDS (FISH), VIRGINIA, IN MAY 2000 (TRUITT ET AL. 2001).

Transect	Substrate	N core samples	Density/m²	Dominant. species	Total N species
MET1	Peat	1,162	181,019	*Mytilus edulis*	12
MET2	Peat	213	33,115	*Mytilus edulis*	7
MET3	Peat	577	89,896	*Mytilus edulis*	10
PARR1	Sand	60	9,285	*Melitidae sp.*	5
PARR2	Sand	34	5,318	*Melitidae sp.*	5
FISH1	Sand	16	2,523	*Parahaustorius*	9
FISH2	Sand	5	861	*Parahaustorius*	5

one isopod. Of the three islands, Parramore had the least diversity, but the second highest density of invertebrates (Table 12). The Melitidae amphipods were by far the most abundant invertebrate species which suggests that they were the Red Knots' main prey. However, observations could not confirm this because the birds held their heads underwater in the wash of the waves while probing.

Fisherman Island had the second highest diversity of invertebrates and the lowest density. The amphipod *Parahaustorius longimerus* was the most abundant, along with three other amphipods, two polychaetes, and two bivalves. Ash-free dry weights were also the lowest among the three islands.

Metompkin Island offered the most food resources for Red Knots in terms of ash-free dry mass, while there was less at Parramore and least at Fisherman. This helps to explain the large numbers of Red Knots observed at Metompkin during past aerial surveys. Without information on stopover times, it is impossible to estimate what proportion of the flyway Red Knot population is supported by this island on migration, but it could be substantial. On 23 May 2005, a dusk count of the Hereford Inlet roost showed 20,000 Red Knots were in Delaware Bay. In the middle of the same day, an aerial count showed 9,150 on the coastal islands of Virginia (B. Watts, pers.comm.).

On Metompkin, the Red Knots roosted over high water on the beach adjacent to the peat banks. As soon as the banks became exposed, feeding activity began and continued for several hours. By half tide or just after, a marked decrease occurred in feeding and most birds were observed preening, loafing, or sleeping. Usually, just before low water, many birds would fly off to the north at a time when the most peat and blue mussels were exposed. This suggests that feeding on blue mussels the birds are able to satisfy their food requirements remarkably quickly.

It is significant to note that none of the core samples from the three islands contained the coquina clam., a common summer resident on many of the Virginia barrier islands. It is believed that in spring 2000, the Red Knot migration probably preceded this bivalve's seasonal migration from just offshore into the intertidal zone of the island beaches.

MIGRATION AND STOPOVER HABITAT—PANAMA

The upper Panama Bay is a critical staging area for shorebirds during the spring. Red Knots forage along the intertidal mudflats that extend several kilometers at low tide. They may also forage within mangroves and sandy beaches near Chitré (Buehler 2002).

MIGRATION AND STOPOVER HABITAT—MARANHÃO, BRAZIL

Maranhão is a migration stopover point during spring and fall for Red Knots. The Red Knots forage on the sandy beaches and mudflats of Campechá Island in the Lençóis Bay and Coroa dos Ovos and Ingleses islands in the Turiaçú Bay. Knots also use extensive mangroves that permeate the interior through the São Marcos Bay and the lower courses of several rivers. Among the important plant species are the red mangrove (*Rizophora mangle*), black mangrove (*Avicenia germinan*), and white mangrove (*Laguncularia racemosa*). The high primary productivity is important to migratory birds (I. Serrano, unpubl. data).

MIGRATION AND STOPOVER HABITAT—LAGOA DO PEIXE, BRAZIL

Lagoa do Peixe National Park is one of the largest stopover grounds for North American migratory waterbirds in the South American continent. The lagoon connects to the sea during winter through wind action, rain, and accumulated water volume in the lagoon, and these processes are supplemented by pumping in summer. This maintains a constant influx of salt water which sustains a rich fauna of

TABLE 12. NUMBERS OF EACH INVERTEBRATE SPECIES COUNTED DURING TRANSECT SAMPLING ON METOMPKIN, PARRAMORE, AND FISHERMAN ISLANDS, VIRGINIA IN MAY 2000 (TRUITT ET AL. 2001).

Species	Number of individuals 1 m from surf	Number of individuals 2 m from surf	Number of individuals 3 m from surf
Metompkin Island			
Bivalves			
Mytilus edulis	16,047	3,224	7,410
Cyrtopleura costata	82	89	264
Polychaete worms			
Nereis succinea	43	85	191
Mediomastus ambiseta	26	0	3
Loimia medusa	0	1	1
Chaetopteros fragment	0	0	1
Heteromastus filiformis	0	5	1
Capitellidae sp.			
Amphipods			
Jassa falcata	20	7	28
Caprela penantis	1	0	0
Eunice norvegica	1	0	0
Gammarus mucronatus	1	0	0
Erichthonius brasiliensis	13	0	0
Isopods			
Cirolana sp.	21	2	10
Miscellaneous			
Fish larvae	1	0	0
Mollusk siphon	1	0	0
Gastropod sp.	1	0	0
Nemertean spp.	3	0	4
Parramore Island			
Bivalves			
Cyrtopleura costata	57	27	
Polychaete worms			
Scolepsis squamata	32	21	
Amphipods			
Melitidae sp.	656	433	
Parahaustorius longimerus	7	1	
Crustaceans			
Emerita talpoida	2	4	
Fisherman Island			
Bivalves			
Cyrtopleura costata	6	12	
Ensis directus	8	0	
Polychaete worms			
Scolepsis squamata	1	2	
Lumbrinereis sp.	1	0	
Amphipods			
Parahaustorius longimerus	222	63	
Trichophoxus epistomus	1	5	
Haustorid sp.	1	0	
Monoculoides edwarsi	1	0	
Miscellaneous			
Nemertean spp	10		

invertebrates all year round. During both northward migration in March-April and southward migration in September-October, Red Knots use the lagoon and the ocean beach for foraging. However, peak numbers have declined from around 10,000 in the mid-1990s to <1,000 in 2003. In the lagoon, the Red Knots' principal prey is the mud snail (*Littoridina australis*; I. Serrano, unpubl. data).

MIGRATION AND STOPOVER HABITAT — PAMPAS REGION, ARGENTINA

In this region available shorebird habitat is found along >1,200 km of shoreline from Buenos Aires, in the mouth of Río de la Plata estuary, to Punta Alta near Bahía Blanca. Bahía de Samborombón and Bahía Blanca estuary contain extensive marshes and mudflats. Tide amplitude is low (2 m on average) and huge intertidal mudflats are present. South of Bahía de Samborombón (Punta Rasa), sandy beaches occur and Laguna Mar Chiquita contains a shallow permanent brackish lagoon connected to the sea.

The highest numbers of Red Knots have been seen during spring migration on ocean sandy beaches backed by dunes southward from Punta Rasa where the area has been heavily modified by urbanization to create appropriate conditions for tourism in summer (Ieno et al. 2004). Feeding studies showed that Red Knot's primary prey is the mud snail (Ieno et al. 2004).

MIGRATION AND STOPOVER HABITAT — PATAGONIAN SHORELINE, ARGENTINA

The Patagonian shoreline consists of the Buenos Aires Province coastline south of Bahía Blanca and includes Río Negro, Chubut, Santa Cruz, and Tierra del Fuego provinces. Critical feeding areas for Red Knots are associated with extensive sandy beaches and mudflats where the primary prey is clams (*Darina solenoides*; Escudero et al. 2003, Albrieu et al. 2004; M. A. Hernández et al., unpubl. data; P. M. González et al., unpubl. data), but also includes polychaetes (e.g., *Travisia olens*; M. A. Hernández et al., unpubl. data) and small crustacea (P. M. González, et al., unpubl. data). Other critical feeding habitats for Red Knots are the restingas, broad, wave-cut rocky platforms extending to the lower intertidal zone, where knots usually feed on blue mussels or another small mussel *Brachidontes rodriguezi* (González et al. 1996, Escudero et al. 2003).

The entire Argentinian coast from Bahía Blanca to the Beagle Channel (Tierra del Fuego) contains sandy beaches and sandflats, mudflats, and restingas which are often covered with a rich invertebrate fauna (Canevari et al. 1998). Gulfs and embayments are important coastal features, and the Patagonian (Tehuelche) gravels form beaches along the shoreline and occur in many places such as the area surrounding Península Valdés and the southern part of the Golfo San Jorge. Restingas are found in many areas below cliff beaches near San Antonio Oeste.

During high tide, foraging areas are usually covered by water and Red Knots roost along the upper shore of beaches, sandbars and shellbars, marshes, and other expansive coastal areas above high-tide line.

MIGRATION AND STOPOVER HABITAT — URUGUAY

The coastline of Uruguay was searched as part of the South American Atlas project in the mid-1980s; no Red Knots were found there (Morrison and Ross 1989). Recent enquiries indicate that Red Knots are recorded in Uruguay very infrequently and in only low numbers (P. M. González, unpubl. data).

WINTER HABITAT — UNITED STATES

As explained in the taxonomy section of this document, the subspecific status of the Red Knots that winter on the western and northeastern coasts of Florida and on the coast of Georgia, South Carolina, and Texas is uncertain. Therefore, on the basis that this population might be *C. c. rufa*, we present the following description of the habitats it occupies.

From South Carolina through Florida, Red Knots winter along sandy beaches. They may also utilize peat banks in Georgia and salt marshes, brackish lagoons, tidal mudflats, and mangroves in Florida. In Texas, wintering Red Knots occur along sandy beaches on Mustang Island and other outer beaches and tidal mudflats and salt marshes on Bolivar Flats.

WINTER HABITAT — CHILE

Bahía Lomas is the main wintering area of *C. c. rufa* in South America (Morrison and Ross 1989, Morrison et al. 2004). It is located near the east entrance of the Straits of Magellan on the northern coast of the main island of Tierra del Fuego (52°28′08″ S; 69°22′54″ W; Fig. 25) and is mainly dominated by intertidal mudflats which tend to be smooth and sandy towards the edges and highly channelled toward the middle. The flats extend for about 50 km and on spring tides the intertidal distance reaches 7 km in places. The substrate of the bay comprises a large area of mud slopes with channels that diminish towards low water.

Since 2003, an ecological study has been conducted on the tidal flats of Bahía Lomas. The main objective has been to determine the composition, distribution, and abundance of the benthic community with special reference its trophic relationship with the Red Knot wintering population. The results indicate that the flats are dominated by three invertebrates: the clam *Darina solenoides*, an amphipod, and a polychaete (Table 13; Espoz et al. 2008). Although each has its own characteristic distribution with respect to tide level, they all tend to increase in abundance towards low water. Of the three species, *Darina solenoides* is the most abundant (Fig. 26) and stable isotope analysis shows that wintering Red Knots are mainly assimilating carbon and nitrogen present in that species (Fig. 27). Therefore *Darina* would appear to be the Red Knots' main

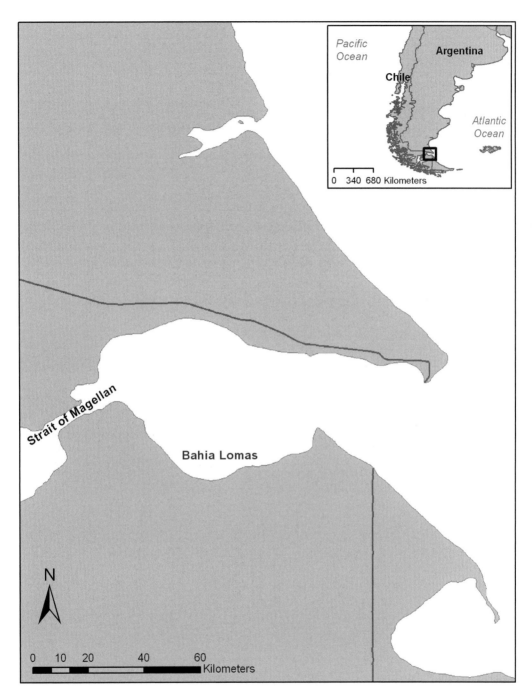

FIGURE 25. Location of Bahía Lomas in Tierra del Fuego, Chile.

TABLE 13. INVERTEBRATES RECORDED IN TRANSECT SAMPLING AT BAHÍA LOMAS, CHILE, AND THE RELATIVE ABUNDANCE OF EACH.

	N	%
Mollusca, Bivalvia		
Darina solenoides	1,815	51.3
Bivalvia (unidentified species)	3	0.1
Mollusca, Gastropoda		
Gastropoda (unidentified species 1)	4	0.1
Gastropoda (unidentified species 2)	3	0.1
Polychaeta		
Paraonidae		
Paraonidae (unidentified species)	875	24.8
Phyllocidae		
Eteone sp.	331	9.4
Nephtyidae		
Aglaophamus sp.	13	0.4
Opheliidae		
Travisia sp.	13	0.4
Euzonus sp.	29	0.8
Spionidae		
Scolelepis sp.	23	0.7
Scolecolepides sp.	165	4.7
Glyceridae		
Glycera sp.	1	0.03
Polychaeta (unidentified species)	11	0.3
Crustacea		
Isopoda 1	13	0.4
Amphipoda (unidentified species 1)	178	5.0
Amphipoda (unidentified species 2)	1	0.03
Others		
Insecta	3	0.1
Insect larvae	20	0.6
Nematoda	20	0.6
Nemertea	11	0.3
Unidentified	3	0.1

prey at Bahía Lomas, just as might be expected in view of the prey taken by Red Knots worldwide (Piersma 1994).

WINTER HABITAT — ARGENTINA

Wintering Red Knots in Argentina are now largely confined to Bahía San Sebastián and Río Grande in the Province of Tierra del Fuego. Knots feed mainly within the mudflats of Bahía San Sebastián and along sandy beaches, mudflats, and restingas in Río Grande (P. M. González, unpubl. data).

WINTER HABITAT — BRAZIL

The main wintering area of Red Knots in Brazil is on the coast of the state of Maranhão where they forage along sandy beaches, tidal mudflats, and mangroves (I. Serrano, unpubl. data).

WINTER HABITAT — PANAMA

A small number of Red Knots winter in the Upper Panama Bay where they utilize the soft, silty mud in the tidal mudflats near Panama City (Buehler 2002).

POPULATION SIZE AND TRENDS

In breeding habitats, Red Knots are thinly distributed across a huge area of the Arctic, where we have no comprehensive understanding

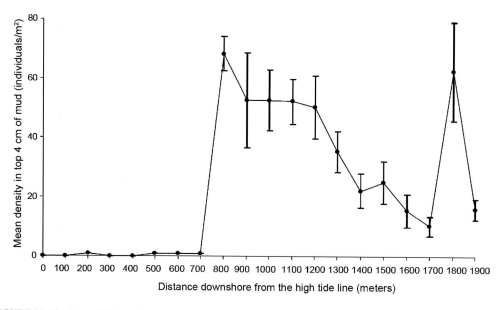

FIGURE 26. The intertidal distribution pattern of *Darina solenoides* at Bahía Lomas, Chile (Espoz et al. 2008).

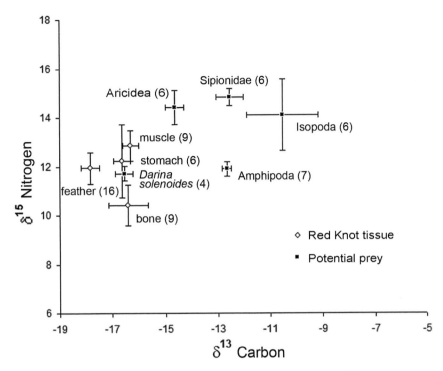

FIGURE 27. Isotopic signatures ($^{13}C/^{12}C$ and $^{15}N/^{14}N$) of tissue samples from Red Knots and benthic invertebrates from the tidal flats of Bahía Lomas, Tierra del Fuego, Chile. Sample size in parentheses (Espoz et al. 2008).

of breeding density or productivity. It is thus necessary instead to rely on surveys in primary wintering and stopover areas as the basis for monitoring population change. Fortunately the *C. c. rufa* population of the Red Knot is one of the best studied long-distance migrant shorebird populations in the world, with surveys taking place in nearly all of the key sites used along its 15,000 km flyway. These give us a reasonably complete picture of its critical habitat throughout the flyway. The surveys have also identified a number of problems in population structure that need to be taken into account in the assessment of population change.

RED KNOT POPULATIONS OF THE AMERICAS

The primary wintering area of the *C. c. rufa* subspecies of the Red Knot is now restricted to three sites on the main island of Tierra del Fuego (Morrison and Ross 1989, Morrison et al. 2004). In recent years, about 70% of the population has been found in just one bay, Bahía Lomas in the Chilean part of the island, with most of the remainder at Río Grande in the Argentinian part with smaller numbers at Bahía San Sebastián (Fig. 28). In the mid-1980s, this population numbered 67,000 and

the wintering area extended northwards along the Argentinian coast from Tierra del Fuego to Río Negro province. Now, the population is not only confined to Tierra del Fuego but has decreased to only 17,211 in 2006.

During migration to its Arctic breeding grounds, *C. c. rufa* stop over in Delaware Bay in late May and numbers counted there have fallen in broad correlation with those in Tierra del Fuego. However, recent studies have shown that Red Knots from two other wintering areas also migrate through Delaware Bay. These are the populations that winter in the southeastern U.S. (mainly Florida) and Maranhão, northern Brazil (Atkinson et al. 2005), the subspecific status of which is uncertain.

The Red Knot population that winters mainly on the west coast of Florida was counted by aerial surveys in the 1980s, and was estimated at between 6,500 and 10,000 by Morrison and Harrington (1992), but counts in the 1993–1994 winter suggest a population of no more than about 4,000 (Sprandel et al. 1997). The most recent estimate is 7,500 birds based on a count of 7,000 Red Knots in South Carolina (April 2003) and 4,000–5,000 in one area in western Florida (November 2004; B. A. Harrington, unpubl. data). Recent evidence suggests that

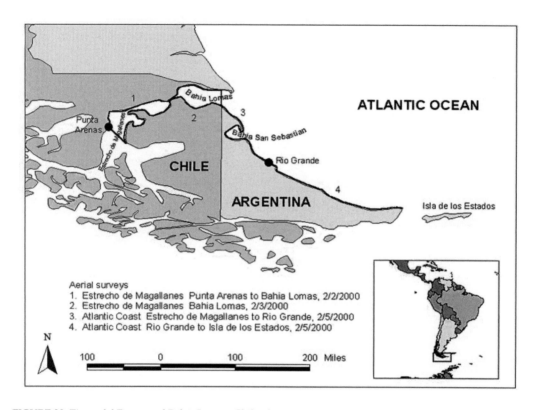

FIGURE 28. Tierra del Fuego and Bahía Lomas, Chile, the primary wintering grounds of *Calidris canutus rufa*.

this population may move with available resources as far north as the coast of Georgia and the winter population there can vary from hundreds in some years to a maximum of 5,000 in others (B. Winn, pers. comm.). There is no reliable evidence of a trend for the Florida wintering population. The count data are very erratic from year to year, probably because of the difficulty of finding Red Knots along Florida's greatly fragmented coastline. All that can be said is that no evidence suggests a major change in the size of the population and that it is probably still of the same order of magnitude as it was in the 1980s. Counts in Cape Romain NWR, South Carolina, indicate declines in the number of Red Knots on passage in both spring and late summer–fall (Fig. 29). It is not known to which wintering population or populations these birds belong. Possibly they are from the Tierra del Fuego population that has shown a clear decline, as described above.

The population wintering in the Maranhão region of Brazil was surveyed in February 2005 with a count of 7,575 (Baker et al. 2005a), which is only slightly below the 8,150 recorded by Morrison and Ross (1989) in the mid-1980s. However, the 20-yr gap between surveys means

that there could have been trends that have not been detected.

In view of current uncertainties about the subspecific status of the northern wintering Red Knots, they are here treated as distinct biogeographic populations and considered separately so far as is possible. *C. c. rufa* breeds in the central and eastern Canadian Arctic, and birds wintering in southern South America are referable to this race. However, it is unclear where the Florida and Maranhão birds breed or whether they are referable to *C. c. rufa* or *roselaari* or even a hitherto undescribed subspecies. Color banding and the isotope signature of flight feathers show that substantial numbers (though probably not all) of the birds that winter in both Maranhão and the southeastern U.S. pass through Delaware Bay during spring migration along with the birds from Tierra del Fuego (Atkinson et al. 2005). Isotope signatures from Southampton Island (P. W. Atkinson, unpubl. data) suggest that some of the Red Knots nesting there are from the northern wintering group, but birds with the orange flags of the Argentinian (Tierra del Fuego) population have also been seen on the same island at East Bay (P. A. Smith, pers. comm.).

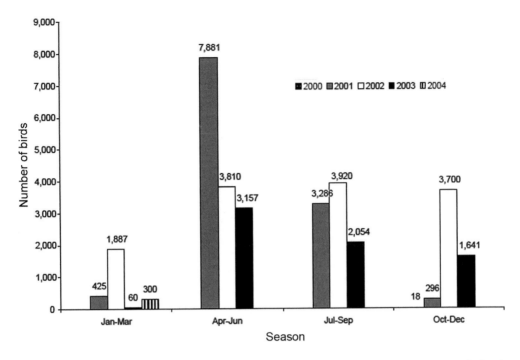

FIGURE 29. The number of Red Knots counted at Cape Romain National Wildlife Refuge, South Carolina, 2000–2004 (Cape Romain NWR, South Carolina DNR, unpubl. data).

If the southeastern U.S. and Maranhão birds are *C. c. roselaari*, the implication is that at least some of them migrate from their wintering areas to Delaware Bay and then to Alaska. Isotope signatures of Alaskan birds (N. Clark, unpubl. data; P. W. Atkinson, unpubl. data) do not support this view. Furthermore, this would seem to be an unlikely scenario because the distance between Florida and Alaska is almost the same as the distance between Delaware Bay and Alaska, but both are well within the capability of Red Knots for a non-stop flight (Weber and Houston 1997) and Delaware Bay is on an approximate great circle route between Maranhão and Alaska. Therefore, the flight from Florida to Delaware Bay would seem unnecessary. However, the possibility that Alaska-bound birds take such a circuitous migration route should not be discounted because it could have arisen in view of what is known about Red Knot evolution. Another factor that might have led to or maintained such a migration route is the existence of an abundant food resource in Delaware Bay in the form of horseshoe crabs' eggs. Therefore, the 5,000–6,000 km cross-continental flight might have been possible from Delaware Bay but not from Florida.

C. c. roselaari certainly use the Pacific coast flyway and at least some winter in California and Baja California (Tomkovich 1992; Page et al. 1997, 1999). However, it has also been suggested that Red Knots wintering in Florida conceivably may include *C. c. roselaari* and that they use a mid-continental route to reach breeding areas in Alaska (Harrington 2001). However, no good evidence supports or refutes this idea.

Color-banding shows little or no interchange between the Red Knots that winter in Maranhão and Tierra del Fuego or between Florida and Tierra del Fuego. No evidence exists for interchange between Florida and Maranhão, but observation rates are too low to accept this as verified (few Red Knots have been marked in Maranhão).

Isotope analysis of primaries from 16 Red Knots caught in Alaska in spring shows that almost certainly they did not molt in Florida (N. Clark, unpubl. data; P. W. Atkinson, unpubl. data). However, although this is inconsistent with *C. c. roselaari* molting and wintering in Florida, it is not proof that they do not because at 35,000–50,000 (Wetlands International 2006) the Alaska population is much greater than the 7,500 wintering in Florida. Therefore, because most of the Alaskan birds must winter elsewhere, a much greater sample than 16 will be necessary to exclude their movement to Florida.

Isotope analysis of primary coverts taken from Red Knots nesting in the main *C. c. rufa* breeding area on Southampton Island, Hudson Bay, showed a southeastern U.S. (or possibly northern Brazil) signature. This confirms that at least some birds wintering in that area are *C. c. rufa* (P. W. Atkinson, unpubl. data; M. Peck, unpubl. data).

Until the taxonomic uncertainties are resolved, the possibility remains that the Maranhão and Florida wintering populations include unknown numbers of *C. c. roselaari* as well as an unknown proportion of *C. c. rufa*. This complicates the assessment because the trend and population size of *C. c. roselaari* are uncertain. The estimate for *C. c. roselaari* in the U.S. Shorebird Conservation Plan (Brown et al. 2001) of 150,000 is based on counts in the 1970s and 1980s is probably a gross overestimate of the population at the time it was published. Current estimates at 35,000–50,000 are much lower (Wetlands International 2006). However, without systematic surveys it is uncertain whether a decline has occurred in the *C. c. roselaari* population. It is likely that all Red Knots using the Pacific flyway are *C. c. roselaari*. However, counts on the U.S. Pacific coast from California to Washington reported by Page et al. (1999) of 9,035 in spring, 7,981 in fall, and 4,813 in winter during 1988–1995 suggest that that flyway comprises no more than about 10,000 birds. It is therefore very difficult to account for even the current *C. c. roselaari* estimate of 35,000–50,000 birds in winter, if it is true that they all winter in the Americas. This is especially so if it were shown that the Florida and Maranhão wintering populations are all *C. c. rufa* as some of the evidence would seem to suggest.

In summary, five known major wintering sites were used by >1,000 Red Knots in the New World. These support a combined total of about 45,000 individuals (Table 14). To this figure a few small populations elsewhere can be added (e.g., 100 in the Upper Bay of Panama in Feb 2002 [Buehler 2002]) and possibly some in western Venezuela where 520 occurred in the mid-1980s (Morrison and Ross 1989). Allowing for some error in counts and estimates, and the fact that some counts are not recent, it would seem unlikely that the total is <40,000 or >50,000.

Assuming that the figures in Table 14 are accurate and discounting small numbers elsewhere, then, depending on whether the populations of uncertain subspecies are all *C. c. rufa* or all *C. c. roselaari*, the population of these two subspecies can range from a *C. c. rufa* population of 17,653–35,728 birds and a *C. c. roselaari* population of 9,035–27,110 birds. This does not take account of the fact that the Alaskan population, assumed to be *C. c. roselaari*, has been estimated at 35,000–50,000 (Wetlands International 2006). However, as discussed below, there is the possibility that many of the Alaskan birds are not *C. c. roselaari* but *C. c. rogersi*.

WINTERING POPULATION TRENDS IN
CALIDRIS CANUTUS RUFA

The uncertainty about the numbers of *C. c. roselaari* and the areas in which it winters is in strong contrast to what is known about the *C. c. rufa* population of Tierra del Fuego. That population has been counted several times since the mid-1980s and (mixed with birds from Florida and Maranhão) every year from 1986–2005 as it passes through Delaware Bay as well as several sites in between. It is the decline in this distinct biogeographic population that is of primary concern.

TABLE 14. RECENT POPULATION ESTIMATES OF RED KNOTS WINTERING IN THE NEW WORLD.

Location	Population	Recent trend	Date	Subspecies	Source
Tierra del Fuego	17,653	major decline	Jan 2005	*rufa*	R. I. G. Morrison (unpubl. data) R. K. Ross (pers. comm.)
Maranhão, northern Brazil	7,575	slight decline	Feb 2005	uncertain	Baker et al. (2005a)
Florida	7,500	not known	2004–2005 Winter	uncertain	B. A. Harrington (unpubl. data)
California, Mexico and possibly farther south	9,035 [a]	not known	Spring 1988–1995 [a]	*roselaari*	Page et al. (1999)
Texas coast	3,000	probable decline	1985–1996 (Jan 2003) [b]	uncertain	Skagen et al. (1999)
Total	44,763				

[a] The figure of 9,035 represents the maximum spring count along the main U.S. Pacific coast during 1988–1995 and probably includes both migrants and wintering birds. Winter counts alone produced 4,813 in the United States 1988–1995 (Page et al. 1999) and 1,082 in Baja California (Page et al. 1997). Presumably, the remaining 3,000 winter elsewhere in Mexico or farther south.
[b] Inquiries suggest that the Texas coast wintering population may now be as little as 300, but there has been no recent census.

Aerial counts during December to early February within the main *C. c. rufa* wintering area in southern South America have shown a catastrophic decline over the 20 yr interval, 1985–2005. The birds are thought to be relatively sedentary at this time of the year, so double counting or missing those that have not yet arrived or have already departed should not have occurred. Moreover, the same observers and survey techniques were used for all the aerial counts in South America. Surveys in the main non-breeding areas are the main method of population estimation for Red Knots recommended by the U.S. Shorebird Conservation Plan (Brown et al. 2001).

In the mid-1980s, the southern wintering *C. c. rufa* population numbered 67,546 and was found along 1,600 km of the Atlantic coast from Tierra del Fuego to Río Colorado in northern Patagonia (Morrison and Ross 1989). By 2006, numbers had fallen to 17,211 and almost the entire population was confined to Tierra del Fuego (Fig. 30). Within Tierra del Fuego, the largest numbers (at least 70% of the population) have always

occurred at Bahía Lomas. There the count fell by about 50% (from over 45,000 to just over 20,000) between 2000 and 2002, remained stable in 2003 and 2004, but then fell again by a further 50% to <10,000 in 2005 (Fig. 30). In Tierra del Fuego as a whole, numbers fell from over 51,000 in 2000 (compared with 53,000 in the 1980s) to the 27,000–31,000 range between 2002 and 2004, and only 17,211 in 2006 (Fig. 30). By 2003, Bahía Lomas held 84% and the combined core areas 98% of all Red Knots counted over the entire wintering range in southern South America. The most recent decreases have occurred mainly in the numbers at Bahía Lomas. At Río Grande in the Argentinian part of Tierra del Fuego, aerial counts show that the population has remained relatively stable at 3,500–5,000 (Fig. 30), though ground counts in November have shown a drop from 6,000 in 2000 to 4,000 in 2004 (Baker et al. 2005a). Knots have almost disappeared from wintering sites outside of Tierra del Fuego on the Patagonian coast of Argentina, falling from over 14,300 in the 1980s to 790 in 2004 (Morrison et al. 2004; R. I. G. Morrison, unpubl. data)

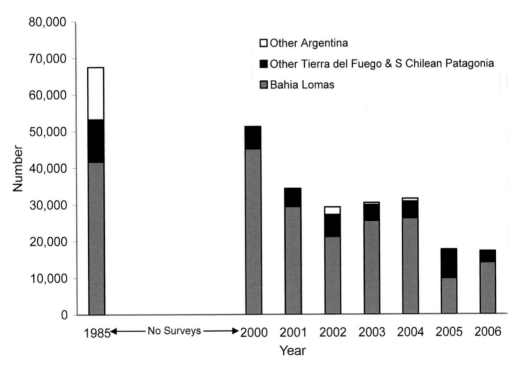

FIGURE 30. The number of Red Knots spending the austral summer in southern South America according to aerial counts made during the *Atlas of Nearctic shorebirds on the coast of South America* project (Morrison and Ross 1989) in 1985 and during 2000–2006. Grey sections are numbers at Bahía Lomas, black sections are other sites in Tierra del Fuego (mainly Río Grande) and southern Chilean Patagonia and white sections are other sites farther north along the coast of Argentina. No counts were made north of Tierra del Fuego in 2000, 2001, or 2005 because reports by ground observers (Ferrari et al. 2002, Escudero et al. 2003) showed that very few Red Knots wintered at any of the sites at which they had previously been reported.

(Fig. 30). This is reflected in surveys at all other sites in Patagonia where Red Knots have occurred during the past 20 yr with 14 out of the 18 sites occupied in 1985 having none in 2004–2005. In the same period, the population of Hudsonian Godwits (*Limosa haemastica*) which also spends the northern winter in Tierra del Fuego but takes the mid-continent flyway to breeding sites in Arctic Canada, remained stable (R. I. G. Morrison, unpubl. data; R. K. Ross, pers. comm.).

Banding studies in Tierra del Fuego invariably show a low proportion of juveniles and it is thought that most winter further north (Baker et al. 2005b). Therefore, the aerial counts of the Tierra del Fuego wintering population will underestimate its true size to the (probably marginal) extent that not all of the juveniles are included.

PASSAGE POPULATION TRENDS

The decline observed in wintering populations is also reflected in surveys of Red Knots at all major stopover sites along the coast of South America. At Bahía San Antonio, where surveys of passage birds are made during March and April, numbers have fallen from 15,000–20,000 in 1990–1997, to 7,000–12,000 in 1998–2002, to 5,000–6,500 in 2003–2005 (Fig. 31). Similar declines have been recorded at Península Valdés (Bala et al. 2001, 2002; Hernández et al. 2004). In Brazil, yearly counts at Lagoa do Peixe fell from a high of 10,000 in 1996 to 5,500–7,000 in 1996–1999, and 900–1,500 in 2001–2003 (Fig. 31). Taken together, these results support the conclusion that the Tierra del Fuego wintering population has declined significantly.

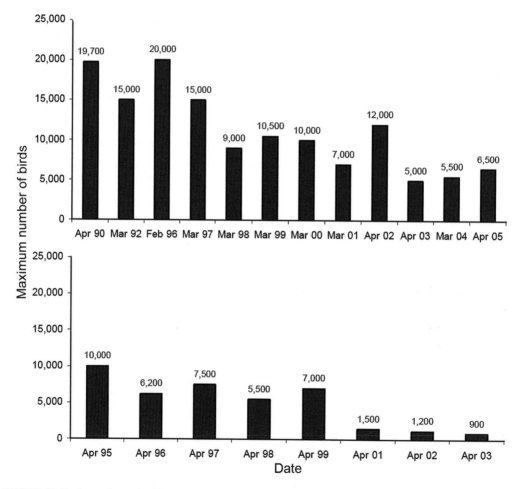

FIGURE 31. Peak numbers of Red Knots during northward passage at (upper) Bahía San Antonio, Argentina 1990–2005 (P. M. González, unpubl. data) and (lower) Lagoa do Peixe, Brazil 1995–2003 (I. Serrano, unpubl. data). Counts at Bahía San Antonio were mostly carried out on a weekly basis throughout February to April. Counts at Lagoa do Peixe were obtained during expeditions that covered the peak spring passage in April.

No regular systematic surveys of Red Knots have happened at any site further north in South America, either on passage or during the northern winter. Baker et al. (2005a) found no evidence of decline in Red Knots wintering in Maranhão, though this was based on just two counts 20 yr apart (1985 and 2005). In South Carolina, the USFWS carried out annual surveys in Cape Romain NWR during 2000–2004 (F. Sanders, pers. comm.; Fig. 29). These show a decline in passage birds similar to that seen in South America with numbers dropping from a March–April high of over 7,000 in 2000 to a low of 3,157 in 2004. Southbound Red Knots also declined from over 3,000 in 2001 and 2002 to 1,641 in 2003.

The longest running survey is the Delaware Bay Aerial Shorebird Survey that was started in 1982–1983 by the New Jersey Audubon Society (NJAS) and has been carried out from 1986 to the present by the NJENSP (Figs. 32 and 33; Clark et al. 1993; K. Clark, unpubl. data). The survey covers both shores of the bay and takes place under similar tidal conditions each week for the 6 wk of the stopover period. Every effort has been made to ensure even and consistent coverage. This has been achieved partly by keeping to the same methodology and partly by minimizing turnover of personnel. In fact the key role of counter has been fulfilled by the same person (K. Clark, NJENSP) since 1986.

The Delaware Bay Aerial Shorebird Survey is not a total census, because it does not cover the adjacent Atlantic coast of New Jersey or the intertidal marshes of Delaware Bay (Fig. 33). Moreover the peak count does not represent the total flyway population because of turnover — some birds may not have arrived, others may have departed. In 2004, for example, Gillings et al. (unpubl. data) estimated that, due to turnover, approximately 24,000 Red Knots passed through the Delaware Bay, despite the peak count being only 13,315 (Fig. 32). It is also likely that turnover rates have varied as the birds have responded to changes in the quantity of food. Overall, turnover rates were probably higher during 1986–1996 when horseshoe crab eggs were abundant than subsequently because of decreased egg availability. Higher turnover in the early years may be the reason for the greater volatility in peak numbers when compared with more recent years (Fig. 32).

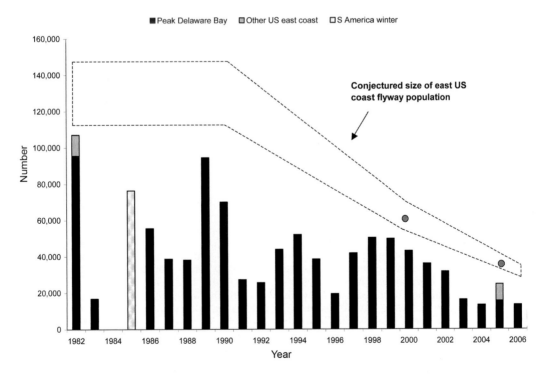

FIGURE 32. Peak counts of Red Knots in Delaware Bay May 1982–2006 as shown by weekly aerial counts. (NJAS (1982–1983), NJENSP (1986–2005). Also shown are simultaneous counts from other U.S. East Coast sites (mainly Virginia), the 1985 South America winter count (Morrison and Ross 1989), the authors' estimate of the total range over which the U.S. East Coast flyway population fluctuated (range enclosed by dashed lines) and the estimates of the flyway population in 1999 of 60,000 (Baker et al. 1999a) and in 2005 of 32,728 (Table 14) shown by gray dots.

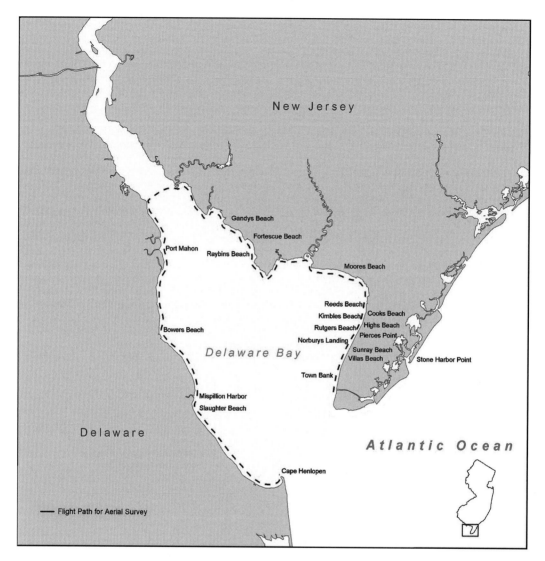

FIGURE 33. Flight path of aerial surveys along the Delaware Bay conducted by the NJDFW.

In 1982 and 1989, the number of Red Knots in Delaware Bay reached peaks of 95,530 and 94,460, respectively. Although peak counts in the intervening years were lower and in some years surprisingly low, no reason exists to suppose that the population declined. In 1985 with no aerial survey in Delaware Bay, for example, the South America count (mainly the far south and Maranhão) was 76,373 to which can be added whatever population was then wintering in Florida. Since the early 1990s, however, the aerial survey has documented a steady decline with only 13,445 in 2006 (Fig. 32).

Figure 32 includes counts made simultaneously with the Delaware Bay peak elsewhere on the East Coast of the U.S. (mainly in Virginia).

Included is the estimate of 60,000 for 1999 by Baker et al. (1999a) and the aggregate counts for the three main wintering populations (Tierra del Fuego, Maranhão and Florida) in 2005 of 32,728 (Table 14).

Until the late 1990s, the peak aerial counts in Delaware Bay were quite erratic from year to year (Fig. 32). Many of these changes are so big that they cannot have reflected changes in the total population because they are demographically impossible. Moreover, they are also far too large to be due to counting error. At this stage we can only speculate about the reasons. Possibly high availability of horseshoe crab eggs led to rapid turnover, leading to a reduction in the count; conversely bad weather may have prevented birds from departing leading to a build-up. It is also possible that in some years many birds exploited food resources, such as *Donax* or mussel spat, elsewhere along the Atlantic coast and did not visit Delaware Bay.

Our conjectured estimate of the U.S. East Coast flyway population is based on the peak aerial counts in Delaware Bay, counts elsewhere along the U.S. East Coast, the 1985 and 2000–2005 aerial counts in Tierra del Fuego, and the counts in Florida and Maranhão referred to above. It also takes into account the fact that peak counts will almost invariably underestimate total stopover population because of turnover (S. Gillings et al., unpubl. data).

In the past it has been assumed that all the Red Knots stopping over in Delaware Bay in May are *C. c. rufa*. This is no longer certain, but the fact that a large proportion of the birds that pass through Delaware Bay are *C. c. rufa* from southern South America is suggested by the fact that the stopover population and the southern South America wintering populations

have shown similar declines (Fig. 32). However, recent studies using carbon and nitrogen isotope ratios of feathers (Atkinson et al. 2005), and resightings of birds marked from other wintering areas have shown that approximately half the birds caught in Delaware Bay in 2004 and 2005 were from the Tierra del Fuego wintering population (Fig. 34). The remaining birds were from the more northerly wintering areas in Florida and Maranhão, Brazil.

The literature includes various estimates for the *C. c. rufa* population in the 1980s and early 1990s in the range of 100,000–150,000 (Harrington et al. 1988, Morrison and Harrington 1992). These estimates were all made on the assumption that *C. c. rufa* includes all birds passing through Delaware Bay, i.e., those wintering in Maranhão and Florida as well as Tierra del Fuego which are consistent with the information presented in Fig. 34. Later, however, Morrison et al. (2001) suggested that *C. c. rufa* numbered as many as 170,000 around the turn of the century by including 18,700

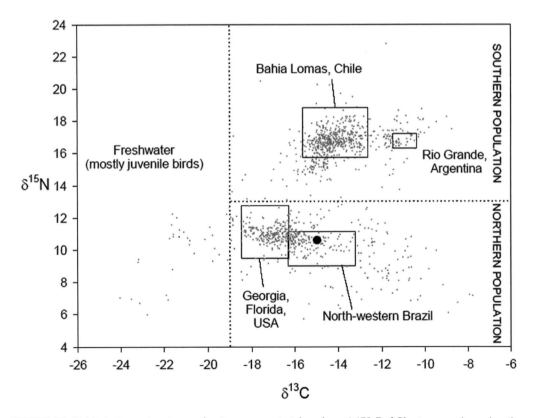

FIGURE 34. Stable isotope signatures of primary coverts taken from 1,150 Red Knots on spring migration through Delaware Bay in May and June 2004 (P. W. Atkinson, unpubl. data). Boxes mark the 90% confidence intervals of birds of known wintering origin. The large dot represents the signature of a tertial taken from a bird nesting on Southampton Island, Nunavut, Canada. Dotted lines show the approximate separation between juvenile birds (with freshwater Arctic signature) and the northern and southern wintering populations.

using the interior flyway. This is presumably why the same figure is mentioned in Brown et al. (2001). However, this figure appears to have been an over-estimation by a factor of almost three for two reasons—Baker et al. (1999a) had already published a much reduced estimate of only 60,000, and the figure of 18,700 is the sum of maximum counts for all sites along the interior flyway for January to June (Skagen et al. 1999), which might involve duplication.

Baker et al. (2004) showed that the reason the Tierra del Fuego population fell by almost 50% between 2000 and 2002 (Morrison et al. 2004) (Fig. 30) was because adult survival declined from an average of 85% in 1994–1998 to only 56% during 1999–2001. They also calculated trends in the population that could be expected if survival either recovered to 85% (Fig. 35a, the best-case scenario) or remained at 56% (Fig. 35b, the worst-case scenario). Subsequent counts during 2003–2005 (Fig. 35b) show that although the population held up in 2003–2004, the sudden drop to only 17,653 in 2005 brought it right back toward the track of the worst case scenario, indicating an increased risk of extinction within the next decade.

Since Fig. 35b was first published, it has been the subject of some misinterpretation. Therefore, we emphasize that its purpose was to demonstrate the consequences of adult survival remaining as low as 56% and not recovering. It assumes constant adult survival, but all studies show that adult survival actually varies

from year to year. Thus there is no expectation that it will remain fixed at any particular value. The fact that the 2003 and 2004 counts were above the 95% confidence limits means that survival was more than 56%; the sudden drop in 2005 suggests that survival was much less than 56%. Therefore, although Fig. 35b predicts possible extinction as early as 2010, the year of extinction is unknowable, neither is extinction certain. The relevance and value of the model is that, combined with the recent counts, it shows that the current population trend is one that carries a considerably increased risk of extinction unless there is effective short term conservation action.

BREEDING AREA POPULATION TRENDS

Although Red Knots can occur in huge flocks, during the breeding season they are spread out thinly across a vast area of the arctic tundra. From 2000–2004, NJENSP conducted regular annual surveys of the density of Red Knot nests in a 9.2 km^2 study area on Southampton Island, Hudson Bay. This showed a decline from 1.16 nests/km^2 in 2000 to 0.33 in 2003 followed by a slight increase to 0.55 in 2004 (Fig. 36). American Golden Plovers (*Pluvialis dominica*) nest commonly in the same study area but their numbers remained stable (Fig. 36). Golden Plovers take the mid-continent flyway to South American wintering areas and do not migrate through Delaware Bay.

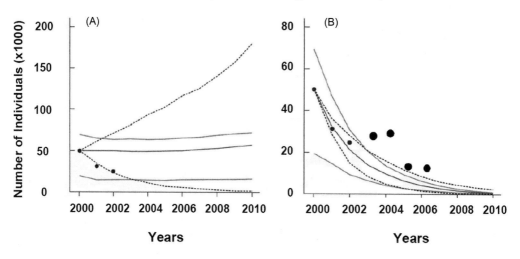

FIGURE 35. Predicted population trends and associated 95% confidence limits of adults (dashed lines), juveniles (lower gray line) and both combined (top gray line) for 10 yr from 2000, with (A) constant adult survival of 85% and juvenile survival being half that of adults ($\lambda = 1$) and (B) constant adult survival of 56% and juvenile survival being half that of adults ($\lambda = 0.66$). The small dots represent the aerial censuses of the over-wintering flock of adults in Tierra del Fuego during 2000–2002, and the large dots are the counts during 2003–2006. The 95% upper and lower confidence limits are based on 1,000 bootstrap iterations. Modified from Baker et al. (2004) and published in this form in Baker et al. (2005a).

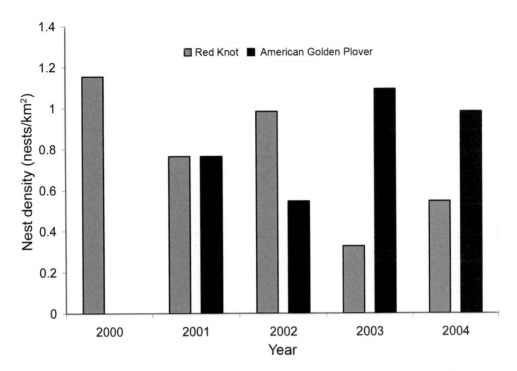

FIGURE 36. Density of the nests of Red Knots and American Golden Plovers in a 9.2 km² study site on Southampton Island, Nunavut, Hudson Bay, Canada, during 2000–2004. American Golden Plovers were not included in the survey until 2001.

SUMMARY OF POPULATION TRENDS

Shorebird life-history traits are characterized by low fecundity (clutch size ≤4 eggs, high nest failure, only one brood per year), delayed maturity, and high annual survival (70–90%; Sandercock 2003). In these respects, the Red Knot is an exemplar of a shorebird. As with most arctic-breeding species, productivity is generally low and in some years can be virtually zero. Productivity depends on the weather, especially its effect on the chicks' thermoregulation requirements and the availability of their invertebrate food and predator abundance. The latter tends to be cyclic with a 3–4 yr period that is closely tied to the abundance of lemmings (Underhill et al. 1993). Years with few lemmings and many predators can be extremely unproductive for Red Knots. However, predator cycles are usually not uniform across all breeding areas so most years there is generally some production of young.

To some extent, periodic changes in the numbers of Red Knots may be related to arctic breeding conditions. However, other shorebird populations that breed in the same areas of the Arctic as Red Knots have experienced these conditions, but, at least during 2000–2004 in a small study area on Southampton Island, have not shown the same recent, sharp decline (Fig. 36) as have Red Knots. Therefore, although some changes in Red Knot populations can be ascribed to arctic breeding conditions, they are unlikely to be the primary cause of the recent declines.

Climate change is predicted to have adverse consequences for many arctic-breeding shorebirds (Rehfisch and Crick 2003). However, no study has yet shown an impact of climate change on Red Knot populations worldwide.

Intensive studies of *C. c. rufa* throughout the west Atlantic flyway only began in 1997 by which time the population had already dropped from the 100,000–150,000 reported in the 1970s and 1980s to close to the 60,000 estimated in 1999 (Baker et al. 1999a). Therefore, we have little information as to what caused this initial decline. Studies since 1997 have shown:

1. The majority of the populations that winters in Tierra del Fuego, Maranhão, and Florida passes through Delaware Bay during northward migration.
2. The Tierra del Fuego population has suffered major decline, but shows no discernible trend of decline in the birds from Florida or Maranhão.

3. A major reduction in the survival of the Tierra del Fuego population from an average of 85% during 1994–1998 to 56% during 1998–2001 coupled with lower rates of recruitment (Baker et al. 2004) was responsible for the decrease in the Tierra del Fuego population from >50,000 in 2000 to 30,000 in 2002–2004.

4. Continued low survival exacerbated by poor arctic productivity was likely responsible for the further fall in the Tierra del Fuego population from 30,778 in January 2004 to 17,653 in January 2005 (P. W. Atkinson, unpubl. data).

5. Birds caught in Delaware Bay in May with a low body mass during 1998–2002 had significantly lower survival than birds caught with a higher mass (after controlling for the general increase in weights that takes place during the stopover) (Baker et al. 2004).

6. Between 1997 and 2003, the proportion of well-conditioned Red Knots in Delaware Bay around the normal departure date at the end of May declined by 70% (Baker et al. 2004)

7. In recent years, especially in 2003 and 2005, substantial numbers of Tierra del Fuego birds have arrived in Delaware Bay later than usual.

8. Since about 1996 an order of magnitude decline has occurred in the availability of horseshoe crab eggs in Delaware Bay.

Worldwide, studies of arctic-breeding shorebirds show that declining populations are often associated with food supply problems at the final spring stopover (International Wader Study Group 2003). Although the precise reason or reasons for the decline in the Tierra del Fuego *C. c. rufa* population are not entirely clear, a major reduction in the availability of horseshoe crab eggs has occurred in Delaware Bay, a critical migration staging site used for refueling prior to the Red Knots' last leg of migration to the Arctic.

Population Size and Trends of Calidris canutus roselaari

C. c. roselaari is thought to breed in Alaska and on Wrangel Island and winter in the Americas, whereas *C. c. rogersi* breeds in northeast Siberia, mainly the Chukotski Peninsula and winters in Australasia (Tomkovich 1992). *C. c. roselaari* are slightly larger than *C. c. rogersi* and more intensely colored in breeding plumage on the belly and under-tail coverts.

In the 1980s, the number of Red Knots seen on spring migration in Alaska was reported to be of the order of 150,000 birds (Morrison et al. 2001). Analysis of the carbon and nitrogen isotope signatures of flight feathers from 16 adult specimens taken during this time indicated that birds molted in two very different regions and, compared to known wintering areas on the eastern seaboard of the Americas, were most similar to habitats found in Tierra del Fuego and northwestern Brazil, i.e., a temperate region and a tropical-subtropical region. However, without further data it is not possible to determine the location of those regions; e.g., the temperate region could be in Australasia (P. W. Atkinson, unpubl. data). More recently, numbers appeared to have dropped to 20,000 (COSEWIC 2006). Brown et al. (2001) states that *C. c. roselaari* numbers 150,000. As with *C. c. rufa*, this appears to be a major over-estimate of numbers at the time it was published in 2001.

If all Red Knots seen in Alaska are *C. c. roselaari* and if all *C. c. roselaari* winter in the Americas, then it is very difficult to account for them in winter—either in the 1980s, when there were 150,000, or today. In the mid-1980s, Morrison and Ross (1989) carried out an aerial count of shorebirds along the entire coast of South America. The only significant numbers of Red Knots recorded were the 67,500 *C. c. rufa* between Tierra del Fuego and Río Negro province, Argentina, and the 8,100 of uncertain status in Maranhão, Brazil. Farther north, no evidence suggests that numbers wintering along the Pacific coast of the U.S. and Mexico ever exceeded more than about 10,000, with another 10,000 in Florida and perhaps 5,000 in Texas. These figures total approximately 100,000. Subtract the definite *C. c. rufa* population and only about 33,000 Red Knots are left that could contribute to the 150,000 *C. c. roselaari* once thought to occur in Alaska. Similarly, if the present *C. c. roselaari* breeding population is 35,000–50,000, it is only possible to account for 9,000–27,000 in the Americas in winter (Table 14). It seems that any of the following hypotheses could explain this situation:

1. Many of the birds seen in Alaska in spring are not *C. c. roselaari* but *C. c. rogersi* (which migrate to Australasia). If so, the current *C. c. roselaari* population may be only the 9,000–27,000 suggested by winter counts. If the *C. c. roselaari* population numbers only 9,000, that subspecies may be even more threatened by the risks associated with small populations (such as extinction through stochastic events and the accumulation of harmful genetic mutation [International Wader Study Group 2003]) than *C. c. rufa*.

2. Part of the *C. c. roselaari* population winters outside the Americas; if so, no one knows where.

3. Major *C. c. roselaari* wintering grounds in the Americas remain to be discovered.

The resolution of which wintering populations are *C. c. roselaari* and which are *C. c. rufa* is important for the effective conservation of both subspecies, especially if one or the other turns out to far less numerous than has previously been supposed. Stable isotope analyses of feathers from Australasian wintering areas are a priority to determine whether staging Alaskan birds are likely to be *C. c. roselaari*, *C. c. rogersi* or a mix of both.

GEOGRAPHIC AREA SUMMARIES

The geographic area summaries in this section discuss location of, and factors affecting, important Red Knot non-breeding (wintering) and migratory stopover areas in South America, U.S., and Canada. These accounts include detailed maps of critical and suitable habitats for Red Knots (Appendix 1).

Identifying critical stopover and wintering sites for Red Knots is an important part of this status assessment. These maps represent current knowledge of areas known to be important migratory stopover and/or wintering habitats and will serve as a starting point for conservation action. These important habitats are classified as critical or suitable according to the following criteria:

Critical habitats:

1. Sites of known importance for Red Knots and are documented by survey.

2. Sites of known importance by expert opinion, and may or may not have survey data available.

3. Sites of known importance that are occupied intermittently (because of naturally fluctuating food resources, human disturbance, beach replenishment, etc.), and may or may not have survey data.

Suitable habitats:

1. Sites of known importance that are occupied intermittently, may or may not have survey data, and are deemed by expert opinion as secondary sites not critical to the persistence of the Red Knot population at its current population level — these sites may become critical if the Red Knot population increases.

2. Sites that were historically used by Red Knot but are now unused although the habitat has not been altered — these sites may become critical if the Red Knot population increases.

Chile

Red Knots visit the coast in the Southern Hemisphere from October to March and are often observed in flocks of over 2,000 birds (Morrison and Ross 1989, Harrington and Flowers 1996); however, since the main flyway is along the Atlantic coast, Red Knots are a rare visitor in most parts of Chile with just a few sightings at Arica (18° S), Río Huasco river mouth (29° S), Valparaiso (33° S), Río Maipo River mouth (33° S), Yali wetland (33° S), and Chiloe Island (42° S; Araya and Millie 1996, Couve and Vidal 2003). Although the flyway follows the Atlantic Ocean, the final destination for the majority of Red Knots is in Chile; specifically Bahía Lomas on the north coast of the main island of Tierra del Fuego (56° S) where 41,700 were recorded in 1985 (62% of the whole population of southern South American at the time; Morrison and Ross 1989). Since then, the total population and the numbers at Bahía Lomas have declined. By 2005, the site held only 9,827 or 56% of the southern population (R. I. G. Morrison, unpubl. data; R. K. Ross, pers. comm.; Fig. 37).

Argentina

In Argentina, *C. c. rufa* occur during migration and the austral summer in tidal wetlands distributed along the Atlantic shore. They spend more than 7 months of the year (September–April) in Argentina, but some individuals (mainly juveniles) can also remain during May and the austral winter. Counts at these sites mirror the severe decline of the population in recent years, and indicate that the birds have contracted into the main sites in Tierra del Fuego.

Aerial censuses conducted by the Canadian Wildlife Service (CWS) along the Patagonian coasts (January 1982) and in Tierra del Fuego (Chile—29 January 1985, Argentina—1 February 1985) reported a total of 67,496 Red Knots of which 24,734 were in Argentina: 10,470 in the Argentinian coast of Tierra del Fuego and 14,264 in the continental Patagonian coast (Morrison and Ross 1989). Small numbers (10–100) were reported to spend the austral summer in Bahía Samborombón, at Punta Rasa, and along the shores of Buenos Aires Province (Myers and Myers 1979, Morrison and Ross 1989, Blanco et al. 1992).

No aerial censuses were carried out in the 1990s, but in the 1994–1995 season a capture-recapture survey was conducted which estimated the total population that winters south of San Antonio Oeste at 74,193 Red Knots with a 95% confidence range of 51,398–111,573

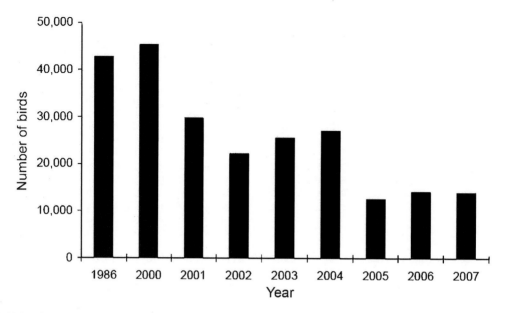

FIGURE 37. Total counts from aerial surveys of Red Knots done in Bahía Lomas, Tierra del Fuego, Chile.

(González et al. 2004). At least 5,000 of these birds were recorded by ground counts in Argentinian Tierra del Fuego (Minton et al. 1996). Although all sites included in 1980s aerial censuses were not visited, small numbers were reported along the shores of Buenos Aires Province (Vila et al. 1994) and at San Antonio Oeste (P. M. González, unpubl. data).

From 2000, aerial censuses showed a dramatic 40% reduction in the core areas of Tierra del Fuego (Morrison et al. 2004). Although not all Argentinian sites were covered by aerial censuses in 2000 and 2001, capture–recapture estimates for the total winter population south of San Antonio Oeste showed the same declining trend (González et al. 2004;

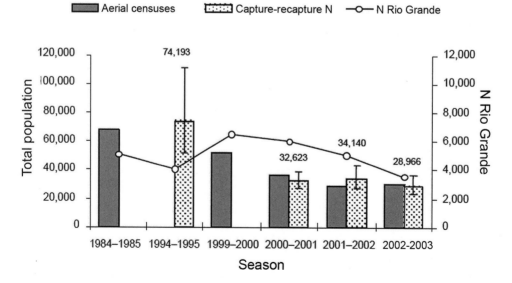

FIGURE 38. Total population estimates (± 95% confidence interval) of Red Knots spending the austral summer south of San Antonio Oeste, Río Negro, Argentina, from capture–recapture methods, compared with aerial census numbers (Morrison and Ross 1989, Morrison et al. 2004,) and number of Red Knots at Río Grande, Tierra del Fuego (González et al. 2004)

Fig. 38). Morrison and Ross (1989) reported important flocks of wintering Red Knots on the Patagonian coast at Península Valdés and Bahía Bustamante in the 1980s, but more recent studies have found none in these areas (L. Bala, pers. comm.; Escudero et al. 2003, Morrison et al. 2004; Table 15; Appendix 1, maps 4, 5, and 6). Therefore, a drastic decline in total numbers has occurred, and also a contraction in the range of the southern wintering population to core areas in Tierra del Fuego. That this change is not simply a redistribution of the birds but a true population decline is also supported by the following: (1) survival estimates and lower recruitment of immatures in this population (Baker et al. 2004), and (2) *C. c. rufa* wintering in northern Brazil are a different population from Tierra del Fuego; no Argentinian or Chilean color-marked Red Knots were found wintering there (Baker et al. 2005a). Moreover, a subsequent decline in Tierra del Fuego numbers to 17,653 was reported in the 2005 season of which 5,000 were seen at Río Grande, Argentina in February (R. I. G. Morrison, unpubl. data).

Based on records from Río Grande (Minton et al. 1996, González et al. 2003), Río Gallegos Estuary (Ferrari et al. 2002) and San Antonio Oeste (González et al. 2004), northward migration begins at the end of January or early February. By the end of April, most Red Knots have already left Argentina although a small number of birds may stay longer, even remaining through the austral winter (usually juveniles; Blanco et al. 1992, Blanco and Carbonell 2001, González et al. 2004).

In the 1980s, important known stopover places for Red Knots were Península Valdés, Chubut Province, where up to 20,000 Red Knots were estimated on passage (Morrison and Harrington 1992), and Bahía Samborombón with Punta Rasa, in Buenos Aires Province where up to 3,000 Red Knots were seen in a single flock (Blanco et al. 1992; Table 16). In the 1990s, San Antonio Oeste in San Matías Gulf was one of most important stopover sites during northward migration, hosting 25–50% of the wintering population from southern Patagonia where up to 20,000 Red Knots were seen at one time (González et al. 2003) (Table 16). Despite being so close to the main wintering areas in Tierra del Fuego (100–300 km away), Río Gallegos estuary was identified as an important stopover site during migration (Ferrari et al. 2002) with a high count of 2,500 Red Knots. Although Morrison et al. (2004) recorded 700 wintering Red Knots in this area in 2002, Ferrari et al. (2002) found no records in December or January from 1997 to 1999. Bahía Bustamante was another area censused regularly in the late 1990s with a highest count of 490 (Escudero et al. 2003; Table 16).

Long-term datasets of regular ground counts (>10 yr) only exist for San Antonio Oeste in San Matías Gulf (January–April, biweekly until 1999, daily to every 10 d from 2000–2005) and for Playa Fracasso (weekly from February–April), in the San José Gulf side of Península Valdés (Fig. 39). Although the highest counts (Table 16) are not necessarily correlated with either the actual number of Red Knots using stopover sites (because of turnover), or with wintering population size (e.g., because birds may bypass

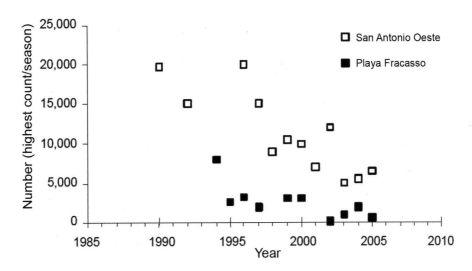

FIGURE 39. Maximum counts of Red Knots during northward migration at two stopover sites in Argentina: San Antonio Oeste and Playa Fracasso in Península Valdés (references in Table 16).

TABLE 15. WINTERING SITES OF RED KNOTS IN ARGENTINA (LOCATIONS GIVEN WITH PROVINCES IN PARENTHESES).

Location	Month	Year	Maximum count	Latitude	Longitude	Source
Río Grande	Jan	1976	3,000–5,000	53°45′ S	67°44.3′ W	Devillers and Terschuren (1976)
Tierra del Fuego	Nov–Dec	1979	5,000			Harrington and Flowers (1996)
	Feb	1985	5,100			Morrison and Ross (1989)
	Feb	1995	4,000			Minton et al. (1996)
	Jan	2000	6,500			G. Escudero (pers. comm.)
	Nov	2000	6,000			Baker et al.(2005b)
	Nov	2001	5,000			Baker et al.(2005b)
	Nov	2002	3,500			Baker et al.(2005b)
	Nov	2003	3,500			Baker et al.(2005b) Morrison and Ross (2004)
	Feb	2004	3,520			R. I. G. Morrison (unpubl. data)
	Feb	2005	5,000			R. I. G. Morrison (unpubl. data)
Bahía San Sebastián	Feb	1985	4,440	53°02.9′ S	68°22′ W	Morrison and Ross 1989
Tierra del Fuego	Feb	2000	2,250			Morrison et al. (2004)
	Feb	2002	50			Morrison et al. (2004)
	Feb	2003	900			Morrison et al. 2004
	Feb	2004	230			R. I. G. Morrison (unpubl. data)
	Feb	2005	100			R. I .G. Morrison (unpubl. data)
Estuario del Río Gallegos (Santa Cruz)	Jan	1998	0	51°30′ S	69°00′ W	Ferrari et al. (2002)
	Dec	2001	1,500			S. Ferrari (pers. comm.)
	Feb	2002	700			Morrison et al. (2004)
	Feb	2003	0			Morrison et al. (2004)
	Dec	2004	800			S. Ferrari (pers. comm.)
	Feb	2005	0			S. Ferrari (pers. comm.)
Bahía Bustamante (Chubut)	Jan	1982	7,400	45°06′ S	66°31′ W	Morrison and Ross (1989)
	Jan	1997	0			Escudero et al. (2003)
	Jan	1998	0			Escudero et al. (2003)
	Jan	1999	0			Escudero et al. (2003)
	Jan	2002	0			Morrison et al. (2004)
	Jan	2003	0			Morrison et al. (2004)
	Feb	2004	0			R. I. G. Morrison (unpubl. data)
	Feb	2005	Not surveyed			
Península Valdés (Chubut)	Jan	1982	3,800	42°30′ S	64°00′ W	Morrison and Ross (1989)
	Jan	2003	0			Morrison et al. (2004)
	Jan	2004	Not surveyed flight restriction			
	Jan.	2005	Not surveyed			R. I. G. Morrison (unpubl. data)
Península Valdés, Fracasso (Chubut)	Jan	1994	0	42°25′ S	64°04′ W	L. Bala et al. (pers. comm.)
	Jan	1995	0			L. Bala et al. (pers. comm.)
	Jan	1996	0			L. Bala et al. (pers. comm.)
	Jan	1997	0			L. Bala et al. (pers. comm.)
	Jan	1999	0			L. Bala et al. (pers. comm.)
	Jan	2000	0			L. Bala et al. (pers. comm.)
	Jan	2002	0			L. Bala et al. (pers. comm.)
	Jan	2003	0			L. Bala et al. (pers. comm.)
	Jan	2004	0			L. Bala et al. (pers. comm.)
	Jan	2005	0			L. Bala et al. (pers. comm.)

Table 16. Stopover sites used by Red Knots in Argentina during northward migration.

Location	Month	Year	Maximum count	Latitude	Longitude	Source
Estuario del						
Río Gallegos	Feb	1998	2,500	51°30′ S	69°00′ W	Ferrari et al. (2002)
(Santa Cruz)	Mar	1999	1,800			Ferrari et al. (2002)
	Mar	2005	1,000			S. Ferrari (pers. comm.)
Bahía Bustamante	Apr	1997	26	45°06′ S	66°31′ W	Escudero et al. (2003)
(Chubut)	Apr	1998	23			Escudero et al. (2003)
	Mar	1999	490			Escudero et al. (2003)
Península Valdés	Apr	1981	20,000	42°30′ S	64°00′ W	Morrison and Harrington (1992)
(Chubut)						
Península Valdés,						
Fracasso	Apr	1994	8,000	42°25′ S	64°04′ W	L. Bala et al. (pers. comm.)
(Chubut)	Mar	1995	2,625			L. Bala et al. (pers. comm.)
	Apr	1996	3,200			L. Bala et al. (pers. comm.)
	Mar	1999	3,020			Bala et al. (2001)
	Apr	2000	3,000			Bala et al. (2002)
	Mar	2002	80			M. Hernández et al. (2004)
	Apr	2003	1,000			L. Bala et al. (pers. comm.)
	Apr	2004	2,000			L. Bala et al. (pers. comm.)
	Apr	2005	500			L. Bala et al. (pers. comm.)
Península Valdés,						
Colombo	Apr	2002	1,500	42°38′ S	64°15′ W	Hernández et al. (2004)
(Chubut)	Apr	2003	250			Musmeci (2005
	Apr	2005	700			L. Bala et al. (pers. comm.)
San Antonio Oeste	Apr	1990	19,700	40°45′ S	64°55′ W	González (1991)
(Río Negro)	Mar	1992	15,000			González et al. (1996)
	Feb	1996	20,000			P.M. González et al. (unpubl. data)
	Mar	1997	15,000			Baker et al. (1999b)
	Mar	1998	9,000			P. M. González and T. Piersma (unpubl. data)
	Mar	1999	10,500			(unpubl. data)
	Mar	2000	10,000			González et al. (2003)
	Mar	2001	7,000			González et al. (2003)
	Apr	2002	12,000			González et al. (2003)
	Apr	2003	5,000			González et al. (2003)
	Mar	2004	5,500			P. M. González et al. (unpubl. data)
	Apr	2005	6,500			P. M. González et al. (unpubl. data)
Punta Rasa	Apr	1988	1,000	36°22′ S	56°45′ W	Blanco et al. 1992
(Buenos Aires)	Apr	1989	3,000			FVSA[a] banding workshop
	Mar	1997	200			Baker et al. (1999b)

[a] FSVA = Fundacion Vida Silvestre Argentina.

San Antonio Oeste after good wintering seasons [González et al. 2003]) or use other beaches at Península Valdés due to changes in sediments at Fracasso beach (V. D'Amico et al., pers. comm.), it is evident that counts in the 1990s were at least 60% higher than during 2000–2005 (Table 16).

In the 1981 season, Morrison and Harrington (1992) estimated that about 20,000 Red Knots occurred on passage in the entire Península Valdés area. However in 2005, thorough weekly ground, boat, and aerial counts from March to May revealed only 700 Red Knots at Colombo beach in the 5th week and 500 at Fracasso beach

in the 7th week. Several individually marked birds were resighted more than once during the season, suggesting that the turnover rate was not very high (V. D'Amico, pers. comm.). Thus, counts at stopover sites are consistent with a declining trend in the wintering population.

Very few sites are known to host Red Knots during their southward migration. For example, at Península Valdés up to 3,800 birds were seen in early October 1980 (Harrington and Leddy 1982), but none have been recorded there during monthly surveys since 1994. At Bahía de San Antonio, 3,500 Red Knots were recorded in October 1992 and 2,500 in October 1997, but only 1,000 in October 2001 (González et al. 2003). At the Río Gallegos estuary, Red Knots have been seen from October–November (Albrieu et al. 2004) with a record of 900 Red Knots in November 1997 (Ferrari et al. 2002). Small numbers have also been recorded in October at La Laguna in Puerto Madryn by Raúl Leon, and at Punta Rasa (Blanco et al. 1992), and Bahía Samborombón (Vila et al. 1994).

Austral winter counts of Red Knots in Argentina (i.e., June–August) are scarce because mainly juveniles occur there. However, a record of 600 exists during the austral winter of 1987 at Punta Rasa (Blanco et al. 1992) where it seems to have been common to see austral wintering Red Knots in the 1980s (Blanco et al. 1992). Small numbers have been at San Antonio Oeste (P. M. González, unpubl. data) as well as 179 at Claromecó (Blanco and Carbonell 2001).

Occasional records of Red Knots have been reported from other sites in Argentina (Table 17). However, because these have not been the subject of systematic surveys, their importance cannot be determined.

Brazil

With an Atlantic coastline of 7,347 km and vast inland wetlands such as the Pantanal, Brazil has a huge amount of shorebird habitat and supporting no less than 25 Nearctic shorebird migrants including Red Knots.

Although Red Knots can occur almost anywhere along the Brazilian shoreline, surveys show that two areas stand out as being of prime importance: the coast of the state of Maranhão in the north and the Lagoa do Peixe National Park in the state of Río Grande do Sul in the south (31° 10′ S, 51° 00′ S; Morrison et al. 1987, Morrison and Ross 1989, Morrison and Harrington 1992, Belton 1994, Nascimento 1995). Passage migrants especially use these

TABLE 17. TOWNS AND PROVINCES IN WHICH RED KNOTS HAVE BEEN OBSERVED IN ARGENTINA.

Place	Records	Date	Latitude, longitude	Source
Laguna Mar Chiquita, Buenos Aires	tens to hundreds	unknown	37°45′ S, 57°25′ W	C. Savigny (pers. comm.) L. Olveira (pers. comm.)
Mar de Cobo, Buenos Aires	tens–few hundreds	unknown	37°46′ S, 57°26′ W	J. Isaac (pers. comm.) D. Blanco et al. (unpubl. data), G. Francia (pers. comm.)
Claromecó, Buenos Aires	tens – hundreds	unknown	38°51′ S, 60°05′ W	
Punta Alta, Buenos Aires	hundreds	unknown	38°54′ S, 62°03′ W	Delhey and Petracci (2004)
Bahía Anegada, Buenos Aires	tens– hundreds	unknown	40°15′ S, 62°16′ W	J. Isaac (pers. comm.)
Caleta de Los Loros, Río Negro	presence	unknown	41°00′ S, 64°01′ W	Canevari et al. (1998) P. M. González (unpubl. data)
Complejo Islote Lobos, Río Negro	800; 3,000; hundreds	unknown	41°26′ S, 65°01′ W	J. P. Chillón (pers. comm.), Morrison et al. (2004)
South Golfo San Matías	1,200; hundreds	unknown	42°00′ S, 65°06′ W	Morrison and Ross (1989), Morrison et al. (2004)
Laguna Puerto Madryn, Chubut	tens	unknown	42°46′ S, 65°03′ W	R. León (pers. comm.)
Punta Tombo, Chubut	presence	unknown	44°02′ S, 65°11′ W	Canevari et al. (1998)
South Golfo Cabo San Jorge to Blanco, Santa Cruz	hundreds– 1,300	unknown	47°12′ S, 65°45′ W	Pérez et al. (1995), Canevari et al. (1998), Morrison and Ross (1989), Morrison et al. (2004)
Ría Deseado (Pta.Foca), Santa Cruz	1,000	unknown	47°44′ S, 65°50′ W	Pérez et al. (1995)
Punta Medanosa, Santa Cruz	3,000	unknown	48°06′ S, 65°55′ W	Pérez et al. (1995), Morrison and Ross (1989)
Cabo Dañoso, Santa Cruz	150	unknown	48°50′ S, 67°13′ W.	Morrison and Ross (1989)
Bahía San Julián, Santa Cruz	tens, 350	unknown	49°21′ S, 67°42′ W.	Hernández (2004), C. Albrieu (pers. comm.)
Puerto Santa Cruz, Santa Cruz	400–500	unknown	50°08′ S, 68°20′ W	S. Imberti (pers. comm.)

areas during northward migration in April-May and during southward migration in September-October. Two factors suggest that passage Red Knots make a direct overland flight between the two: the general lack of records from the rest of the Brazilian coast, and an observation of 10 adults in September 1989 in the southern Pantanal in the state of Mato Grosso do Sul (19°30′ S, 56°10′ W; Centro Nacional de Pesquisa para Conservação das Aves Silvestres [CEMAVE], unpubl. data). Although it is not known whether Red Knots regularly stop over in the Pantanal or whether the 10 birds had been forced to land there as a result of weather conditions, it does indicate that they take the overland route.

The north coast of Maranhão also supports the largest wintering population in South America outside Tierra del Fuego (I. Serrano, unpubl. data; Morrison and Ross 1989, Baker et al. 2004, Baker et al. 2005a). During the breeding season small numbers of non-breeding birds (mainly juveniles) remain on the coast of Maranhão and Río Grande do Sul (Belton 1994), and in the Lagoa do Peixe National Park (Nascimento 1995). Other records of Red Knots along the Brazilian coast are insignificant.

It became clear during censuses carried out on the South American coast in 1982 and 1986 (Morrison and Ross 1989) that the regions of Salgado Paraense (State of Pará) and Reentrâncias Maranhenses (State of Maranhão) on the north coast are among the most important shorebird sites in Brazil. A total of 398,000 shorebirds were counted including 8,324 Red Knots.

Ground surveys were conducted by CEMAVE-IBAMA (Brazilian Institute of the Environment and Renewable Natural Resources) in 1990 and 1994 in October and November and from April to the second week of May along the coasts of the state of Amapá (Nascimento 1998) and in 1991 and 1995 on the coast of Maranhão (I. Serrano et al., unpubl. data). Activities included capture of migratory Nearctic shorebirds with mist-nets, banding (metal bands and color bands), and gathering of biometric data (molting, sex, age, weight, etc.).

In November 1992, 760 Red Knots were counted in Baía dos Lençóis near Campechá Island and in November 1993 1,398 were at the same site. Between 12 April and 5 May 1995, a ground survey was carried out along the north-northeast coast of the states of Ceará and Maranhão, including the mouth of the Gurupi River on the border between the states of Pará and Maranhão. Over 450 km were surveyed and several areas east of the Cabelo da Velha, including Lençóis Bay (Campechá Island) and Turiaçú Bay were found to hold large numbers of Red Knots (Table 18), particularly Coroa dos Ovos Island and Ingleses Island (I. Serrano et al., unpubl. data). In view of the dates of these observations, it is likely that the birds counted included both passage migrants that had overwintered in Argentina or Chile as well as birds that had wintered locally. In February 2005, an aerial census of the key coastal wetlands of Maranhão revealed a total of 7,575 Red Knots, the most (5,000) in Turiaçú Bay and on Coroa dos Ovos Island (Baker et al. 2005a). Therefore, only a slight (7%) decline had occurred in the population since the previous winter count in the mid-1980s, well within the likely counting error (Table 19). Although the 1995 and 2005 surveys were made using different methods and took place at different seasons, they both indicate that the Turiaçú Bay is the most important area for Red Knots.

TABLE 18. NUMBER OF RED KNOTS COUNTED ON THE NORTH COAST OF MARANHÃO, BRAZIL, IN APRIL AND MAY 1995 (I. SERRANO ET AL., UNPUBL. DATA).

Locality (bays)	Latitude, longitude	Estimated number
São Marcos	02°20′ S, 44°20′ W	50
Cumã	02°17′ S, 44°23′ W	0
Capim	01°29′ S, 44°49′ W	4
Cabelo da Velha	01°40′ S, 44°40′ W	90
Lençóis	01°22′ S, 44°56′ W	600
Turiaçú	01°25′ S, 45°06′ W	11,198
Total		11,942

TABLE 19. NUMBER OF RED KNOTS RECORDED ON THE COAST OF MARANHÃO, BRAZIL.

Source	Season	Count
Morrison and Ross (1989)	Winter	8,150
I. Serrano et al. (1995, unpubl. data)	Spring (Apr–May)	11,942
Baker et al. (2005a)	Winter (Feb)	7,575

CEMAVE records show that four Red Knots captured in Maranhão had been banded in Delaware Bay, U.S.—two in the Coroa dos Ovos Islands in November 1993, and two in Campechá Islanda in December 2003. Banding also shows that during northward migration, birds marked in Lagoa do Peixe may stop over on the Maranhão coast. One color-banded individual was seen at Lagoa do Peixe on northward passage in 1987 and again in Maranhão in May the same year. The same bird was observed in Delaware Bay in May 1988 and 1990 (Antas and Nascimento 1996). Another Red Knot was banded by CEMAVE on 10 May 2001 at Campechá weighing 165 g and recaptured only 11 d later at Slaughter Beach, Delaware. This is the shortest migration time recorded for an individual Red Knot between Maranhão and Delaware Bay. Based on theoretical estimates of flight capability, Red Knots weighing >160g can reach 5,000 km, the distance involved. Visual scaning for color-banded Red Knots in the Coroa dos Ovos and Campechá Islands in February 2005 (Baker et al. 2005a) showed that 12 out of 663 Red Knots had been marked in Delaware Bay.

Recent resightings of color-banded Red Knots in Maranhão and isotopic analysis of feathers shows that the Maranhão wintering population is distinct from that of Tierra del Fuego (Baker et al. 2005a). In May 2005, observations in Delaware

Bay (NJENSP, unpubl. data) revealed at least three birds that had been banded in Maranhão (one in October 2004 and two in February 2005). Despite the low number of birds captured in the October 2004 and February 2005 expeditions (10 and 38, respectively), this is a strong indication of the importance of the Maranhão coast both for wintering and as a stopover location during northward migration of birds from Tierra del Fuego.

Lagoa do Peixe National Park is located in the southernmost region of Brazil, between the Atlantic Ocean and Lagoa dos Patos (Appendix 1, map 9). The park is one of the most important wintering grounds and stopover sites for North American migratory shorebirds.

The 35-km lagoon connects to the sea especially during winter during high wind, and when rain accumulates water in the lagoon. In summer, pumping sustains a constant influx of salt water. In this way, the lagoon has developed a rich invertebrate fauna all year round, making it an important source of food for migratory birds due to its high primary productivity. The major food resource for Red Knots at Lagoa do Peixe appears to be the mud snail.

Ground counts of Red Knots carried out in the Lagoa do Peixe National Park by CEMAVE (unpubl. data) during the month of April 1995–2003 show a decrease of numbers of Red Knots especially since 2001 of >90% (Fig. 40). Other

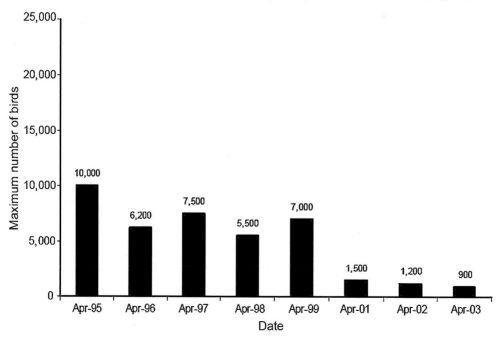

FIGURE 40. Peak numbers of Red Knots recorded in Lagoa do Peixe National Park, Brazil, 1995–2003 (CEMAVE/IBAMA).

published counts of Red Knots at Lagoa do Peixe include 7,000 in April 1984 (Harrington et al. 1986), 11,000 birds (Lara-Resende and Leuwemberg 1987) and 8,900 birds (Vooren and Chiaradia 1990). According to Belton (1994) 1,000 individuals were seen at the end of May. During the breeding season, a small number of non-breeding birds (probably 1-yr-olds) remain at Lagoa do Peixe (Belton 1994). Two birds color-banded at Lagoa do Peixe were later seen during southward migration on the coast of South Carolina on 28 July 1986.

During northward migration, most birds arrive at Lagoa do Peixe in March and the last birds are seen at the end of April, when birds occur on the northernmost beaches in the state of Río Grande do Sul. The last migrants are seen at Santa Catarina in mid-May (Antas and Nascimento 1996). After Lagoa do Peixe, the next stop is in Maranhão and then Delaware Bay, U.S. One color-banded bird from Lagoa do Peixe was encountered in the Presquile Provincial Park, Lake Ontario, Canada. Others have been seen in Florida in the second week of May (CEMAVE, unpubl. data).

About 8,900 migratory shorebirds have been banded by CEMAVE-IBAMA between 1984 and 2004 at the Lagoa do Peixe National Park, including 2,698 Red Knots, 1,871 White-rumped Sandpipers (*Calidris fuscicollis*), 745 Ruddy Turnstones (*Arenaria interpres*), and 658 Sanderlings. Red Knots have provided the most recaptures, especially in the U.S. (Delaware Bay) and Argentina (San Antonio Oeste and Río Grande); CEMAVE, unpubl. data).

Panama

Ten shorebird counts were made by Buehler (2002) between 5 January and 15 April 2002 in the upper Panama Bay: five close to Panama City, two at Río Pacora, and one at Chitré. These show that up to 200 Red Knots occurred during winter (January) and 300 during northward passage (March) (Table 20).

In the Costa del Este area of Panama City, where prime roosting sites were recently lost to housing development, flocks of up to 80,000 shorebirds were observed flying continuously for the duration of the high tide.

Two Red Knots were seen with orange color-marking flags on the tibia, indicating that they had been banded in Argentina. One, with the flag on the left tibia and no color bands, was seen on 20 February 2002 and had probably been banded at Río Grande, Tierra del Fuego, in February 1995. The other, with the flag on the right tibia and a red band on the left tarsus, was seen on 15 and 28 March 2002 and had been banded at San Antonio Oeste, Patagonia, in March 1998. Many of the Red Knots seen in January and February 2002 were identified as juveniles because they had yellowish legs.

The first Red Knots showing breeding plumage were observed on 15 March 2002 when the proportion was 20%. By 28 March, the proportion had increased to 70% with a similar figure on 7 April. By 15 April 2002, the majority of Red Knots had left the area and of the ten birds that remained, only one was in breeding plumage.

United States Fish and Wildlife Service Region 2 – Texas

During 1980–1996, flocks of Red Knots in excess of 1,000 were recorded from several sites on the Texas coast especially during winter (January) and spring passage (April–May), with over 2,800 on one occasion at Mustang Island Beach (Skagen et al. 1999; Table 21). Since that period, however, numbers have been much lower with the largest number recorded only 300, at Bolivar Flats, Galveston County, on 30–31 January 2003 (B. A. Harrington, unpubl. data). Bolivar Flats, which are managed by the Houston Audubon Society, is now the only site where small numbers of Red Knots (5–10) are seen regularly in winter with smaller numbers on the outer gulf beaches. Slightly greater numbers occur during migration (around 20). Christmas bird count (CBC) data from 1997–1998 (the only year for which data were available) shows a total of 36 Red Knots in the state.

The Gulf Coast Bird Observatory confirms that former estimates of 4,000 Red Knots on passage through Texas may now be high by as much as an order of magnitude. An important caveat to these figures is that there have been no systematic surveys for Red Knots in Texas

TABLE 20. COUNTS OF RED KNOTS AT THREE SITES IN PANAMA BETWEEN 5 JANUARY AND 15 APRIL 2002 (BUEHLER 2002).

Location	Date									
	5 Jan	19 Jan	2 Feb	21 Feb	24 Feb	28 Feb	15 Mar	28 Mar	7 Apr	15 Apr
Panama City	200	200				100	250	300	250	10
Río Pacora			20		5					
Chitré				100						

TABLE 21. RECORDS OF RED KNOTS ON THE TEXAS COAST DURING 1980–1996 (SKAGEN ET AL. 1999).

Maximum count	Latitude (°N)	Longitude (°W)	Location
January through June			
2,838	27.70	97.20	Mustang Island Beach, Texas
2,460	27.80	97.10	Airport, Port Aransas, Texas
900	26.00	97.10	Boca Chica Beach, Cameron County, Texas
800	28.20	96.60	Matagorda NWR, Texas
750	29.50	94.60	Bolivar Flats, Texas
575	26.30	97.40	Laguna Atascosa NWR, Texas
184	27.40	97.40	Padre Island National Seashore, Texas
81	26.20	97.20	South Padre Island, Texas
55	28.50	96.60	Magnolia Beach, Indianola Island, Calhoun County, Texas
48	27.60	97.30	Laguna Madre, Corpus Christi, Texas
48	28.90	95.10	San Luis Pass, Galveston Island, Texas
40	29.20	95.80	Big Reef, Galveston Island, Texas
40	29.40	94.60	Shore east of Bolivar Flats, Galveston Island, Texas
July through December			
1,443	27.70	97.20	Mustang Island Beach, Texas
1,439	27.40	97.40	Padre Island National Seashore, Texas
280	26.30	97.40	Laguna Atascosa NWR, Texas
250	28.20	96.60	Matagorda NWR, Texas
111	27.60	97.80	Beach on border of Nueces County and Kleberg County, Texas
88	27.80	97.10	Airport, Port Aransas, Texas
45	29.50	94.60	Bolivar Flats, Texas
30	26.10	97.20	South Padre Island, Texas
29	28.30	96.80	Burgentine Lake, Aransas NWR, Texas
28	26.00	97.10	Boca Chica Beach, Cameron County, Texas
27	27.60	97.30	Laguna Madre, Corpus Christi, Texas
12	27.70	97.60	Nueces County, Texas
10	29.20	95.80	Big Reef, Galveston Island, Texas

and there is nearly 1,000 km of outer coastline in the state from Port Arthur to Brownsville and 3,700 km of shoreline. Therefore, it is quite possible that substantial numbers of Red Knots occur in Texas and are undetected.

Three observations suggest that the Red Knots that occur in Texas belong to the *C. c. rufa* subspecies. First, Oberholser (1974) identified a winter specimen from Cameron County as *C. c. rufa*. Second, an orange-flagged bird from Argentina was seen on the Texas coast in May 2004. Third, an individually flagged bird that had been banded in Delaware Bay in May 2003 was seen on the Texas coast in August–September 2005 (B. Ortego, pers. comm.; W. Burkett, pers. comm.; J. Arvin, pers. comm.).

United States Fish and Wildlife Service Region 4 – Florida

Red Knots have been documented in Florida in all months of the year (Appendices 2, 3) but are seen most frequently from November–May. During November–February, they are most commonly observed on the west coast where the highest number of 6,500 was recorded at Casey Key Beach on 23 January 1979 (Appendix 3). However, the second highest count of 5,000

was on the east coast on 23 March 1978 at Anastasia Island, St. Johns County.

The number of Red Knots that currently winter in Florida is very uncertain and no recent count has been as high as the 6,500 recorded in 1979. ISS counts during 1993–1994, suggest a population of no more than about 4,000 (Sprandel et al. 1997). These were recorded at 27 of the 60 most important shorebird sites in Florida between 16 December 1993 and 1 March 1994 (Table 22; Appendix 1, maps 11, 12, and 13). Evidence from Florida Christmas bird counts obtained by averaging data for each circle during 1980–1989 suggests a minimum state population of 2,928. More recently, 4,000–5,000 were recorded at a single site in western Florida in November 2004 (B. A. Harrington, unpubl. data). Although the data are sparse, we conjecture that the state population may currently be in the region of 7,500. Our reasons are:

1. The 2004 observation was at just one site whereas in 1993–1994 Red Knots were found at 27 sites so it is likely that at least some of those sites would still support the species.

2. Knots are regularly recorded on the coast of South Carolina in early April. These include a flock of 7,000 in early April

TABLE 22. LOWEST AND HIGHEST NUMBER OF RED KNOTS COUNTED ON THE COAST OF FLORIDA IN FOUR COUNTS BETWEEN 16 DECEMBER 1993 AND 1 MARCH 1994, ORDERED ACCORDING TO THE MAXIMUM NUMBER RECORDED.

Site name	Count (lowest–highest)	Location (latitude, longitude)
Shell Key	113–775	27°40 5′, 82°44.0′
Caladesi Island, Hurricane Pass	6–300	28°03.0′, 82°49.3′
Passage Key	0–300	27°33.5v, 82°44.5′
Capri Pass (a.k.a. Key Island)	31–286	25°58.45′, 81°44.82′
Island north of Bunces Pass (now contiguous with Shell Key)	0–280	27°40.0′, 82°44.0′
Little Estero Island	0–241	26°25.0′, 81°54.0′
Palm Island Resort	51–223	26°53.5′, 82°20.5′
Caladesi Island, Dunedin Pass	0–165	28°01.0′, 82°49.45′
Merritt Island NWR, Black Point Drive	0–164	28°40.2′, 80°46.37′
Lanark Reef	1–147	29°52.4′, 84°35.3′
Honeymoon Island	31–122	28°04.0′, 82°49.5′
Lake Ingraham, SE End	0–122	25°08.67′, 81°05.2′
Yent Bayou	0–116	29°47.4′, 84°45.5′
Three Rooker Bar (N and S ends)	0–79	28°07.0′, 82°50.5′
Carrabelle Beach	0–69	29°50.0′, 84°40.5′
Anclote Key (N and S ends)	0–64	28°12.5′, 82°51.0′
Snake Bite Channel	0–60	25°08.13′, 80°53.79′
Courtney Campbell Causeway SE, (2 sites)	0–39	27°58.0′, 82°33.0′
Ding Darling NWR, tower stop	0–30	26°75.5′, 82°08.0′
Ft. DeSoto NW End	0–7	27°37.5′, 82°42.0′
Lido Beach	0–7	27°19.5′, 82°35.0′
Ft. DeSoto East End	0–2	27°38.0′, 82°44.5′
Kennedy Space Center, Pad 39B	0–2	28°37.48′, 80°36.7′

2003 (B. A. Harrington, unpubl. data). It is thought that it would be too early for these birds to have come from South America and that they had probably wintered in Florida. Extensive searches for color bands were made with 163 sightings of marked individuals, but no Red Knots marked in South America were found.

3. Calculations based on resightings of color-banded Red Knots wintering in Florida made between 1981 and 2004 consistently suggest that the population could be even larger than 7,500 (10,000 or more). The error associated with these calculations and the lack of reports of large numbers suggests that the estimates from band resightings may be too high (B. A. Harrington, unpubl. data), but they do suggest relatively consistent numbers through the years.

The evidence of the size of the population of Red Knots wintering in Florida is therefore far from satisfactory and although the figure of 7,500 is used throughout this review, it should be regarded with considerable caution. Systematic surveys to determine the exact size of this important population should be treated as a high priority.

United States Fish and Wildlife Service Region 4 – Georgia

The barrier coast of Georgia, approximately 160 km long, supports measurable numbers of Red Knots from about mid-July through May. During a 6-wk period in June and early July, only a few birds might be found in some remote locations. Clearly, the most significant documented event involving Red Knots in Georgia is the annual fall staging event that can include as many as 10,000 birds at one time. Less well-understood is the biology of the Red Knots that winter in Georgia, and those that migrate through Georgia in the spring (Table 23).

The fall staging phenomenon with large numbers of Red Knots was first discovered in September 1996. This area is remote, and it is very likely that Red Knots have been staging in this area prior to 1996. Knots in large but variable numbers have been recorded every September since 1996. The staging event appears to have a focal area at the mouth of the Altamaha River, where extensive river-generated shoals become exposed at lower tides creating vast areas of feeding habitat for the Red Knots (Fig. 41). The use area includes the south-

TABLE 23. IMPORTANT RED KNOT STOPOVER AND WINTER LOCATIONS IN GEORGIA.

Site name	Importance to fall staging (scale 1–20) N of birds	Importance to winter (scale 1–20) N of birds	Importance spring to migration (scale 1–20) N of birds
Little Tybee Island	none (1)	medium (10) 10–100	low (5) 10–1,000
Ogeechee River Bar	none (1)	low (5) 10s	high (15) 100s
Wassaw Island	none (1)	medium (10) 100–1,000	high (15) 100–1,000
Ossabaw Island	none (1)	high (15) 10–1,000	high (15) 10–1,000
St. Catherines Island	none (1)	high (15) 10–1,000	medium (15) 100
St. Catherines Bar	none (1)	medium (8) 10–100	medium (12) 10–100
Grass Island	none (1)	low (5) 10	high (18) 100–1,000
Blackbeard Island	none (1)	medium (10) 10–100	medium (10) 10–100
Sapelo Island	very high (15) 1,000	medium (10) 10–100	medium (10) 10–100
Wolf Island	very high/critical (20) 1,000–10,000	medium (8) 10–100	high (17) 100–1,000
Little Egg Island Bar	very high/critical (20) 1,000-10,000	medium (8) 10–100	medium (15) 10–100
Little St. Simons Island	very high/critical (20) 1,000–10,000	medium (10) 10–100	high (15) 100
Sea Island	none (1)	medium (10) 10–100	low (5) 10–100
Gould's Inlet, St. Simons Island	none (1)	medium (12) 10–100	medium (10) 10–100
Jekyll Island	none (1)	low (5) 10–100	medium (8) 10–100
Little Cumberland Island	none (1)	low (3) 10	lLow (5) 10
Cumberland Island	none (1)	high (15) 100–1,000	medium (12) 100

ern beaches of Sapelo Island (national estuarine research reserve), Wolf Island and its bar (national wildlife refuge), Little Egg Island Bar (state natural area), and Little St. Simons Island (privately owned, undeveloped) (Appendix 1, map 14).

Temporally, Red Knots begin to arrive in late July and early August, build in number into mid-September, and disperse by mid-October. The length of stay for individual birds is not yet known. Birds banded in Delaware Bay, South Carolina, and Georgia make up nearly 100% of

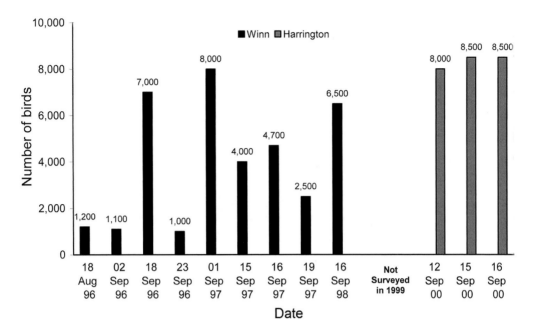

FIGURE 41. Number of Red Knots counted at Altamaha Estuary, Georgia, 1996–1998 (B. Winn, unpubl. data) and 2000 (B. A. Harrington, unpubl. data).

the individually color-marked Red Knots seen in the fall staging event, and throughout the winter in Georgia.

The number of wintering Red Knots in Georgia varies between and within years. Results of an annual winter survey for the entire Georgia coast show the minimum number of Red Knots to be in the hundreds of birds, and the highest to be nearly 5,000. The distribution of wintering Red Knots is generally unpredictable and dispersed over much of the barrier coast. The distribution appears to be linked closely with the abundance and availability of *Mulinia* clams.

Spring migrant use of the Georgia coast has not been studied well. Knots appear to increase in number during late April and May. Knots banded in Georgia and South Carolina can be seen with Red Knots banded in Delaware Bay, Argentina, and Chile. Red Knot use of horseshoe crab eggs appears to increase during the last 2 wk of May in specific locations. By early June, Red Knots have moved out of Georgia

United States Fish and Wildlife Service
Region 4 — South Carolina

Four surveys were conducted in the Cape Romain area and one in St. Helena Sound during the period 2001–2004. The Cape Romain surveys suggest Red Knot numbers peak in April and May during spring passage and then

again in late August, September and October during fall passage (Appendix 1, map 15).

The graph of combined Bulls Island and Cape Romain NWR data (Fig. 42) indicate that Red Knot numbers declined between 2001 and 2004. Bulls Island beach surveys suggest a 75% decline in Red Knots moving through in the spring from 2002–2004. The Cape Romain NWR surveys often did not include Bulls Island, which is part of Cape Romain NWR. Therefore, numbers can be added for a more accurate total of Red Knots in the Refuge.

Few surveys have occurred in the area north of Cape Romain to Pawley's Island. Most of this coastline is undeveloped and remote. The habitat appears optimal for Red Knot and they are often observed there. Deveaux Bank and Bird Key, south of Charleston, are South Carolina Department of Natural Resources preserves for seabird nesting. These areas are visited in April to post the nesting area. Flocks of 200–400 Red Knots have been observed on these islands during April although formal surveys have not been conducted. Systematic surveys are required to document abundance, distribution and habitat use by Red Knots in coastal South Carolina. Surveys for shorebirds were conducted between 1997 and 2004 in the Cape Romain region north of Charleston, South Carolina (Fig. 42, Table 24). The amount of coastal habitat surveyed differed between years, so it is difficult to determine trend for

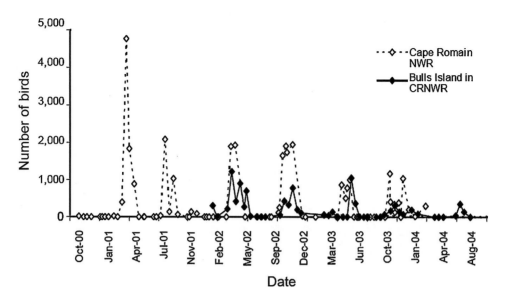

FIGURE 42. Red Knot surveys conducted between 2000 and 2004 in the Cape Romain region of Charleston, South Carolina (sources provided in Table 24).

TABLE 24. RED KNOT SURVEYS CONDUCTED BETWEEN 2000 AND 2004 IN THE CAPE ROMAIN REGION OF CHARLESTON, SOUTH CAROLINA.

Cape Romain NWR (S. Dawsey, pers. comm.)		Bull's Island, Cape Romain National Wildlife Refuge (D. Cubie, pers. comm.; P. Nugent, pers. comm.)	
Date surveyed	N birds	Date surveyed	N birds
30 Oct 2000	18	28 Jan 2002	303
15 Nov 2000	0	11 Feb 2002	5
27 Nov 2000	0	18 Mar 2002	219
12 Dec 2000	0	1 Apr 2002	1,210
11 Jan 2001	0	15 Apr 2002	417
18 Jan 2001	0	29 Apr 2002	900
27 Jan 2001	0	13 May 2002	274
8 Feb 2001	0	20 May 2002	694
26 Feb 2001	25	3 Jun 2002	20
11 Mar 2001	0	24 Jun 2002	9
26 Mar 2001	401	8 Jul 2002	0
9 Apr 2001	4,771	22 Jul 2002	0
19 Apr 2001	1,825	9 Sep 2002	49
6 May 2001	885	23 Sep 2002	426
22 May 2001	0	7 Oct 2002	327
8 Jun 2001	0	21 Oct 2002	778
10 Jun 2001	0	5 Nov 2002	201
12 Jul 2001	0	18 Nov 2002	110
21 Jul 2001	0	3 Feb 2003	58
4 Aug 2001	36	18 Feb 2003	44
19 Aug 2001	2,080	3 Mar 2003	135
3 Sep 2001	140	17 Mar 2003	4
17 Sep 2001	1,030	7 Apr 2003	0
2 Oct 2001	65	21 Apr 2003	4
3 Nov 2001	0	5 May 2003	1,047
10 Nov 2001	0	19 May 2003	368
17 Nov 2001	140	2 Jun 2003	6
6 Dec 2001	91	16 Jun 2003	0
1 Jan 2002	0	30 Jun 2003	0
8 Jan 2002	0	28 Jul 2003	0

TABLE 24. CONTINUED.

Cape Romain NWR (S. Dawsey, pers. comm.)		Bull's Island, Cape Romain National Wildlife Refuge (D. Cubie, pers. comm.; P. Nugent, pers. comm.)	
Date surveyed	N birds	Date surveyed	N birds
16 Jan 2002	0	11 Aug 2003	0
30 Jan 2002	0	25 Aug 2003	72
16 Feb 2002	0	15 Sep 2003	167
14 Mar 2002	0	29 Sep 2003	310
29 Mar 2002	1,887	14 Oct 2003	142
12 Apr 2002	1,923	27 Oct 2003	74
16 May 2002	0	24 Nov 2003	191
25 Jun 2002	0	15 Dec 2003	81
9 Jul 2002	0	9 Feb 2004	0
5 Aug 2002	0	23 Feb 2004	0
11 Aug 2002	0	9 Mar 2004	0
4 Sep 2002	121	19 Apr 2004	41
7 Sep 2002	253	4 May 2004	350
17 Sep 2002	1,646	17 May 2004	140
28 Sep 2002	1,900	7 Jun 2004	0
1 Oct 2002	1,730		
20 Oct 2002	1,940		
22 Nov 2002	30		
2 Dec 2002	0		
5 Jan 2003	0		
2 Feb 2003	60		
3 Mar 05 0			
21 Mar 2003	0		
2 Apr 2003	864		
16 Apr 2003	510		
21 Apr 2003	782		
30 Apr 2003	996		
14 May 2003	5		
24 May 2003	0		
29 May 2003	0		
27 Jun 2003	0		
8 Jul 20030			
21 Jul 2003	0		
12 Aug 2003	0		
27 Aug 2003	0		
12 Sep 2003	1,164		
14 Sep 2003	415		
27 Sep 2003	345		
29 Sep 2003	130		
12 Oct 2003	386		
19 Oct 2003	0		
26 Oct 2003	1,035		
15 Nov 2003	202		
6 Dec 2003	18		
10 Jan 2004	300		

entire period. Surveys of the same area during the period 2001–2004 show a decline in Red Knots peak numbers in April and May and then in late August, September, and October (Figs. 43–45). The Cape Romain region was surveyed in 1988–1989. High counts for surveyed sites were also recorded in May and August through September suggesting these months are peak migration months in South Carolina.

United States Fish and Wildlife Service
Region 4 – North Carolina

Based on the limited survey information and anecdotal observations by wildlife professionals and local ornithologists, the following sites, presented from south to north, are believed to be important stopover and wintering areas for Red Knots (Table 25; Appendix 1,

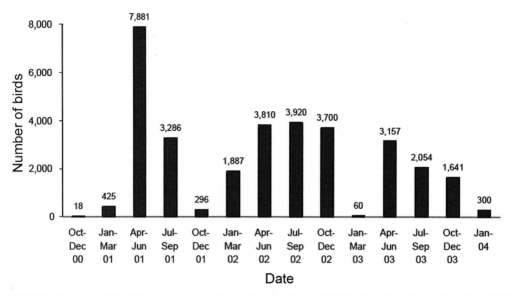

FIGURE 43. Number of Red Knots counted at Cape Romain National Wildlife Refuge, South Carolina, 2000–2004 (S. Dawsey, pers. comm.).

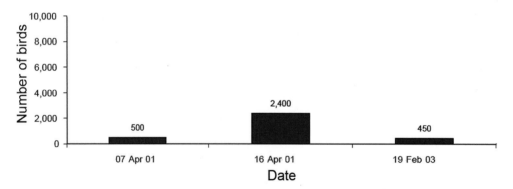

FIGURE 44. Number of Red Knots counted at Harbor Island, South Carolina, 2001–2003 (B. A. Harrington, unpubl. data).

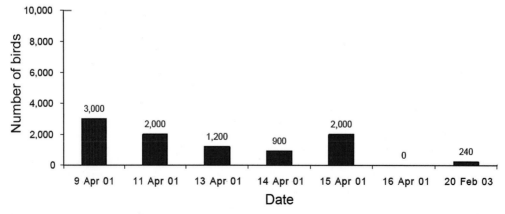

FIGURE 45. Number of Red Knots counted at Hunting Island, South Carolina, 2001–2003 (B. A. Harrington, unpubl. data).

TABLE 25. STOPOVER AND POTENTIAL WINTERING AREAS FOR RED KNOTS IN NORTH CAROLINA.

Location	Spring	N	Fall	N	Winter	N
Tubbs Inlet	28 April 2004	500	–	–	–	–
	5 April 2005	90	–	–	–	–
Ocean Isl. Beach	25 April 1986	200	–	–	–	–
Fort Fisher	–	–	–	–	Consistent winter use; CBC[a] also records Red Knots at this location (J. Fussell pers. comm.)	~30
Bear Is.-	18 May 1985	200	–	–	February (year	2
Bogue Inlet	19 May 1989	1,250	–	–	unknown)	–
	May (late 1990s) (J. Fussell, pers. comm.)	max. 100	–	–	–	–
Bird Shoals	–	–	–	–	Winter (J. Fussell, pers. comm.)CBC[a]	Max. 100
	–	–	–	–		~4
Cape Lookout Nat. Seashore North Core Banks	Early May, 2005	1,000[b]	–	–	–	–
Cape Hatteras Nat. Seashore Ocracoke	Early May, 2005	1,000[b]	–	–	–	–
Pea Island NWR	–	–	–	–	November (year unknown)	100
Rachel Carson Reserve	–	–	–	–	Winter consistent use (J. Fussell, pers. comm.)	100
Cedar Island NWR	May consistent use (J. Fussell, pers.comm.)	50–200 individuals	–	–	–	–

[a] Christmas Bird Count.
[b] These counts may represent the same birds.

map 16). Available information suggests Red Knots are consistently using coastal areas of North Carolina during spring and fall migration. Knots are wintering in North Carolina in limited numbers. Systematic surveys during migration and wintering seasons are necessary to determine distribution, abundance and habitat use of coastal areas by Red Knots.

On Tubbs Inlet, 90 Red Knots were observed foraging on the ocean side of the island in early April 2005 and 500 Red Knots were observed roosting on the bay side of the island in late April 2004. Little or no information is available concerning use of Red Knots during fall or winter months.

Fort Fisher State Historic Site hosts a natural rock outcrop that appears to be an important feeding area for small numbers of birds each winter and almost certainly in migration. Approximately 30 Red Knots are recorded there each winter by J. Fussell (pers. comm.) and the CBC.

Bear Island and Bogue Inlet regularly host small numbers of Red Knots. The maximum number recorded in spring was 60 individuals and two birds were observed in winter (February). Historically, good numbers of Red Knots occurred at the outer beaches of Bear

Island. This area has not been systematically surveyed.

Bird Shoals is potentially an important wintering site for Red Knots. A few Red Knots have been recorded at this site during the CBC in December. J. Fussell (pers. comm.) has documented up to 100 birds here in the winter. No systematic surveys have been conducted during spring or fall migration to determine shorebird abundance.

Surveys conducted in 1992–1993 revealed moderate numbers of Red Knots using the Outer Banks of Cape Lookout National Seashore during migration and in winter (Dinsmore et al. 1998). Most observations during this study were on North Core Banks. Recent observations suggest that South Core Banks and North Core Banks have significant numbers of Red Knots. About 1,000 birds were observed on the north end of North Core Banks in early May, 2005. Good numbers were observed foraging on outer beach of South Core Banks2006. North Carolina Nongame and Endangered Wildlife Program started an ISS survey at New Drum Inlet on the north end of South Core Banks. This survey will continue in the fall. Portions of Cape Lookout are important stopover sites. The east end of Shackleford Banks has extensive intertidal flats

TABLE 26. NUMBER OF RED KNOTS OBSERVED DURING THE 2001–2002 INTERNATIONAL SHOREBIRD SURVEY ON CLAM SHOAL, NORTH CAROLINA.

Date	N
14 February 2001	80
26 July 2001	–
16 August 2001	–
10 October 2001	218
31 October 2001	398
9 January 2002	305
21 February 2002	–
18 April 2002	31
15 May 2002	25

bordering Bardens Inlet and Back Sound and is considered a suitable migratory stopover for Red Knots in spring

Approximately 1,000 Red Knots were observed on south end of Ocracoke on Cape Hatteras National Seashore in early May 2005. These may be the same birds observed on North Core Banks. Red Knots numbering from 10–200 (maximum = 400) are observed on Ocracoke (S. Maddock, pers. comm.)

Results of the ISS on Clam Shoal (Table 26) indicate this site is an important wintering area and is used during spring and fall migration.

Refuge staff at Pea Island NWR conduct shorebird surveys and record small numbers of Red Knots. Staff recorded a peak of 100 birds in November. This site is likely serving as a stopover and wintering location for Red Knots.

A consistent number of about 100 Red Knots are observed in winter at the Rachel Carson Reserve (J. Fussell, pers. comm.).

Small numbers of Red Knots (50–200 individuals) are regularly seen in the spring along a 9.6-km stretch of beach on the Pamlico Sound Shoreline of Cedar Island, part of which is within Cedar Island NWR (the northwest end).

United States Fish and Wildlife Service Region 5 – Virginia

On 23 May 2005 at the request of the NJDFW, Bryan Watts of the Center for Conservation Biology and Barry Truitt of TNC's Virginia Coast Reserve conducted an aerial survey of Virginia barrier islands for Red Knots. The survey resulted in a total estimate of 9,150 Red Knots along the island chain. Significant concentrations were observed on Wreck Island, Paramore Island, Hog Island, and Myrtle Island.

Aerial surveys conducted throughout the springs of 1994 – 1996 by the same observers and using the same techniques showed that Red Knot migration on the Virginia Barrier Islands peaks during the third weak of May. The peak estimate during these 3 yr was 8,955 birds documented on 21 May 1996. The estimate for 2005 is within 200 individuals of the peak estimate from 10 yr earlier. It should be noted that the Chimney Pole Marsh-Sandy Island complex inside Quinby Inlet was surveyed in 2005 (710 Red Knots detected) but not in the mid-1990s. Although overwhelming evidence shows that the Red Knot population within the Western Hemisphere has experienced dramatic declines, current use of the Virginia Barrier Islands by migrating Red Knots appears to be similar to the mid-1990s (Tables 27–29,

TABLE 27. RESULTS OF AERIAL SURVEYS CONDUCTED AT LOW TIDE FOR RED KNOTS ALONG OUTER BEACH SURF ZONE OF VIRGINIA BARRIER ISLANDS FROM VIRGINIA–MARYLAND BORDER TO MOUTH OF CHESAPEAKE BAY IN 1995[a], 1996[b], AND 2005 (B. WATTS, PERS. COMM.; B. TRUITT, PERS. COMM.).

Site	1995	1996	2005
Assateague Island	57	174	60
Wallops Island	20	395	0
Assawoman Island	500	214	0
Metompkin Island	1,915	1,272	230
Cedar Island	486	1,622	200
Dawson Shoals			
Parramore Island	2,485	1,758	1,040
Chimney Pole Marsh	n/a	n/a	710
Hog Island	1,260	1,243	1,115
Cobb Island	675	1,030	780
Little Cobb Island	0	0	0
Wreck Island	5	31	4,250
Ship Shoal Island	42	150	75
Myrtle Island	90	150	500
Smith Island	423	883	100
Fisherman Island	0	0	90
Total	7,958	8,922	9,150

[a] Results for the 1995 survey represent the high count of five surveys conducted between 25 April and 30 May 1995. See Table 28 for results of all 1995 surveys.
[b] Results for the 1996 survey represent the high count of six surveys conducted between 27 April and 10 June 1996. See Table 29 for results of all 1996 surveys.

TABLE 28. RESULTS OF AERIAL SURVEYS CONDUCTED AT LOW TIDE FOR RED KNOTS ALONG OUTER BEACH SURF ZONE OF VIRGINIA BARRIER ISLANDS FROM VIRGINIA–MARYLAND BORDER TO MOUTH OF CHESAPEAKE BAY IN 1995 (B. WATTS, PERS. COMM.; B. TRUIT, PERS. COMM.).

SITE	25 April 1995	9 May 1995	16 May 1995	24 May 1995	30 May 1995
Assateague Island	0	0	0	57	418
Wallops Island	0	0	190	20	5
Assawoman Island	0	0	0	500	5
Metompkin Island	0	20	1,000	1,915	34
Cedar Island	0	0	10	486	80
Dawson Shoals					
Parramore Island	0	20	505	2,485	1,095
Hog Island	0	0	155	1,260	655
Cobb Island	0	0	940	675	700
Little Cobb Island	0	0	0	0	0
Wreck Island	0	0	0	5	5
Ship Shoal Island	0	0	95	42	30
Myrtle Island	0	0	175	90	120
Smith Island	0	0	305	423	140
Fisherman Island	0	0	0	0	8
Total	0	40	3,375	7,958	3,295

TABLE 29. RESULTS OF AERIAL SURVEYS CONDUCTED AT LOW TIDE FOR RED KNOTS ALONG OUTER BEACH SURF ZONE OF VIRGINIA BARRIER ISLANDS FROM VIRGINIA–MARYLAND BORDER TO MOUTH OF CHESAPEAKE BAY IN 1996 (B. WATTS, PERS. COMM.; B. TRUITT, PERS. COMM.).

SITE	27 April 1996	5 May 1996	13 May 1996	21 May 1996	1 June1996	10 June1996
Assateague Island	0	0	0	235	174	0
Wallops Island	0	0	0	0	395	0
Assawoman Island	0	0	0	0	214	0
Metompkin Island	0	0	0	2,150	1,272	0
Cedar Island	0	0	400	1,940	1,622	0
Parramore Island	0	0	1,035	1,459	1,758	0
Hog Island	0	0	60	947	1,243	200
Cobb Island	0	0	0	30	1,030	0
Little Cobb Island	0	0	0	0	0	0
Wreck Island	0	0	85	25	31	0
Ship Shoal Island	0	0	80	30	150	0
Myrtle Island	0	0	0	55	150	0
Smith Island	0	0	20	1,713	883	0
Fisherman Island	0	0	0	0	0	3
Total	0	0	1,680	8,584	8,922	203

Fig. 46). Volunteers have conducted weekly shorebird surveys along the outer beach surf zone of Chincoteague NWR since 1992 (Table 30). Extensive shorebird surveys conducted by the late Claudia P. Wilds at Chincoteague in the 1970s and 1980s indicated that most of the Red Knots documented in the area were found on Tom's Cove Beach.

Surveys of the outer beach surf zone of Fisherman Island NWR at the southern tip of the Delmarva Peninsula indicate very little use of the island by the Red Knots during spring migration (Tables 27–29). It should be noted that over 200 Red Knots were documented on the island in May of 2005 (P. Denmon, pers. comm.). In 2004, refuge personnel initiated systematic fall shorebird surveys following ISS protocol (Table 31). One year of results indi-

cate very little use of the island by Red Knots between August and October.

Ten years of shorebird survey data along the ocean facing beaches of Back Bay NWR and False Cape State Park suggest that the number of Red Knots using those beaches during spring migration is insignificant relative to the amount of use received by the barrier islands bordering the Delmarva Peninsula (D. Schwab, pers. comm.).

Shorebird surveys conducted during a May 2000 invertebrate study, showed that Red Knot numbers peaked on Metompkin Island on 19 May with approximately 3,000 birds present and on Parramore Island on 21 May with approximately 3,000 present. A total of 68 banded and flagged birds were noted, with 37 from Argentina, 27 from Delaware Bay, and four from Brazil.

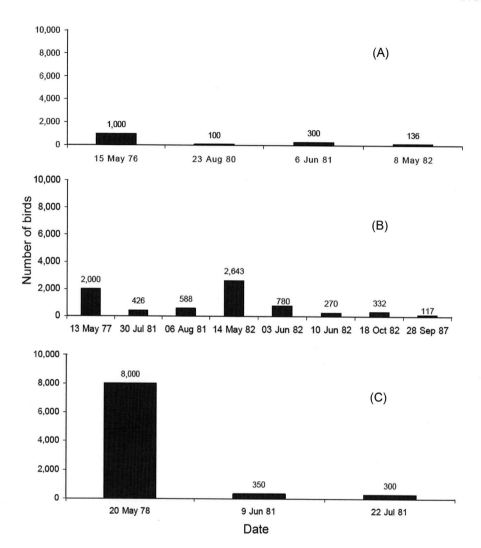

FIGURE 46. Number of Red Knots counted at (A) Wallops Island, (B) Chincoteague, and Metompkin Island, Virginia, 1976–1982 (B. A. Harrington, unpubl. data).

TABLE 30. GROUND SURVEYS FOR RED KNOTS ON CHINCOTEAGUE NATIONAL WILDLIFE REFUGE, 1992–2003. NUMBERS INDICATE PEAK COUNT [a].

	1992	1993	1994	1995	1996	1997	1998	1999	2000	2001	2002	2003
January	0	0	0	0	0	0	0	0	0	0	6	0
February	0	4	0	0	0	0	0	0	0	0	0	0
March	1	0	0	0	0	0	0	0	0	0	0	0
April	0	0	1	0	0	0	0	0	0	0	7	0
May	15	36	47	144	133	73	54	90	5	0	543	4
June	28	9	124	98	5	11	42	48	13	66	282	0
July	105	27	58	143	3	62	25	1	0	2	8	0
August	209	106	306	20	5	13	0	0	3	4	88	24
September	23	19	65	99	10	5	1	0	0	1	35	0
October	37	0	0	0	8	0	0	0	0	0	1	55
November	26	2	0	12	1	1	4	0	0	0	0	0
December	0	1	11	25	52	8	0	0	0	1	64	0

[a] One to five counts conducted monthly at varying tidal stages.

TABLE 31. RESULTS OF SHOREBIRD SURVEYS CONDUCTED ON FISHERMAN ISLAND NATIONAL WILDLIFE REFUGE, VIRGINIA, FOLLOWING INTERNATIONAL SHOREBIRD SURVEY PROTOCOL IN 2004[a].

Date	N Red Knots
11 August 2004	0
24 August 2004	0
7 September 2004	0
13 September 2004	2
23 September 2004	0
7 October 2004	1
14 October 2004	0

[a] Data collected and provided to Fisherman Island NWR by volunteers.

Various studies and surveys documenting Red Knot use of habitats in Virginia are summarized as follows:

1. Chesapeake Bay, western shore, various years—no systematic survey data exists for the isolated beaches that occur along the western shore of the Chesapeake Bay. These areas are almost certainly used by Red Knots during migration, but in unknown numbers. Over 200 individuals have been observed at Plumtree Island, NWR in mid-May. Fewer numbers have been observed at Goodwin Island. Other areas that may be used by Red Knots include the beaches at Newpoint Comfort, Melford Haven and Grandview Beach (B. Watts, pers. comm.).

2. Chesapeake Bay, western shore (Craney Island), 1975—shorebird surveys conducted on Craney Island 2–3 d/wk from 18 February through 17 July 1975 recorded large numbers of shorebirds of various species but only a single Red Knot near the end of May (Shopland 1975).

3. Lower western shore salt marshes, 1992—surveys conducted for birds using 30 salt marshes along the lower western shore of the Chesapeake Bay between 6 May and 10 July 1992. More than 1,800 shorebirds were recorded including three Red Knots (Watts, 1992).

4. Lower western shore salt marshes, 1993—tidepool surveys within salt marshes of the lower western shore of the Chesapeake Bay were conducted from 25 April through 23 October of 1993. Several hundred shorebirds were recorded using tidepools but no Red Knots were observed (Allen 1995).

5. Chesapeake Bay, Eastern Shore, various years—no systematic survey data exist for the Eastern Shore of the Chesapeake Bay. Flocks of >500 Red Knots have been observed during aerial surveys over Plantation Creek, Northampton County, Virginia (B. Watts, pers. comm.).

6. Lower Delmarva mainland, 1991–1992—shorebird surveys within 400 agricultural fields in Northampton County, Virginia from March 1991 to February 1992 recorded more than 20,000 observations of 21 species. Only one observation of a Red Knot was made during the study. This individual was observed in May (Rottenborn 1992).

7. Beaches of Norfolk and Virginia Beach, 1992—shorebird surveys were conducted along six beach segments within Norfolk and Virginia Beach from 8 February to 11 June, 1992 with >3,000 observations including <50 Red Knots (McLean 1993).

To date, no formal resighting surveys have been conducted in Virginia. In 2005, casual scans of Red Knot flocks on Virginia's barrier islands during spring migration revealed a number of observations of birds that were banded throughout their range (Appendix 1, map 17). This suggests that the development of a formal and systematic spring migration resighting survey effort on the barrier islands would be worthwhile expenditure of time and resources.

United States Fish and Wildlife Service
Region 5 – Maryland

The state of Maryland does not conduct or sponsor any organized surveys that include Red Knots, and no research, monitoring or management efforts regarding Red Knots have been done in the state (G. Therres, pers. comm.). Suitable habitats do exist within the state including: Hart Miller Island, Assateague Island, and Poplar Island. Poplar Island is located off the Chesapeake Bay coastline, about 54 km south of Baltimore in Talbot County. At the time of this writing no accessible records of sightings of Red Knots had been made within the state.

United States Fish and Wildlife Service
Region 5 – New Jersey and Delaware

The Delaware Bay is a migratory stopover of hemispheric importance for Red Knots and at least five other species of shorebird including Ruddy Turnstone, Sanderling, Dunlin, Short-billed Dowitcher (*Limnodromos griseus*), and Semipalmated Sandpiper. This section presents information specific to New Jersey and Delaware habitats and shorebird populations. Historic and current research has been conducted from the perspective of the Delaware Bay ecosystem because migratory shorebirds use the entire bay to meet their energetic needs.

Delaware Bay, a major estuary of the U.S. middle Atlantic coastal region, is located at the mouth of the Delaware River in the states of Delaware and New Jersey. Delaware Bay serves as critical stopover habitat for migrating shorebirds, especially during the spring migration when it supports some of the highest numbers recorded in the lower 48 states (Clark et al. 1993). Many of these migrants rely heavily on the eggs of horseshoe crabs, which come to spawn in Delaware Bay in high numbers (Castro and Myers 1993, Tsipoura and Burger 1999). Because a significant proportion of the Red Knot population moves through Delaware Bay during the spring migration, this area is of critical concern.

Delaware Bay is fringed by extensive coastal marshes and mudflats typically fronted by a sandy barrier beach. The sandy barrier beaches overlay marsh sediments (generally a fibrous peat formed by the root mat of the marsh plants) and vary in thickness from a thin veneer to about 2-m thick (Phillips 1986a). The back beaches, above normal high tide, form a low dune and are often colonized by common reed (*Phragmites australis*; Phillips 1987). The intertidal portions of these sandy barrier beaches are of special significance as these are the locus of horseshoe crab spawning activity and the Red Knots' foraging activities. At a bay-wide scale, the use of intertidal beaches as horseshoe crab spawning habitat is limited in the north (Sea Breeze in New Jersey and Woodland Beach in Delaware) by low salinity and by ocean-generated energy in the south (North Cape May, New Jersey, and Broadkill, Delaware).

Not surprisingly, migratory shorebird abundance is spatially variable within the Delaware Bay estuary as a consequence of these larger bay-wide patterns of horseshoe crab abundance and spawning activity. In their study of site selection of migratory shorebirds in Delaware Bay, Botton et al. (1994) found that migrant shorebirds, including Red Knots, showed a strong preference for beaches with higher numbers of crab eggs. Shorebirds were recorded to aggregate near shoreline discontinuities, such as salt-marsh-creek deltas and jetties that acted as concentration mechanisms for passively drifting eggs. Foraging and roosting shorebirds also react to human disturbance and are often displaced from prime foraging areas (Burger 1986, Erwin 1996). Thus near-shore development or high human use may lower a beach's value as optimal shorebird foraging habitat. During the spring 2005 migratory period, NJDFW took aggressive measures to limit access of people and pets to key stretches of beach habitat as a means of minimizing disturbance to foraging

and resting shorebirds. These various studies suggest that a complex array of factors determines the optimality of particular Delaware Bay beaches as horseshoe crab spawning and shorebird foraging habitat.

Aerial surveys of migrating shorebirds have been conducted along Delaware bayshore since 1982 (Dunne et al. 1982, Kochenberger 1983, Clark et al. 1993). In 1982 and 1983, surveys were done by NJAS up to three times in the stopover period; since 1986 surveys have followed a standardized method (Clark et al. 1993). All bayshore surveys were conducted from Cape May Canal to Cohansey River in New Jersey, and Cape Henlopen to Woodland Beach in Delaware (Appendix 1, maps 19 and 20). Surveys were conducted once per week for the 6-wk period of early May to mid-June each year. Aerial survey data are summarized as a single-day peak count of Red Knots each year (Table 32). These survey data are analyzed in conjunction with other data sources within this document. A simple correlation analysis shows that Red Knot counts have declined by 52%; however, birds' length of stay is a strong influence when calculating the population

TABLE 32. PEAK COUNTS OF RED KNOTS OBSERVED IN AERIAL SURVEYS OF DELAWARE BAY SHORELINE.

Year	N Red Knots
1982[a]	95,530
1983[b]	16,859
1984	No survey
1985	No survey
1986[c]	55,531
1987	38,750
1988	38,190
1989	94,460
1990	45,785
1991	27,280
1992	25,595
1993	44,000
1994	52,055
1995	38,600
1996	19,445
1997	41,855
1998	50,360
1999	49,805
2000	43,145
2001	36,125
2002	31,695
2003	16,255
2004	13,315
2005	15,345
2006	13,445
Geometric mean	34,279
Correlation with year	−0.52 (P = 0.009)

[a] 1982 by Dunne et al. (1982).
[b] 1983 by Kochenberger (1983).
[c] 1986–2005 by Clark et al. (1993).

trend in the bay. As the horseshoe crab egg food source declines, birds must spend more time in the bay, and the likelihood of counting the same birds in multiple weekly surveys increases. Such a scenario would mean the actual decline is >52%.

Aerial survey data were mapped to illustrate the distribution of Red Knots in two time periods: 1986–1990 and 2001–2005 representing pre- and post-horseshoe crab decline, respectively. The survey data were summarized into the 5-yr periods, the total number of Red Knots summed (across the entire study area) and the percentage of the total 5-yr sum calculated for each beach segment. The survey data were analyzed as percentages to examine the spatial distribution of beach use on a relative, rather than an absolute basis.

Comparison of the maps for these two time periods suggests that the spatial distribution of Red Knot use has changed (Fig. 20). During the 1986–1990 time period, the Red Knots were relatively evenly distributed along the New Jersey shoreline from Reeds Beach to Ben Davis Point. However, during the 2001–2005 a greater concentration appeared to be in the Norbury's Landing to Reed's Beach area and the Egg Island Point to Gandy's Beach area. During 1986–1990, Red Knots were relatively evenly distributed along Delaware shoreline from Bowers Beach through Bombay Hook NWR, with a major concentration in the Slaughter Beach-Mispillion Harbor area. During 2001–2005, a much greater concentration occurred in the Slaughter Beach-Mispillion Harbor and Bowers Beach areas. Mispillion Harbor should be noted as the site of incredibly high concentrations consistently containing upward of 15–20% of all the Red Knots recorded on the Bay.

Other areas of the Bayshore were recorded as receiving comparatively minimal use by Red Knots; for example, the Cape May Peninsula south of Norbury's Landing, the central (Big Stone Beach) and eastern most (Prime Hook-Broadkill Beach to Cape Henlopen) sections of the Delaware shoreline. It is interesting to note that these low bird use areas coincide with areas of low horseshoe crab spawning activity as recorded by Smith et al. (2002a).

In addition to the aerial surveys, ground-based surveys have been conducted by NJENSP to identify other high use areas for Red Knots during the spring stopover. In particular, large numbers of Red Knots have been recorded using the Stone Harbor Point area on the Atlantic coast of Cape May County, New Jersey (Sitters et al. 2001, unpubl. data). Stone Harbor Point and adjacent islands contain undeveloped sand beach/bar, mudflat, and salt marsh and serve as both foraging and resting habitat for Red Knots. In 2001, Red Knots were surveyed roosting (Table 33) and feeding (Table 34) in the Stone Harbor Point area, reaching a maximum count of 18,000 on 28 May 2001. In 2005, H. P. Sitters (unpubl. data) recorded both nighttime counts in the area and the presence of telemetered Red Knots (Table 35). These data suggest possibly all Red Knots in Delaware Bay were using the Stone Harbor Point area for nighttime roosting in late May 2005, and underscore the importance of this area for the population.

Thus, while the Delaware Bay intertidal beaches are essential for horseshoe crab spawning and are the egg resource for Red Knots, migrating shorebirds including the Red Knot move actively between Delaware Bay habitats with changes in the tidal cycle (Burger et al. 1997; H. P. Sitters, unpubl. data). Shorebirds use all these habitats for foraging and resting

TABLE 33. NUMBERS OF RED KNOTS ROOSTING AT HIGH WATER BY DAY AND AT DUSK AT STONE HARBOR POINT, NEW JERSEY, DURING MAY 2001 (H. P. SITTERS, UNPUBL. DATA).

Date	Time of high tide	N Red Knots roosting	Day or dusk
9 May	1032 H	152	day
10 May	1120 H	100	day
21 May	2011 H	11,000	dusk
22 May	2050 H	14,000	dusk
23 May	0922 H	700	day
23 May	2130 H	15,000	dusk
24 May	1008 H	1,200	day
27 May	1253 H	12,000	day
28 May	1353 H	18,000	day
29 May	1451 H	15,000	day
30 May	1550 H	3,200	day
1 June	1747 H	3,000	day
2 June	1841 H	1,500	dusk
3 June	1931 H	2,000	dusk

TABLE 34. OBSERVATIONS OF RED KNOTS FEEDING IN THE STONE HARBOR AREA WETLANDS DURING MAY 2001 (H. P. SITTERS, UNPUBL. DATA).

Date in May	Time of low water	N Red Knots in wetlands	Time observed	Knots Location	Total daily counts of Red Knots
4	1258 H	2	1400–1445 H	Grassy Sound	2
5	1346 H	250	1120–1530 H	Great Sound	250
7	1519 H	500	1415–1630 H	Great Sound	500
8	1602 H	700	1420–1740 H	Great Sound	700
9	1644 H	700	1500–1815 H	Great Sound	700
10	1724 H	1,400	1630–1830 H	Great Sound	1,400
17	1100 H	43	0930–1230 H	Great and Jenkins Sound	43
19	1239 H	300	1015–1450 H	Jenkins Sound	300
21	1404 H	700	1445–1500 H	Stone Harbor	700
22	1448 H	800	1440–1510 H	Back-bay Stone Harbor	
		200	1530–1555 H	Grassy Sound	
		3,500	1600–1625 H	Stone Harbor	3,500
23	1533 H	130	1330 H	Stone Harbor	
		156	1340 H	Back-bay Stone Harbor	
		350	1400–1500 H	Back-bay Stone Harbor	
		200	1520–1550 H	Grassy Sound	
		150	1615 and 1637 H	Back-bay Stone Harbor	
		700	1630 H	Stone Harbor	850
24	1618 H	600	1445–1700 H	Back-bay Stone Harbor	
		500	1445–1700 H	Back-bay Stone Harbor	
		37	1740 H	Stone Harbor	1,200
27	0647 H	6,500	0930–1000 H	Stone Harbor	
	1847 H	3,000	1745–1845 H	Stone Harbor	
		5,000	1745–1845 H	Back-bay Stone Harbor	8,000
28	0743 H	250	0800–0900 H	Stone Harbor	
		950	0800–0900 H	Back-bay Stone Harbor	
	1950 H	3,000	1800–1900 H	Stone Harbor	
		2,200	1800–1900 H	Back-bay Stone Harbor	5,500
29	0845 H	3,000	0945 H	Stone Harbor	
		7,000	0955–1040 H	Jenkins Sound	7,000
		5,000	2000–2015 H	Back-bay Stone Harbor	5,000
30	0949 H	400	1100 H	Stone Harbor	
		2,000	1130 H	Jenkins Sound	2,400
31	1048 H	700	1100 H	Stone Harbor	
		1,800	1100 H	Back-bay Stone Harbor	
		3,000	1130 H	Jenkins Sound	5,500

TABLE 35. SUMMARY OF RED KNOT EVENING AND NIGHT COUNTS AND NUMBER OF RADIO-TAGGED RED KNOTS AT HEREFORD INLET, STONE HARBOR, NEW JERSEY, DURING 19–31 MAY 2005 (H. P. SITTERS, UNPUBL. DATA).

Date	Time of high tide	Time of observations	Red Knots counted	Radio-tagged Red Knots recorded
19 May	1735 H	1800–1900 H	3,500	
20 May	1821 H	1800–1900 H	4,500	
21 May	1904 H	1900 H	4,500	
22 May	1946 H	1900–2000 H	13,000	
23 May	2029 H	1900–2000 H	20,000	
24 May	2114 H	1900–2030 H	16,000	
25 May	2204 H	2030 H	14,000	21
		2100 H		28
26 May	2259 H	2030 H	14,000	16
		2315 H		33
27 May	2359 H	2350 H		30
29 May	0059 H	0040 H		26
30 May	0159 H	0215 H		25
31 May	0257 H	0305 H		20

depending on location, seasonal date, time of day, tide, and species. Though the beaches are of critical importance, during high tide they are often too narrow for foraging, and the birds go elsewhere, including nearby salt marshes, tidal mudflats, and creeks. Radio telemetry has documented flights by Red Knots across Delaware Bay from Mispillion Harbor and across Cape May Peninsula to use the sand beach and salt marshes near Stone Harbor Point for foraging, resting, and roosting (H. P. Sitters, unpubl. data). Burger et al. (1997) suggested that in addition to the massive food resource provided by spawning horseshoe crabs, Delaware Bay's complex mosaic of coastal habitat types of mudflats, beaches, tidal creeks, and salt marshes is essential to maintain the large migrant shorebird population. H. P. Sitters (unpubl. data) suggested that Red Knots move to Atlantic coast habitats in the Stone Harbor area when horseshoe crab eggs are limited on the bayshore; they will forage on mussel spat when that is available. In recent years Red Knots made daily flights to roost at Stone Harbor even though they foraged at Mispillion in Delaware and Fortescue in New Jersey (H. P. Sitters, unpubl. data). This suggests that safe, predator-free roost sites are also of critical importance.

United States Fish and Wildlife Service
Region 5 — New York

The Red Knot does not occur in high numbers in the Jamaica Bay area. The East Pond, an impoundment that is part of the Jamaica Bay Wildlife Refuge, is the most common location where Red Knots occur (Appendix 1, map 21).

Plumb Beach is also a site where Red Knots feed on horseshoe crab eggs. Plumb Beach is the prime location for horseshoe crab spawning in the Jamaica Bay area. Several other secondary sites serve as suitable habitat for Red Knots. Gerritsen Inlet (Saltmarsh Nature Center and city parks) has an extensive shoreline that is used by Red Knots and other shorebirds. Red Knots are also consistently seen in the area of Far Rockaway, Long Beach, and Jones Beach.

Although most of the Long Island shorebird experts queried do not believe these secondary areas host large numbers of Red Knots, these sites are used consistently by small numbers of Red Knots during spring and fall migration and should be considered suitable.

United States Fish and Wildlife Service
Region 5 — Connecticut

The state of Connecticut does not have habitat deemed critical to Red Knots, though there is

some consistent use in the state by a small number of birds (J. Dickson, pers. comm.). Records indicate, however, that Red Knot populations within the state have declined. CBC data from 1972–2001 indicate that the highest numbers of Red Knots in the state occurred in 1986 (20 Red Knots recorded) and in 1992 (27 Red Knots recorded). Based on surveys by the Connecticut Department of Environmental Protection, the maximum number of Red Knots found in the state during migration surveys was 90, during August 1984. The maximum observance rate of Red Knots in surveys was <22%, typically between May and October (Varza 2004).

Important habitats in Connecticut may include the Housantonic River mouth (four Red Knots observed in 2001) which is a key migratory corridor. Specifically, the outer bars — Short Beach on the south side of Milford Point in the Housantonic River mouth — was the site of all the recorded Red Knots activity. Other areas that may be important to Red Knots in Connecticut are Milford Point (Milford), Long Beach (Stratford), and Sandy Point (West Haven) where small numbers of birds (<9 Red Knots recorded in these location in 2001) have been recorded (Appendix 1, map 22; Varza (2004). The sand bars on Cockenoe Island (Westport) are regularly used by three–six Red Knots during spring and fall migration according to data from Connecticut Audubon and the Connecticut Ornithological Association.

United States Fish and Wildlife Service
Region 5 — Rhode Island

No historic records exist of large numbers of Red Knots using coastal areas of Rhode Island during spring or fall migration. Red Knots occur consistently but intermittently and in low numbers, at three of five important shorebird migratory stop overs in Rhode Island — Napatree Point-Sandy Point Island, Westerly; Ninigret Pond, Charlestown; and Quicksand Pond, Little Compton (Appendix 1, map 22). In an historical compilation of Rhode Island birds, R. L. Ferren (unpubl. data) cites only a single count of >100 birds. Maximum counts on any given site rarely exceed 50 individuals. No stopover sites in Rhode Island are considered to be critical for Red Knots; however, existing stopover sites for Red Knots tend to be areas that host relatively large concentrations of other shorebirds as well.

The movement of Red Knots through Rhode Island on northward migration in spring is decidedly uni-modal, peaking between the third week of May and the first week of June. Conversely, the number of Red Knots on southward migration (July–October) is generally greater than spring but much more sporadic, with a loose peak around 22 August. The intermittent nature of Red Knot use of Rhode Island stopovers may be related to inclement weather; that is, storms or fog may force coastal or pelagic migrating Red Knots to seek safe roosts or foraging areas along the Rhode Island shoreline. While most shorebird species moving through Rhode Island have regular and predictable migration patterns, the Red Knot stands out as a species with unpredictable migration patterns, particularly on southward migration. At Napatree Point, where shorebird surveys have been conducted regularly (C. Raithel, pers. comm.) since 1980, high (25+ birds) Red Knot counts have been recorded between 1982 and 2004 (Table 36).

It is evident in contrast to R. L. Ferren (unpubl data), that large counts of Red Knots are much more likely to occur in fall (three of the 19 records above were in spring). The sporadic nature of Red Knot migration is evident even in these cursory numbers. High counts (≤100 individuals) occurred in only 10 of 24 yr of this survey. Some years are apparently much better for Red Knots than others in Rhode Island. For example, seven of the 19 high counts occurred in 1989. This phenomenon could simply be due to autocorrelation in the data—when large numbers of Red Knots appear in Rhode Island, they tend to stay for a while and are therefore counted repeatedly. However, the spread of fall dates (between 21 July and 25 September) for high counts is similarly unusual for Rhode Island shorebirds—most species display a very predictable bimodal or uni-modal fall pattern. These numbers suggest that the variance in survey counts for the Red Knot (at least in this area) is higher than that for other shorebirds.

It would be interesting if the sporadic nature of Red Knot migration in Rhode Island (relative to other shorebird species) is related to its demonstrably greater vulnerability, because examples with other species groups where high variation in breeding cycles and/or habitat use seem to be linked to vulnerability at landscape scales. Other researchers have suggested that Red Knots use highly ephemeral resources, such as mussel spat and small surf clams (*Donax variabilis*), and Red Knot distribution from year-to-year likely depends on the abundance of these food resources. It is unknown if this is a factor contributing to Red Knot abundance and distribution on coastal Rhode Island.

However, the sporadic nature of Red Knot use of some coastal areas all along the eastern seaboard suggests Red Knots may have a narrower foraging niche in time and space than other species. As long as a heterogeneous mixture of suitable habitats exists, and prey are available at least in some locations, Red Knots can persist. However, as habitats become lost to disturbance, development, abundant predators, and subject to activities that reduce prey availability (e.g., beach replenishment), foraging, and roosting options for Red Knots become limited. Particularly on northbound migration where time is critical, these factors are likely to negatively impact the population.

United States Fish and Wildlife Service
Region 5 – Massachusetts

During southward migration, regions on Cape Cod and Massachusetts Bay are important migration staging sites (Appendix 1, map 23). To identify major stopover locations, we searched

TABLE 36. SUMMARY OF SPRING AND FALL MIGRATION SURVEYS FOR RED KNOTS IN RHODE ISLAND BETWEEN 1982 AND 2004 (C. RAITHEL, PERS. COMM.).

Spring migration			Fall migration		
Year	Day	N Red Knots	Year	Day	N Red Knots
1982	2 Jun	60	1984	11 Aug	43
1983	22 May	26	1989	15 Aug	33
2002	4 Jun	28	1989	22 Aug	67
			1989	5 Sep	36
			1989	11 Sep	32
			1989	21 Sep	65
			1989	22 Sep	72
			1989	25 Sep	25
			1990	9 Aug	32
			1990	13 Aug	51
			1994	22 Aug	51
			1996	21 Jul	55
			2000	21 Aug	33
			2000	5 Sep	31
			2000	6 Sep	47
			2004	22 Aug	50

historical records in publications such as *Records of New England Birds* (1939–1972), volumes in migration seasons of *Audubon Field Notes* (and its successor *American Birds*) (1948–1999), *Bird Observer of Eastern Massachusetts* (1970–2002), and the ISS (1974–2002). In general, these sources (except the ISS, which follows prescribed count routines) record early and late arrival dates, and often, maximum seasonal counts.

Where available, maximum counts during south migration were made during south migration in each of three regions of Massachusetts (the coast North of Boston, Western Cape Cod Bay, and Eastern Cape Cod; B. A. Harrington, unpubl. data; Appendix 1, map 23). Although maximum counts are difficult to statistically assess, a strong correlation (r^2 = 0.90, P < 0.001) exists between maximum and mean ISS counts of Red Knots during south migration in Massachusetts (B. A. Harrington, unpubl. data), indicating that maximum counts are a reasonable metric for an historic review.

The historic count data summarized in Fig. 47 indicate relatively consistent use of eastern Cape Cod locations by Red Knots during the last 50 yr, as well as less regular periods when high numbers used sites on Western Cape Cod Bay. In contrast, the North Shore of Massachusetts was relatively little used by Red Knots throughout the 50 yr.

It is appropriate to note that Massachusetts is clearly used by southbound Red Knots with South American destinations during July and August. However, it also is clear that numbers of Red Knots using the Massachusetts coast are substantially lower than the numbers that pass through Delaware Bay during the northward migration (Fig. 48; Morrison and Harrington 1992). The banding locations were identified for 327 of the 334 color-banded Red Knots found in Massachusetts during southward migration. Most (75%, N = 245) of the identified birds had been marked on Delaware Bay, 23% (N = 77) had been marked in South America, and only five (2%) had been marked in South Carolina. None from Georgia were found. The frequencies of marked Red Knots from different banding locations were not statistically significantly different from the frequencies found in Delaware Bay (χ^2 = 10.54, df = 5, P > 0.05).

United States Fish and Wildlife Service Region 5 – New Hampshire

New Hampshire does not host large numbers of staging Red Knots. At the time of writing, the Nongame Program of the New Hampshire Department of Natural Resources does not conduct any surveys, monitor or have any available data on Red Knots within the state. All records for this state are from bird sightings submitted to New Hampshire Audubon. According to these reports, no more than 50 Red Knots were ever seen at any one place in New Hampshire from 1986–2004. Though not seen in large numbers, intermittent use seems to occur at least three locations — Hampton Harbor, Seabrook Harbor, and White and Seavey islands (Appendix 1, maps 24 and 26; Audubon Society of New Hampshire, unpubl. data).

United States Fish and Wildlife Service Region 5 – Maine

The state of Maine conducts coast-wide counts between July and September of shorebirds to identify shorebird habitats (Table 37; L. Tudor, pers. comm.). Currently, it is not believed that Maine provides Red Knots with critical stopover habitats. Red Knots are usually not seen on northward migration, always on southward migration. Habitats that may possibly be important for Red Knots include Petite Manan Island and Bluff and Stratton islands (Appendix 1, maps 24, 25, and 26). The most productive staging area for shorebirds in Maine is Lubec and Sprague Neck (Appendix 1, maps 24 and 25). In 1979 and 1980, these areas were surveyed intensively, only 11 Red Knots were recorded at Lubec and 64 Red Knots were recorded at Sprague Neck. In 1989, the state of Maine began intensive shorebird surveys to locate and designate critical staging areas. Surveys were concentrated on one section of coastline per year, with surveys completed in 1995. Areas were surveyed every 2 wk at varying tides starting in mid-July through the end of September. Since 1995, the state has monitored key sites in Washington County and has started collecting data for the Program for Regional and International Shorebird Monitoring (PRISM). PRISM is being implemented by the Canada-U.S. Shorebird Monitoring and Assessment Committee formed in 2001 by the Canadian Shorebird Working Group and the U.S. Shorebird Council. PRISM is based on the shorebird conservation plans recently completed in Canada and the U.S. and provides a single blueprint for implementing both of these plans. For more information see http://www.fws.gov/shorebirdplan/USShorebird/downloads/PRISMOverview1_02.doc

These surveys start in mid-July and go through end of September, covering select areas every 2–3 wk. The state also cooperates with non-government organizations working on nesting tern islands which record shorebird numbers, these data are collected from June to end of July with scattered data collected in August.

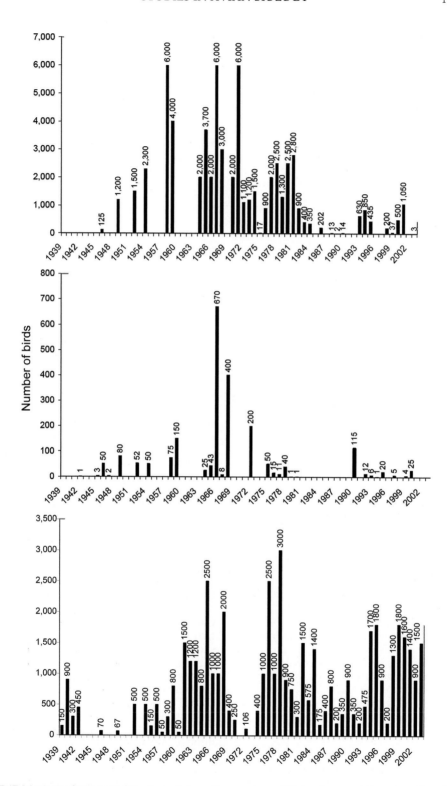

FIGURE 47. Maximum historic Red Knot counts from three regions of Massachusetts: (A) western Cape Cod, (B) North Shore, and (C) eastern Cape Code during southbound migration (B. A. Harrington, unpubl. data).

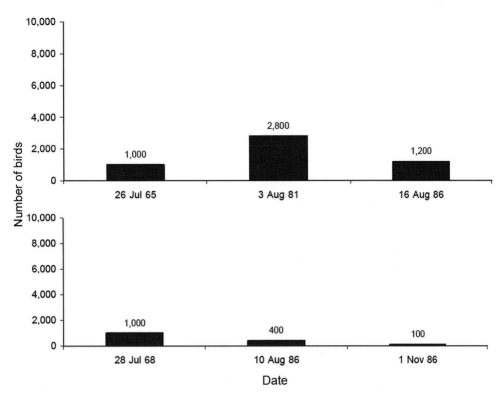

FIGURE 48. Number of Red Knots counted at Scituate (upper) and Monomoy (lower), Massachusetts, 1965–1986 (B. A. Harrington, unpubl. data).

Canada

Although the entire adult population of *C. c. rufa* breeds in Arctic Canada, estimating the population on its arctic breeding grounds is problematical owing to very low breeding densities (e.g., Southampton Island), lack of detailed habitat maps and information, and the need to extrapolate over very large areas. Trends may be derived from counts at migration areas, though in North America such counts may involve mixtures of populations from different wintering areas. For *C. c. rufa* wintering in southern South America, the most authoritative counts are those conducted at the main wintering sites in Tierra del Fuego.

During spring migration in North America, it appears that many *C. c. rufa* may fly directly to the breeding grounds from Delaware Bay. Large flights of Red Knots have been observed passing northward through southern James Bay at the end of May or start of June (R. I. G. Morrison, unpubl. data; M. Peck, unpubl. data), having probably flown directly from Delaware Bay (Morrison and Harrington 1992). Large concentrations are occasionally found around Lake Ontario (e.g., 400 at Presqu'ile Provincial Park

on 18 May 1969, 1,500 at Prince Edward Point on 30 May 1979,and 1,000 near Amherstview on 21 May 1985), though these probably represent weather-related dropouts from the main migration (McRae 1982, Weir 1989, Morrison and Harrington 1992). The sighting of a Red Knot that had been color-banded at Lagoa do Peixe in southern Brasil at Presqu'ile Provincial Park indicates that these birds include migrants from the southern *C. c. rufa* population. Knots are rare in spring on the Atlantic coast of Canada, where food resources have not yet recovered from winter ice conditions. Farther west along the route of the interior flyway, occasional observations have been made of Red Knots occurring briefly in atypical habitats during spring migration; these are likely to involve birds wintering in Florida (or Maranhão). For example, 2,500 were seen on a burned over stubble field near Last Mountain Lake, Saskatchewan, on 21 May 1972 (Skagen et al. 1999). Such records probably again relate to migrants bound for the western edge of *C. c. rufa's* breeding range being forced to land during poor weather. We know of no similar records in more recent years.

The number of Red Knots occurring at autumn migration stopover sites in Canada,

TABLE 37. RED KNOT SURVEY DATA FOR MAINE (1980–2004).

Date	N Red Knots	Location
Aug 1989	115	Hog Bay, Franklin, Hancock County
Sep 1989	27	Hog Bay
Aug 1985	10	Spruce Island, Deer Isle, Hancock County
Jun 2004	2	Ship Island, Tremont, Hancock County
May 1988	38	Over Point, Milbridge, Washington County
May 1989	15	Over Point
Oct 1988	12	Over Point
Oct 1989	9	Over Point
Aug 2004	1	Over Point
Aug 1989	14	Petit Manan Island, Milbridge, Washington County
Aug 1999	4	Petit Manan Island
Jul 2004	6	Petit Manan Island
Sep 1989	8	Petit Manan Point, Steuben, Washington County
Sep 1980	80	Holmes Creek, Cutler, Washington County
1980	87	Sprague Neck, Cutler, Washington County
Sep 1994	26	Sprague Neck
Aug 1994	10	Mash harbor, Addison, Washington County
Aug 2004	1	Flat Bay, Addison, Washington County
Sep 1991	10	West River-Indian River, Addison Jonesport, Washington
1980	11	Lubec Flats, Lubec, Washington County
Sep 1980	25	Lubec Flats
Sep 1991	6	Lubec Flats
Aug 1994	25	Lubec Flats
Sep 1996	10	Lubec Flats
Sep 1996	18	Lubec Flats
Sep 2002	13	Lubec Flats
Oct 2002	4	Lubec Flats
Aug 1993	53	Eastern Egg Rock, St George, Knox County
Jul 1993	26	Eastern Egg Rock
Jul 1994	20	Eastern Egg Rock
Aug 1994	7	Eastern Egg Rock
Sep 1993	16	Scarborough Marsh, Scarborough, Cumberland County
May 1985	26	Biddeford Pool, Biddeford, York County
Jul 1993	14	Bluff and Stratton Island, Old Orchard Beach, York County
Jul 1993	6	Bluff and Stratton Island
Aug 2004	5	Bluff and Stratton Island
Aug 2004	3	Bluff and Stratton Island

such as James Bay, the Bay of Fundy, and on the Mingan Islands in the Gulf of St. Lawrence, is greater than in spring (Hicklin 1987; R. I. G. Morrison, unpubl. data; M. Peck, unpubl. data). Large numbers of Red Knots pass southward through the southwestern coast of Hudson Bay (Manitoba and Ontario) and the western and southern coasts of James Bay during July and August (Hope and Shortt 1944, Manning 1952, Ross et al., pers. commun.). Mainland coastal surveys in late July 1990 and early August 1991 resulted in totals of 23,251 and 15,055, respectively (R. I. G. Morrison and R. K. Ross, unpubl. data). The southeast corner of Akimiski Island also appears to be important for Red Knots, with 6,900 being observed on a survey in late August 1995 (R. K. Ross, pers. comm.). Counts of 100–350 Red Knots have been recorded on the south coast of James Bay in Quebec (Aubry and Cotter 2001). Currently, the most important area for Red Knots on migration in eastern Canada is along the north shore of the St. Lawrence River in Quebec and the Mingan archipelago where counts of 1,000 or more have been made in late July or early August in several years (Étude des Populations d'Oiseaux du Québec, unpubl. data; Y. Aubry, pers. comm.; Fig. 49). During July to September 2006, 842 different individually banded Red Knot from elsewhere in the west Atlantic flyway were seen amongst those stopping over on the Mingan Islands. Most (585) had been banded during northward migration in Delaware Bay, but as many as 217 had been banded in Argentina and Chile confirming that the majority belonged to the *C. c. rufa* population that winters in southern South America (Fig. 49; Y. Aubry, pers. comm.). In view of the approximate proportion of banded birds in the *C. c. rufa* population (~10%) and the fact that some are likely to have been missed, it would seem probable that around a half of the flyway population stopped in the Mingan Islands in

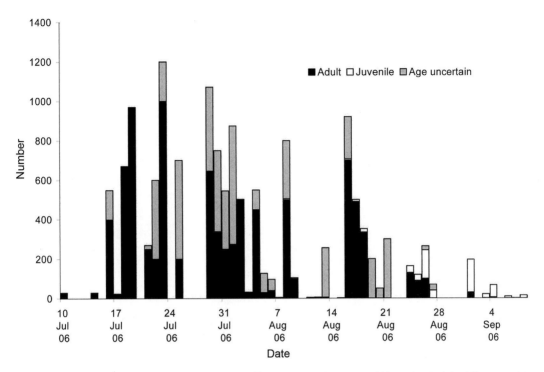

FIGURE 49. Counts of Red Knots on four islands (Nue, Grande, Quarry, and Niapiskau) of the Mingan archipelago in the Gulf of St Lawrence, Quebec, Canada, during July–September 2006 (Y. Aubry, pers. comm.).

2006. The islands are granitic and their shores are mostly rocky. However, on their southern sides there are small intertidal flats of gravel or sand that support an abundance of invertebrates (*Mytilus*, *Littorina*, and *Gamarus* spp.) suitable for foraging Red Knots. These invertebrates are mostly attached to the *Fucus* spp.and the other algae that cover the flats.

Up to the early 1980s, Red Knots were moderately numerous during southward migration in the upper Bay of Fundy, but fell rapidly to low levels in the mid 1980s and have remained at low levels since then. This may represent a withdrawal from relatively peripheral areas as the population started decreasing. Trend analyses of data from both Quebec and the Atlantic provinces of Canada have indicated significant declines (Morrison et al. 2006).

THREATS

Under section 4 of the Endangered Species Act 1973 (ESA), a species that is endangered or threatened may be listed as such if it is endangered or threatened because of: (1) the present or threatened destruction, modification, or curtailment of its habitat or range, and/or (2) overutilization for commercial, recreational, scientific, or educational purposes, and/or (3) disease or

predation, and/or (4) the inadequacy of existing regulatory mechanisms or other natural or manmade factors affecting its continued existence.

Threats are therefore listed under these headings. In principle, a threat is only important if it has or may have an adverse impact on an animal's evolutionary fitness — its ability to survive and reproduce. In conservation science, perceived threats are often assumed to have fitness implications, but except where actual mortality occurs this is seldom proved. Therefore, a major focus of *C. c. rufa* studies has been to measure adult survival and attempt to identify those factors that lead to its reduction. This has met with some success, as described below. Nevertheless several threats are identified which in our opinion are likely to have fitness consequences, but we are unable to prove that this is the case.

THREATS TO HABITATS IN DELAWARE BAY DURING SPRING MIGRATION

The principal known threat to a substantial proportion of Red Knots in the Americas is the dwindling supply of their main food resource at their final spring stopover in Delaware Bay, the eggs of the horseshoe crab. As described in the habitats section, this once abundant resource has declined through the exploitation of the adult crabs.

As discussed in the population size and trends section, a greater or lesser proportion of three wintering populations of Red Knots pass through Delaware Bay during northward migration. However, as far as can be ascertained, only the Tierra del Fuego wintering population has undergone a major decline. Those wintering farther north, in the southeastern U.S. and Maranhão, have shown no clear trend. The main difference between these populations is that the Tierra del Fuego birds have a much longer, time-constrained migration that carries a greater risk of arriving in Delaware Bay in poor condition and/or late, whereas the latter fly a relatively short distance and may arrive on time and in better condition. Either way, the Tierra del Fuego birds have a greater need for an abundant food supply in Delaware Bay than the others. Therefore, the decline in the availability of food resources, especially horseshoe crab eggs, may have the greatest impact on the long-distance migrants rather than those that have not traveled as far. Alternatively, the lack of food in Delaware Bay is not the immediate problem, but the birds are arriving there late and/or in poor condition because of difficulties farther south along their migration route. Therefore, they have lower survival because they have less time to obtain the resources they require.

Although the precise role of reduced food supplies in Delaware Bay has not always been clear, in some years its impact has been patent. In 2003, for example, crab spawning was delayed probably as a result of low water temperatures (Weber 2003) and although the Red Knot stopover was also later than usual, the birds failed to achieve their normal rate of mass gain (Atkinson et al. 2007, L. J. Niles et al., unpubl. data). In contrast, in 2004 the stopover and the availability of crabs' eggs was more closely synchronous and the birds achieved good weight gains despite the fact that that overall egg densities were little different to the previous year (Atkinson et al. 2007; L. J. Niles et al., unpubl. data).

When the Red Knots leave for the Arctic, they not only need resources for the 3,000-km non-stop flight across territory without food supplies, but they also need additional resources to ensure their survival during the first few weeks after arrival when little food is available. Therefore, the food supply in Delaware Bay is crucial for their survival and ability to reproduce successfully. This is demonstrated by studies that show that birds caught at a lower weight in Delaware Bay (controlling for date) were less likely to be observed in future years

than heavier birds and were therefore assumed to have lower survival (Baker et al. 2004).

Without doubt, the main reason for the reduced availability of horseshoe crab eggs (Fig. 22) to shorebirds on the Delaware Bay beaches is the over-exploitation of the adult crabs (Figs. 13 and 21). However, three factors exacerbate the situation and have the effect of reducing the availability of eggs further: (1) beach erosion reducing the amount of optimal crab spawning habitat, (2) disturbance by people, dogs, and potential predators, and (3) competition from gulls, especially Laughing Gulls (*Larus atricilla*). These are considered below.

Delaware Bay's sandy barrier beaches are dynamic features that respond in a generally predictable manner, migrating landward by storm overwash as the bayward shoreline is also retreating landward in the face of continued sea-level rise (Phillips 1986a). While future rates are difficult to predict, the current level of sea-level rise in Delaware Bay is generally thought to be about 3 mm/yr (Phillips 1986a). This has resulted in erosion of the bay's shorelines and a landward extension of the inland edge of the marshes. During 1940–1978, Phillips (1986a) documented a mean erosion rate of 3.2 m/yr for a 52-km long section of New Jersey's Delaware Bay, Cumberland County shoreline and indicated that this was a high rate of erosion compared to other estuaries. The spatial pattern of the erosion was complex with differential erosion resistance related to local differences in shoreline morphology (Phillips 1986b). Phillips' (1986a, 1986b) shoreline erosion studies suggest that bay-edge erosion is occurring more rapidly than the landward/upward extension of the coastal wetlands and that this pattern is likely to persist.

Galbraith et al. (2002) examined several different scenarios of future sea-level rise as a consequence of global climate change and project major losses of intertidal habitat in Delaware Bay due to continued sea-level rise. Under the 50% probability scenario, Delaware Bay is predicted to lose 60% or more of the shorebird intertidal feeding habitats by 2100. Under more extreme sea-level rise, Delaware Bay may actually have a net gain of intertidal flats as the coastline moves further inland converting dry land to intertidal habitat. However, this prediction assumes that the coastal protection structure do not constrain the ability of shorelines to move landward. Within the Delaware Bay system, as elsewhere in the mid-Atlantic region, coastal development and shoreline protection activities are expected to interfere with the longer-term landward migration of shorelines (Najjar et al. 2000). Though Delaware Bay is less developed than many similar stretches of mid-Atlantic coastline, some optimal crab-spawning beach habitat is also the site of existing shoreline residential development. Significant sections of the Delaware Bay shoreline have already been impacted by shoreline stabilization projects. Coupled with continuing sea-level rise and shoreline erosion, the demand for additional shoreline protection structures is expected to increase (Najjar et al. 2000). Shoreline stabilization or armoring projects employing bulkheading, riprap, or other solid beach-fill can either completely eliminate intertidal sand beach habitat or sufficiently alter sediment quality and beach morphology to negatively affect the suitability of the remaining habitat for horseshoe crab spawning (Botton et al. 1988, Myers 1996). Beach replenishment through offshore pumping of sandy sediments (as carried out along several sections of the Delaware shore but not New Jersey) provides an alternative means of beach stabilization as well as creating potential crab-spawning habitat. Smith et al. (2002c) evaluated the effects of beach nourishment on spawning activity, egg density, egg viability and sediment-beach characteristics on Delaware Bay beaches; however, all factors that affect the function of beach replenishment for crab-spawning and shorebird foraging habitat have not yet been fully evaluated. The fact that during 2002–2005 more Red Knots on average fed on the New Jersey side of the bay (where no replenishment has taken place) than on the Delaware side (Fig. 23) suggests that beach replenishment may not have a major impact on the value of beaches as crab-spawning habitat. Besides affecting crab-spawning-Red Knot-feeding habitat, erosion has also led to loss of sites used by Red Knots for roosting, especially around Mispillion Harbor.

Threats to Habitat in Massachusetts

Potential threats to Red Knot habitats in Massachusetts include human development and beach replenishment.

Threats to Habitat in North Carolina

Along the coast, threats to migrant and wintering Red Knot habitat include beach stabilization works (nourishment, channel relocation, and bulkhead construction), and housing development. This particularly applies at Tubbs Inlet.

Threats to Habitat in South Carolina

A large area of the South Carolina coast is protected due to public ownership and conservation easements. Few opportunities exist to increase the amount of protected coastal land. Coastal counties are experiencing annual human population growth rates of 2–3%. Wetlands are being degraded by pollution, development, and oil spills; invertebrates are declining due to pollution; and horseshoe crabs are over-harvested.

Threats to Habitat in Florida

Shoreline hardening, dredging, and deposition, including beach-nourishment activities, are significantly altering much of Florida's coastline. Similarly, beach-raking activities alter the natural characteristics of the beach zone. Despite the fact that all of these activities require permits, there is no centralized documentation of their location or extent. Furthermore, the impacts on Red Knots and other shorebirds is not well known but is thought to be significant.

Threats to Habitat in Brazil

Very little is known about the Red Knots that winter on the coast of Maranhão. They occur along 150 km of highly fragmented shore which is difficult to survey, even from the air, and difficult to access (Baker et al. 2005a). Among the most important threats that can be identified is petroleum exploration in the sea on the continental shelf, as well as iron ore and gold mining, which leads to loss of coastal habitat through the dumping of soil, oil pollution, mercury contamination, and uncontrolled urban spread along the coast. Mangrove clearance has also had a negative impact on Red Knot habitat by altering the deposition of sediments which leads to a reduction in benthic prey.

At the Lagoa do Peixe National Park, the main management activities relate to the controlling of water levels in the lagoon and ameliorating the effects of *Pinus* afforestation. Red Knots feed on snails and other invertebrates around the edges of the lagoon and the abundance and availability of this food supply depends on water levels. Connection between the lagoon and sea occurs naturally mainly during winter and spring when a combination of southerly winds and rainfall opens the sandbar through water pressure. Closure occurs as a result of the deposition of sand in the lagoon mouth during northerly and northeasterly winds. Farmers use pumps to drain water from their lands and this can have a major effect on the level of the lagoon. During drought years, like 1997, the sandbar cannot be closed due to strong continental drainage that limits deposition at the mouth of the lagoon. It is the periodic exchange of water with the sea that allows invertebrates to colonize the lagoon and provide a food resource for migratory shorebirds. Although water levels are controlled to some extent by pumping, any factor that interferes with this, such as nearby farmers draining their land, is a threat to the value of this important site for Red Knots.

Another threat to Lagoa do Peixe is the uncontrolled *Pinus* afforestation of land in the vicinity, which probably has the effect of lowering the water table (IBAMA, unpubl. data). In some areas, the plantations appear to help siltation of the lagoon by altering the movement of sand dunes. *Pinus* harvesting leads to the appearance of gullies, which contribute to higher erosion. According to the management plan (IBAMA 1999), studies were to be conducted on the impact of *Pinus* forests, but no results have been published to date.

THREATS TO HABITAT AT MIGRATION STOPOVER
SITES ALONG THE ATLANTIC COAST OF PATAGONIA,
ARGENTINA

Oil pollution is a threat in Reserva Provincial de Río Chico para Aves Playeras Migratorias (RPRCAPM) and Reserva Urbana Costera del Río Chico, at Bahía Bustamante (where 15% of Red Knots were polluted with oil in a study in 1979 [Harrington and Morrison 1980]), and at Península Valdés. However, oil pollution has recently decreased significantly along the Patagonian coast (J. L. Estévez, pers. comm.). Development and associated pollution are threatening the RPRCAPM (created in 2001) and Reserva Urbana Costera del Río Chico (created in 2004). This comprises filling in of the tidal flat and marshes for urban use, location of a rubbish dump near shorebird feeding, and roosting sites as well as pollution from urban waste. At the Bahía San Antonio Natural Protected Area (created in 1993) major potential exists for pollution from a soda ash factory which began to operate in 2005 and from port activities which are likely to expand as the factory increases production. In the Bahía Samborombón reserve (created in 1979) threats come from urban and agrosystem expansion and development.

THREAT OF OIL POLLUTION AND POSSIBILITY OF
OTHER UNIDENTIFIED FACTORS AFFECTING THE
PRINCIPAL *CALIDRIS CANUTUS RUFA* NON-BREEDING
SITE AT BAHÍA LOMAS, CHILE

The region of Magellan, Chile, has traditionally been an important producer of oil and natural gas since the first oil discovery was made in 1945 within 10 km from the bayshore in Manantiales. Even though local oil activity has

diminished over the last 20 yr and only covers a small percentage of national demand, it is a resource that is still exploited. Oil is extracted by drilling on land and offshore, the latter with no new drillings in the last 8 yr. Bahía Lomas, located at the eastern end of the Magellan Strait on the northern coast of Tierra del Fuego, has several oil platforms. Most are static, and several have been closed within the last year as the oil resource has been depleted. Apparently, no incentive exists to continue drilling in the Straits of Magellan. However, on the nearby Atlantic Ocean coast of Argentina, oil drilling has been increasing in the last 10 yr. The boat traffic from oil production in the Straits of Magellan is another potential risk as significant oil spills may occur with detrimental consequences similar to two recorded incidents in the vicinities of the bay (48,500 metric tons from the Metula in 1974 and 90 metric tons from the Berge Nice in 2004).

Although the potential threat to the Red Knot population would appear to be significant, no incidents have been reported of Red Knots being affected by oil either directly by major contamination of the plumage or indirectly through their food supplies (though small amounts of oil have been noted on some birds caught (A. D. Dey, unpubl. data; L. J. Niles, unpubl. data). However, major declines at Bahía Lomas have not been mirrored at nearby Río Grande (Fig. 50), suggesting a possible problem at Bahía Lomas. If so, it is more likely to be connected with the oil industry than anything else because that is virtually the only significant human activity in the area.

The possibility that problems at Bahía Lomas are entirely responsible for the *C. c. rufa* population crash would seem unlikely in view of the observation that it is birds at a lower weight in Delaware Bay that have lower survival (Baker et al. 2004). Nevertheless, there could be a connection between birds leaving Bahía Lomas in poor condition and arriving in Delaware Bay in poor condition. Another scenario is that, though much smaller than Bahía Lomas, Río Grande is a preferred site. Therefore, just as Red Knots have deserted sites further north along the Patagonian coast since 1985 becoming more and more concentrated in what is presumably the better non-breeding area of Tierra del Fuego, they may now be doing the same within Tierra del Fuego, deserting Bahía Lomas for Río Grande. These are matters that deserve further investigation.

OIL POLLUTION THREAT AND HUMAN DISTURBANCE
AT THE ONLY OTHER MAJOR NON-BREEDING SITE AT
RÍO GRANDE, ARGENTINA

Most of the sites used by Red Knots at Río Grande on the Atlantic coast of the Argentinian

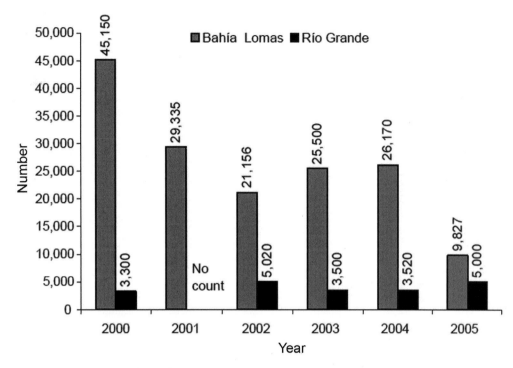

FIGURE 50. Aerial counts of Red Knots (*Calidris canutus rufa*) on major wintering areas in southern South America, January–February 2000–2005 — Bahía Lomas and Río Grande, Chile. All sites are in the main wintering area (Morrison et al. 2004).

part of Tierra del Fuego are within the Reserva Costa Atlántica de Tierra del Fuego created in 1992. However, as at Bahía Lomas, the area is important for on- and off-shore oil production with the potential for oil pollution, especially from oil tankers loading around Río Grande City. Again, no direct evidence exists of Red Knots having being affected by oil pollution but it remains a threat.

The Red Knots frequently suffer human disturbance while feeding and roosting around Río Grande city, especially by people using all terrain vehicles and motor cycles, as well as from walkers, runners, fishermen, and dogs.

THREATS TO RED KNOT HABITAT IN CANADA

The shorebird habitats of the Mingan Islands in the Gulf of St Lawrence, Quebec, are at risk because of the proximity of ships carrying oil, titanium, and iron through the archipelago to the Havre-St-Pierre Harbour. In March 1999, one ship spilled 44 metric tons of crude oil that came ashore in the Mingan area. A similar accident occurring during the July–October stopover could have a serious impact on Red Knot feeding areas.

OVER UTILIZATION FOR COMMERCIAL, RECREATIONAL, SCIENTIFIC, OR EDUCATIONAL PURPOSES

In the U.S., no overutilization of the Red Knot for commercial, recreational, or educational purposes has been identified. However, hunting migratory shorebirds for food used to be common among local communities in Maranhão, Northern Brazil. They provided an alternative source of protein and birds with high subcutaneous fat content for long migratory flights were particularly valued (I. Serrano, unpubl. data). According to local people, the most consumed species were Red Knot, Black-bellied Plover (*Pluvialis squatarola*), and Whimbrel (*Numenius phaeopus*), though no data are available as to the number of birds taken. Local people say that although some shorebirds are still hunted, this practice has greatly decreased over the past decade and hunting is not thought to amount to a serious cause of mortality.

HAVE SCIENTIFIC STUDIES CONTRIBUTED TO THE RED KNOT'S DECLINE?

It is sometimes claimed that the more intrusive forms of avian research, such as catching birds for banding and examination, has a detrimental effect. The most serious form that overutilization for scientific purposes might take would be if it affected the birds' ability to survive and reproduce and so contributed to the population decline.

Bird banding has been carried out across the world, especially in Europe and North America, for over a century. Virtually all taxa have been banded at one time or another and the practice has come under considerable scrutiny. In most countries, bird banding is highly regulated and limited to trained personnel only. As such, it is considered a valuable and safe research tool. If it led to significant mortality or atypical behavior, it would not be permitted. Moreover, there would be no purpose in doing it because the whole point is to study what birds do naturally. Some bird populations that have been the subject of intensive banding studies have increased while others have decreased. In Europe, for example, the Icelandic race of the Black-tailed Godwit (*Limosa limosa*) has increased, but the western European race has declined, yet both have been banded extensively (Wetlands International 2006).

As to *C. c. rufa*, the banding effort has been fairly constant since intensive studies began in 1997, yet the population has remained stable between some years but declined dramatically between others (Figs. 30 and 32). Moreover the number of birds caught annually (about 1,000 in Delaware Bay plus 300 in South America) is relatively small compared with some of the year-to-year population declines (14,000 from 2004–2005), so most of the birds that disappeared, presumed dead, had never been caught. Therefore, it can be concluded that scientific studies have not been responsible for the major decline of *C. c. rufa*.

Each year, about 50 of the birds caught in Delaware Bay have been the subject of radio-telemetry studies in which a 2-g radio-tag has been glued to their backs. The tags are expected to drop off after 1–2 months through the natural replacement of skin. These birds, like the remainder of Red Knots caught, are also fitted with individually numbered color-flags. Resighting studies in subsequent years show that the annual survival of birds that had been radio tagged was no different to that of birds there had merely been banded (P. W. Atkinson, unpubl. data).

Do Scientific Studies Cause Significant Disturbance to Red Knots?

Harrington (unpubl. data) evaluated the response of Red Knots to disturbance associated with research activities, including cannon-net catches. Observers recorded the frequency of disturbance events and time spent in flight during attempts to catch shorebirds with cannon nets and at the same sites when catch attempts were not conducted. Disturbance events recorded when there was no catching were attributed to sources unrelated to research activities. Results indicate that the mean hourly disturbance rate during catch attempts was 13.0 versus 11.7 when catch attempts were not being conducted; this is not a statistically significant difference (t-test, P > 0.05). Harrington also compared the duration of flights by Red Knots that were disturbed by research-related activities (N = 145) with that of Red Knots that were disturbed by natural causes, (N = 179). About 20% of the Red Knots that were timed flew out of sight, so their flight duration could not be determined. The proportion of Red Knots that flew out of sight during natural disturbance events (21%) was similar to the proportion that flew out of sight during research activities (21%). Of the remaining sample, flights of Red Knots from natural causes tended to be shorter than for Red Knots disturbed by researchers. Harrington also found no statistically significant difference in the mean number of calories used by Red Knots reacting to natural disturbances and Red Knots reacting to the activities of researchers. Analysis of research-related disturbance data for Ruddy Turnstones produced results similar to those for Red Knot, i.e., tests did not detect statistically significant differences between natural and research-related disturbances.

Steps to Minimize Disturbance by Research Activities

In recent years, especially since 2003, considerable care has been taken to minimize disturbance caused to shorebirds in Delaware Bay by researchers. Catching, in particular, has been limited in terms of total numbers caught, frequency, and catch size consistent with the twin aims of monitoring annual survival and weight gain. Moreover most close observation (e.g., to read inscribed color flags) has been carried out, when possible, from well-concealed sites including blinds.

Disease or Predation

In Europe and North America, the study of shorebirds over most of the past 30 yr has been conducted in what Butler et al. (2003) called a predator vacuum arising from greatly depleted raptor populations caused by persecution and pesticide poisoning. Only in the past decade have these shown recovery to pre-World War

II levels in temperate North America. Butler et al. (2003) demonstrated how recovering raptor populations appear to have led to changes in the migratory strategies of some shorebirds. These include lower numbers of shorebirds, reduced stopover length, and lower mass in the more dangerous sites. However, increased raptor numbers have not yet been shown to affect the size of shorebird populations. Given that Red Knots spend most of the year in regions where raptor populations were never greatly affected by persecution and poisoning (Arctic Canada and South America), it would seem unlikely that increased raptor predation has been responsible for the population decline.

In the Arctic, 3–4 yr lemming cycles give rise to similar cycles in the predation of shorebird nests. Therefore, when lemmings are abundant, arctic foxes, and jaegers concentrate on them and shorebirds breed successfully, but when lemmings are in short supply few shorebird eggs or chicks survive (Summers and Underhill 1987). It is evident that these cycles have always affected the productivity of arctic-breeding shorebirds and lead to fairly minor year-to-year changes in otherwise stable populations. We have no reason to suppose that increased arctic nest predation has been responsible for the long-term decline in the *C. c. rufa* population. However, unsuccessful breeding seasons have contributed to at least some recent reductions in the population.

Potential predators of shorebirds, especially Peregrine Falcons, red foxes (*Vulpes vulpes*), and feral cats (*Felis catus*), are possibly more of a threat to Red Knots in Delaware Bay as sources of disturbance than as agents of mortality. Over the past decade, Peregrine Falcons in North America have largely recovered from reduced numbers in the mid 20th century caused by persecution and pesticide poisoning. Now, several pairs nest close to both shores of Delaware Bay. However, they are almost all using artificial nest sites and it is likely that without these Peregrine Falcons would be largely absent, as they probably were before their numbers crashed. The disturbance they cause to Red Knots in Delaware Bay has not been properly evaluated. This should be done and, if it is found to be significant, steps taken to reduce its impact by removal or relocation of the nesting towers.

An epizootic disease resulting in large-scale mortality of Red Knots reported from the west coast of Florida in December 1973 and November 1974 was caused by a protozoan parasite, most likely an undescribed sporozoan species (Harrington 2001). Further reports on Red Knot mortality in Florida in 1981 were due to *Plasmodium hermani* (Harrington 2001).

In 1981, Harrington (2001) reported an adventitious molt in Red Knots caused by a mallophagan parasite (Mallophaga, Menoponidae) in feather shafts. On 7 April 1997, 26 Red Knots, 10 White-rumped Sandpipers, and three Sanderlings were found dead or dying along 10 km of beach at Lagoa do Peixe, southern Brazil. The following day, another 13 dead or sick Red Knots were found along 35 km of beach nearby (Baker et al. 1999b). Some, but not all of these birds, were infected with hookworms (*Acanthocephala*). Although hookworms can cause death, it would seem more likely that the mortality had another cause. Smaller mortalities of spring migrants with similar symptoms of malaise have also been reported from Uruguay in recent years.

Since December 2003, blood and feather samples have been collected in Brazil not only from Red Knots but also from several other shorebird species for genetic variability studies and stable isotope analysis. In the course of these studies in February 2005, all of a sample of 38 Red Knots caught in Maranhão was found to be heavily infected with ectoparasites. The birds were much less than the usual fat-free mass of Red Knots (Baker et al. 2005a). Recent studies have shown that tropical wintering shorebirds have a higher incidence of parasites and pathogens than those wintering at higher latitudes (Mendes et al. 2005). However, without further studies, it cannot be known whether this observation is typical of Red Knots wintering in that area or peculiar to one winter, or whether such infestation leads to significant mortality, or whether it can be passed on to other populations such as when Tierra del Fuego birds stopover in Maranhão during northward or southward migration. Nevertheless the potential importance of this observation is considerable if it is shown that ectoparasite infection leads to a loss of fitness. No systematic effort has yet been made to assess the parasite load of birds passing through Delaware Bay, but fieldworkers have noticed ectoparasites on a substantial number of Red Knots caught there (C. D. T. Minton and L. J. Niles, unpubl. data). This is a factor worthy of further investigation.

Since 2002, migratory birds in Brazil have been tested for viruses including West Nile, Newcastle, and avian influenza by the National Health Foundation in collaboration with Instituto Brasileiro do Meio Ambiente dos Recursos Naturais Renováveis and Centro Nacional de Pesquisa para Conservação das Aves Silvestres. To date, avian influenza type H2 has been found in one Red Knot, Mayaro virus in seven Red Knots, and equine encephalite virus in another (Araújo et al. 2003).

The Inadequacy of Existing Regulatory Mechanisms

Several regulatory issues have negatively influenced the protection of Red Knots. Most have arisen because Red Knots range over such a large area that coordinating conservation regulations is not just an interstate issue in the U.S. but also the subject of international diplomacy.

C. c. rufa breeds in one country (Canada), uses stopovers in at least four countries (U.S., Brazil, Argentina, and Chile) and winters in mostly different locations in the same four countries (Fig. 50). The birds also use spring stopovers in all Atlantic coast states from Florida to New Jersey, wintering sites in at least three states, and autumn stopover sites in all eastern states from New England to Florida (Figs. 51 and 52).

In the U.S., the Red Knot is protected from hunting but has special status in only two states—New Jersey where it is has threatened status and Georgia where it is a species of special concern (Fig. 53). In April 2007, the Committee on the Status of Endangered Wildlife in Canada determined that *C. c. rufa* was endangered. In Brazil it is being proposed for listing as endangered. In Chile, both the Red Knot and its habitat are protected. The federal law that regulates hunting (LEY No. 19.473) includes the Red Knot in the list of protected species. All coastal habitats (extending to 300 m inland from the high-tide line) are managed by the Chilean Navy and are the property of the national government. Argentina does not allow the Red Knot to be hunted and specifically protects it from subsistence hunting. Both Chile and Argentina are among the 101 parties to The Convention on the Conservation of Migratory Species of Wild Animals which, at its meeting in November 2005, determined that the *C. c. rufa* subspecies of the Red Knot was endangered and as such added it to Appendix 1 of the convention. Under the terms of the convention the parties agree to strive towards strictly protecting animals listed in Appendix 1, conserving or restoring the places where they live, mitigating obstacles to migration, and controlling other factors that might endanger them (http://www.cms.int). The U.S., Canada, and Brazil are among the minority of countries that are not yet parties to the convention.

Inadequacies of the Federal and Regional Regulatory System

The existing regulatory system creates a number of problems for the conservation of Red Knots stopping over in Delaware Bay in that different agencies have jurisdiction over the protection of horseshoe crabs and their eggs on the one hand and Red Knots on the other. The birds are under the legal jurisdiction of the USFWS, and the horseshoe crabs are under the legal jurisdiction of the Atlantic States Marine Fisheries Commission (ASMFC) which has the authority to set quotas for adoption by the states. The ASMFC is overseen by the National Marine Fisheries Service (NMFS) which has ultimate responsibility for the management and conservation of living marine resources. Presently, NMFS has limited its involvement to participating in the ASMFC subcommittees and has not taken any regulatory action to protect crabs or birds. Individual states have authority to implement more restrictive harvest regulations than those set by the ASMFC and have done so on numerous occasions.

The ASMFC has promulgated a horseshoe crab management plan to conserve the horseshoe crab resource based on the current commercial uses of the crab for bait and for the biomedical industry, and the competing needs of migratory shorebirds and the federally listed, loggerhead turtle (*Caretta caretta*). The protection of the adult horseshoe crab population as food source for the loggerhead turtle is specifically identified in the plan with the recognition that the plan should be coordinated with the federal agencies having jurisdiction over the turtle population. Migratory shorebirds, and specifically the Red Knot, and their reliance on horseshoe crab eggs are also identified and discussed in the management plan. The plan specifically protects the food resource of the loggerhead turtle pursuant to Section 7(a)(2) of the ESA; the food resource of the Red Knot is not similarly protected. Although the ASMFC does not have direct legal jurisdiction to protect the food resource for the Red Knot, it has taken steps to improve horseshoe crab egg availability including decreasing harvest quotas, more efficient use of crabs as bait, and facilitating a horseshoe crab sanctuary at the mouth of Delaware Bay.

In contrast, the USFWS does have authority to protect the birds under the Migratory Bird Treaty Act (40 Stat. 755; 16 U.S.C. 703-712) (MBTA) which provides that no migratory bird can be taken, killed, or possessed unless in accordance with the provisions of the treaty. The MBTA is the only current federal protection provided for the Red Knot. The MBTA prohibits take of any migratory bird, which is defined as: to pursue, hunt, shoot, wound, kill, trap, capture, or collect, or attempt to pursue, hunt, shoot, wound, kill, trap, capture, or collect. However, other than for nesting sites, which are not located in the U.S., the MBTA provides no authority for protection of habitat or food

FIGURE 51. Important *Calidris canutus rufa* breeding, stopover, and wintering areas in the Western Hemisphere

resources. Human disturbance is cited as one of the major threats to Red Knots throughout its migratory range within the U.S. Therefore, the MBTA provides inadequate protection to the Red Knot in that it does not afford Red Knots protection from human disturbance on migratory and wintering areas or ensure protection of food resources.

Under the Endangered Species Act 1973, a species may be designated as threatened or

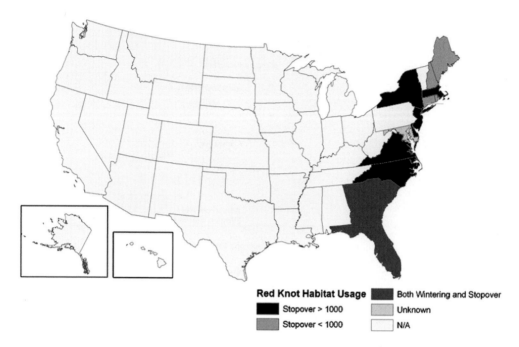

FIGURE 52. Important *Calidris canutus rufa* stopover and wintering areas in the United States.

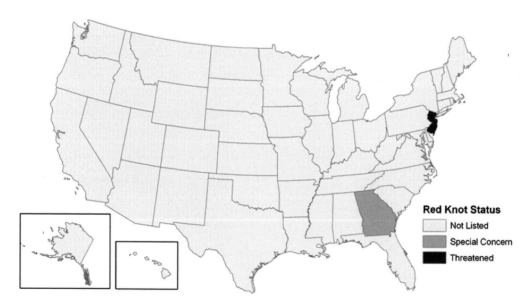

FIGURE 53. Red Knot state legal status in each state in the U.S.

endangered. However, this may be precluded through lack of resources if there are species of higher conservation priority. Therefore, species whose listing is warranted may receive none of the benefits of listing including those involving little or no cost. This is a shortcoming that needs to be addressed.

INADEQUACIES OF REGULATORY SYSTEMS IN INDIVIDUAL STATES

Without adequate federal coordination, the attempts of individual states to conserve Red Knots have lacked consistency. This has led to substantial gaps in protection, especially when horseshoe crab fishermen have exploited differences in regulations among states.

In 1996, New Jersey restricted the harvest of horseshoe crabs when it was confronted with mounting evidence of the decline of crabs, eggs, and shorebirds, particularly Red Knots. In response, the horseshoe crab fishermen took crabs but landed them in Delaware and Maryland. The following year, Delaware and Maryland followed New Jersey's lead and instituted increased restrictions on the horseshoe crab harvest. That year the fishermen harvested crabs but landed them in Virginia. Subsequently, the ASMFC imposed modest restrictions to the harvest and fishermen attempted to land crabs in Pennsylvania while Virginia disregarded the ASMFC restrictions. After the development and implementation of the Horseshoe Crab Management Plan, which regulated landings coast-wide, the problem was solved, but this experience makes it clear that individual states alone without federal or regional coordination cannot adequately protect wide-ranging inter-jurisdictional species such horseshoe crabs or shorebirds.

Another inadequacy of regulatory mechanisms relates to the protection of Red Knots from disturbance. NJDFW has been protecting beaches used by shorebirds from disturbance since 1985. In 2003, the Division closed seven beaches to all human use during the peak of the shorebird stopover. The reason for the closure was to increase the availability of eggs for shorebirds by preventing repeated disturbances, which have been demonstrated to be significantly detrimental to the birds' ability to feed (Burger et al. 2007). Moreover, disturbance by humans and dogs often increases the competitive advantages of gulls because gulls adapt more easily than shorebirds to repeated disturbance (Burger et al. 2007). Only in the state of New Jersey is the Red Knot listed as a threatened species and, as such, provided with legal protection. In all other states, no legal basis exists for preventing disturbance (Fig. 53). The need to protect Red Knots from repeated disturbance on beaches also applies during southward migration in autumn as shown by recent studies (D. Mizrahi, pers. comm.).

In Delaware, even if the Red Knot was listed as a state endangered species, the listing would only pertain to collection, possession, transportation, and sale. No regulatory mechanisms protect the habitat of Delaware state-listed species or to permit regulation of activities such as chronic disturbance, destruction of habitat, or removal or depletion of food resources.

Regulation of human use of the inter-tidal zone is greatly complicated by variation between states in ownership and jurisdiction of the foreshore. In New Jersey, for example, most inter-tidal areas are owned by the state and managed by the state's Tideland Council, whereas in Delaware lands can be privately owned to the mean low-tide line. Thus, in New Jersey restrictions on activities that may interfere with shorebird foraging or roosting apply statewide. In eight sections of beach, use can be eliminated entirely. However, in Delaware, restrictions can only be applied to state-owned lands and lands designated as Delaware River and Bay Shoreline Refuge (Smyrna River to St. Jones River). At present, Delaware does not have legal authority to restrict or eliminate activities that would disturb shorebirds on all privately owned beaches including the harvest of horseshoe crabs unless the beach is voluntarily registered as a horseshoe crab sanctuary. Similar legal barriers to restrict disturbance of wintering shorebirds exist in nearly all Atlantic coast states. These state-by-state variations in jurisdiction create significant impediments to region-wide or nationwide restrictions to protect shorebirds and horseshoe crabs.

CURTAILMENT OF HABITAT USE FROM DISTURBANCE BY PEOPLE AND DOGS

Human disturbance can have an adverse effect on shorebird foraging and this depends on the degree of disturbance and the availability of other suitable feeding areas. Disturbance compels birds to pay the energetic cost of flying to a new area, it may reduce the amount of time that the birds are able to feed, and can prevent them from feeding in the most preferred sites. Any overall reduction in energy intake as a result of these responses is the net impact of disturbance on energy budgets (Davidson and Rothwell 1993). Disturbance, however, may have little impact on birds if there are suitable foraging areas nearby in which they can feed.

In Delaware Bay the spectacle of shorebirds and spawning horseshoe crabs draws hundreds of bird watchers to beaches during the spring migratory stopover (Burger et al. 1995). The beaches are also vulnerable to the usual beach activities, such as walking, jogging, fishing, and dog walking. Disturbance along the New Jersey shore of Delaware Bay was first investigated in 1982, with further studies in the 1980s, 1990, and 2002 (Burger et al. 2004). The results show that the average period that that a beach was disturbed during any hour of the day dropped from 32.9 min in 1982 to 3.2 min in 2002. This was the direct result of increased management efforts by the NJDFW. Though the period of disturbances decreased during this period, it appears that the birds' sensitivity to disturbance increased. In 1982, 30% of shorebirds disturbed at Reeds Beach South and 98% at Reeds Beach North flew away when disrupted by people and did not return within 10 min. In 2002, 98% and 93% respectively did not return, with an increasing proportion of disturbance coming from dogs.

When shorebirds are disturbed by people and dogs on their foraging beaches, they usually respond by flying away. When there were no restrictions on disturbance in the 1980s, shorebirds were disturbed for over half of the time by day and when all beaches were disturbed the shorebirds often returned to the same beaches (Burger et al. 2004). When most beaches were protected from disturbance in 2002, the shorebirds were able to move to nearby beaches that were undisturbed. Therefore, management that restricts human activities on Delaware Bay beaches is shown to be effective in creating disturbance-free beaches necessary for feeding and resting shorebirds.

Starting in 2003, major sections of the New Jersey shore have been closed to human use during the peak of the stopover at the initiative of the NJDFW in order to reduce disturbance to shorebirds by people and dogs. Before this, disturbance of the beaches was a particular problem, especially during Memorial Day weekend. In 2001, for example, all 18,000 Red Knots that had previously been feeding on the bayshore spent the weekend on the Atlantic coast in the vicinity of Stone Harbor (H. P. Sitters, unpubl. data).

An additional source of disturbance is that caused by off road vehicle (ORV) use. Although not quantified, areas along the Delaware shore are occasionally used by ORVs. The frequency and duration of this type of disturbance varies but can have a major impact if ORVs remain at a specific location for an extended period of time. An ORV driving along a beach without stopping may have a relatively insignificant effect. However, when they are used with great frequency or for long periods (such as when they are used for recreation as opposed to transportation), ORVs probably cause shorebirds to leave and not return.

Disturbance by people is not limited to direct use of Delaware Bay beaches. Low-energy beaches, particularly those along the mouths of tidal creeks and rivers have been identified as optimum horseshoe crab spawning habitat. Where these have high levels of boat traffic, such as at Mispillion Harbor, disturbance due to the presence, noise, speed, or wake of boats is likely to be considerable (B. A. Harrington, unpubl. data). Preliminary results indicate that

boat traffic in Mispillion Harbor represents a significant source of disturbance to feeding shorebirds, particularly when boats travel at high speed (B. A. Harrington, unpubl. data).

In Massachusetts disturbance by humans and dogs has been identified as a threat to Red Knots.

In Virginia some of the potential threats Red Knots currently face on the barrier islands include frequent interruptions in foraging and roosting bouts caused by humans and an introduced breeding population of Peregrines Falcons.

Along the coast of North Carolina, threats to migrant and wintering Red Knots include human disturbance, especially at the following key sites:

1. Tubbs Inlet—human disturbance.
2. Bear Island/Bogue Inlet—some human disturbance at inlet and nearby bath house during the spring and summer months but very limited at present.
3. Bird Shoals—human disturbance primarily during the spring and summer months.
4. Cape Lookout National Seashore—human disturbance including beach driving during spring and summer months.
5. Cape Hatteras National Seashore—human disturbance including beach driving during spring-summer months.
6. Pea Island—human disturbance during the spring and summer months.
7. Clam Shoal—this site is fairly inaccessible, but more people have visited it in recent years so possibly human disturbance during the spring and summer months is increasing.

A large area of the South Carolina coast is protected due to public ownership and conservation easements. Few opportunities exist to increase the amount of protected coastal land. The biggest threat to Red Knots is disturbance by boats, humans, and dogs, even in Cape Romain NWR. Presently in South Carolina, only two islands (in Cape Romain NWR) are closed to boat landings that are known to be important Red Knot loafing and foraging areas. Coastal counties are experiencing annual human population growth rates of 2–3%.

In Georgia, human disturbance (pedestrians, dogs, boats, and bicyclists) is the most significant threat to important winter and stopover habitats for Red Knots.

In Florida, it appears that the most immediate and tangible threat to migrant and wintering Red Knots is chronic disturbance (Niles et al. 2006). However, with the exception of a few federally owned sites, most beaches experience very high human disturbance rates which are increasing. While almost all foraging habitat and most roosting sites are in public ownership, very few locations are managed in any way for winter or passage shorebirds. Seasonal posting in Florida is done primarily for beach-nesting birds during the spring and summer months. Publicly owned lands, if managed at all, are generally under tremendous recreational pressure from a rapidly growing human population. Some sites receive incidental protection under restrictions designed to protect other resources (combustible motor exclusion zones to protect sea grass beds or homeland security restrictions at ports, military installations, space center, etc.).

In Argentina, human disturbance is a threat on the beaches at Reserva Provincial de Río Chico para Aves Playeras Migratorias and Reserva Urbana Costera del Río Chico (tourism), on Península Valdés (tourism, with dogs a particular problem, and fishermen with cats [L. Bala, pers. comm.]), in the Bahía San Antonio Natural Protected Area (beach tourism), and in Bahía Samborombón (tourism).

Red Knots frequently suffer human disturbance while feeding and roosting around Río Grande city, especially by people using all-terrain vehicles and motor cycles, as well as from walkers, runners, fishermen, and dogs.

COMPETITION FROM GULLS

Gulls are both competitors for food and potential predators of shorebirds. They take advantage of abundant horseshoe crab eggs, particularly on that part of the New Jersey bayshore that lies close to their Atlantic coast breeding colonies. During 1979–2004, numbers of two common species, Laughing Gull and Herring Gull (*Larus argentatus*), fluctuated widely but with a no statistically significant long-term trend. However, Greater Black-backed Gulls (*L. marinus*) increased significantly (Table 38). Number of gulls using the New Jersey bayshore for feeding has not changed significantly (Sutton and Dowdell 2002). During 1992–2002,

the number of gulls recorded in single-day counts on accessible New Jersey bayshore beaches ranged from 10,000–23,000.

Gull breeding colonies in Delaware are not located as close to the bayshore beaches as in New Jersey. However, immature, non-breeding, large gulls (Greater Black-backed Gull and Herring Gull) and some Laughing Gulls (most likely from New Jersey breeding colonies) do congregate on the Delaware shore during the spring, especially at Mispillion Harbor. Though gull numbers have been recorded along the Delaware bayshore in recent years, there are insufficient long-term data to show populations trends.

Although total gull numbers have shown no significant long-term trend (Table 38), the effect of their competition on the shorebirds may have increased as a result of the decline in the availability of horseshoe crab eggs. Burger et al. (2007) found that gulls are more tolerant of human disturbance than shorebirds. When disturbed by humans, gull numbers returned to pre-disturbance levels within 5 min. Even after 10 min shorebird numbers failed to reach pre-disturbance levels. Shorebirds showed a particularly strong reaction to dogs; when disturbed by a dog, shorebirds did not return to the same beach. Red Knots are also more vigilant when feeding near gulls and most spend more time watching out for gulls to the detriment of time spent feeding (J. Burger, unpubl. data).

Thus the size and aggression of gulls, coupled with their greater tolerance of human disturbance, give them the advantage over shorebirds in prime feeding areas. In the present scenario of limited availability of good feeding beaches, gulls appear to be an increasing threat to Red Knots in the Delaware Bay.

The influence of gulls on horseshoe crab egg densities has been shown to be significant through exclosure experiments conducted by Virginia Polytechnic Institute (S. Karpanty, pers. comm.). Burger et al. (2004) found that

TABLE 38. AERIAL SURVEY COUNTS OF GULLS ON THE ATLANTIC COAST OF NEW JERSEY (D. JENKINS, UNPUBL. DATA).

Year	Laughing Gull	Herring Gull	Great Black-backed Gull	All gulls
1979	59,914	5,802	128	65,844
1983	58,267	5,237	260	63,764
1985	54,434	4,720	226	59,380
1989	58,797	7,097	293	66,187
1995	39,085	6,828	781	46,694
2001	80,253	9,814	1,036	91,103
2004	52,765	5,347	795	58,907
Mean	57,645	6,406	503	64,554
Correlation with year (r_s)	−0.29 (P > 0.05)	0.39 (P > 0.05)	0.93 (P = 0.003)	−0.18 (P > 0.05)

gulls out competed all shorebird species including Red Knots for horseshoe crab eggs, and that the influence of gulls increases with repeated disturbance. In contrast to shorebirds, people walking dogs caused gulls to leave but they returned shortly after the disturbance ended.

Red Knot foraging efficiency is also adversely affected by the mere presence of gulls. Hernández (2005) found that the foraging efficiency of Red Knots feeding on horseshoe crab eggs decreased by as much as 40% when feeding close to a gull.

RISKS ASSOCIATED WITH SMALL POPULATION SIZE

The threat to *C. c. rufa* may become further increased if the population drops below about 10,000 because Baker et al. (2005a) has shown that, due to their low genetic variability, the effective size of shorebird populations is much smaller than numbers censused (i.e., not all individuals contribute to the gene pool). As a result, census populations of 5,000–10,000 are likely to be especially vulnerable to the accumulation of harmful genetic mutations. Small populations are also at greater risk from the effects of stochastic events. This applies especially those which, like the Red Knot, are highly dependent on a small number of sites.

WEATHER-RELATED THREATS TO RED KNOTS

Cold and/or wet weather during the brief arctic summer can have a severely adverse effect on the breeding success of shorebirds (van de Kam et al. 2004). Global climate warming may lead to alterations in arctic weather patterns. These may be beneficial to shorebirds if they lead to warmer, longer breeding seasons but this is by no means certain (Rehfisch and Crick 2003).

In the very long term global warming may lead to large-scale habitat changes which will be greatly exacerbated by vegetation responses to increased atmospheric carbon dioxide (Rehfisch and Crick 2003). It has been predicted that this may lead to a 65% decrease in tundra habitat over a large area of the Arctic (Cramer 1997). If so, Red Knot breeding habitat would become so scarce that there is little doubt that this would restrict the size of its population.

SUMMARY OF LAND OWNERSHIP AND EXISTING HABITAT PROTECTION FOR POPULATIONS

Appendix 4 summarizes details of the ownership of all land considered to be important for Red Knots throughout the western Atlantic flyway. This appendix also indicates the approximate percentage of land that is subject to some arrangement for habitat protection. However, it should be noted that the nature of such arrangements varies from place to place and in only a very few cases is the arrangement specifically for the benefit of Red Knots.

PAST AND CURRENT CONSERVATION AND HABITAT MANAGEMENT ACTIVITIES UNDERTAKEN TO BENEFIT THE SPECIES

As part of this assessment, biologists representing each state and country were contacted and were requested to outline management efforts for Red Knots. We found that no management efforts are directed specifically at Red Knots along the entire length of the flyway except in the area of Delaware Bay. However, many global, national, regional, and state-specific management and conservation efforts have been implemented to benefit shorebirds in general, including the Red Knot.

THE RAMSAR CONVENTION ON WETLANDS

The Convention on Wetlands, signed at Ramsar, Iran in 1971, is an intergovernmental treaty which provides the framework for national action and international cooperation for the conservation and wise use of wetlands and their resources. Presently the convention has 146 contracting parties with 1,463 wetland sites, totaling 125,400,000 ha, designated for inclusion in the Ramsar List of Wetlands of International Importance.

The mission of the convention agreed at the eighth meeting of the Conference of the Contracting Parties in Valencia in 2002 is to promote the conservation and wise use of all wetlands through local, regional, and national actions and international cooperation, as a contribution towards achieving sustainable development throughout the world (http://www.ramsar.org).

WESTERN HEMISPHERE SHOREBIRD RESERVE NETWORK

The network is a voluntary, non-regulatory coalition of over 160 private and public organizations in seven countries working together to study and conserve shorebirds throughout their habitats. Membership in Western Hemisphere Shorebird Reserve Network (WHSRN) provides the site with international recognition as a major host for shorebirds. The network now includes 46 officially designated sites that are responsible for managing >80,940,000 ha. Member sites are located in Argentina, Brazil, Peru, Suriname, Mexico, U.S., and Canada. Further, almost 150 more sites are in Canada and the U.S. alone that are known to meet WHSRN site criteria but have not yet joined the network.

Of the 47 species of migratory shorebirds in North America, five are predicted to decline by 25% or more over the next 5 yr and 16 others have projected or actual population declines of 5–20%. Habitat degradation at critical staging, breeding, and non-breeding sites may be a major factor along with many problems that a migratory species encounter.

IMPORTANT BIRD AREAS PROGRAM

National Audubon Society, as the partner for BirdLife International, is working to identify a network of sites that provide critical habitat for birds. This effort known as the Important Bird Areas Program (IBA) recognizes that habitat loss and fragmentation are the most serious threats facing populations of birds across America and around the world. By working through partnerships, principally the North American Bird Conservation Initiative, to identify those places that are critical to birds during some part of their life cycle (breeding, wintering, feeding, and migrating) it is hoped to minimize the effects that habitat loss, and degradation have on bird populations. Unless the rapid destruction and degradation of habitat can be slowed, populations of many birds may decline to dangerously low levels. The IBA program is a global effort to identify areas that are most important for maintaining bird populations, and focus conservation efforts at protecting these sites. In the U.S., the IBA program has become a key component of many bird conservation efforts, for example, Partners in Flight, North American Waterbird Conservation Plan, and the U.S. Shorebird Conservation Plan.

CONVENTION ON THE CONSERVATION OF MIGRATORY SPECIES OF WILD ANIMALS 1979

The Convention on the Conservation of Migratory Species of Wild Animals (also known as CMS or Bonn Convention) aims to conserve terrestrial, marine and avian migratory species throughout their range. It is an intergovernmental treaty, concluded under the aegis of the United Nations Environment Program, concerned with the conservation of wildlife and habitats on a global scale. Since the convention came into force, its membership has grown steadily to include 101 Parties (as of 1 January 2007) from Africa, central and South America, Asia, Europe, and Oceania. At the instigation of Argentina, the Conference of the Parties to the Convention meeting in November 2005

determined that the *C. c. rufa* subspecies of the Red Knot was endangered and as such added it to Appendix 1 of the convention. Under the terms of the Convention the Parties agree to strive towards strictly protecting animals listed in Appendix 1, conserving or restoring the places where they live, mitigating obstacles to migration and controlling other factors that might endanger them (http://www.cms.int).

NATIONAL WILDLIFE REFUGES

Refuge managers in USFWS regions 2, 4, and 5 were solicited for information on management plans that might affect Red Knots. Management efforts for shorebirds are taking place in many wildlife refuges in the flyway, but most focus on impoundment management that aim primarily at species likely to forage in moist soil, such as Semi-palmated Sandpiper, Dunlin, Short-billed Dowitcher, and Greater Yellowlegs (*Tringa melanoleuca*). The Red Knot feeds primarily on small mussels and clams normally associated with tidal sands, and would only benefit indirectly from impoundment management for shorebirds. While not the focus of specific management efforts, Red Knots benefit from the creation of safe high tide or nighttime roosts on the small islands formed by the natural topography of shallow water impoundments.

THE INTERNATIONAL SHOREBIRD SURVEY AND PROGRAM FOR REGIONAL AND INTERNATIONAL SHOREBIRD MONITORING

In 1974, the Manomet Center for Conservation Sciences organized the ISS to gather information on shorebirds and the wetlands they use. Information gathered by ISS cooperators over the last 30 yr show some disturbing trends. The data have long suggested that several shorebird species were declining rapidly, but until recently the design of the ISS did not allow for a sensitive statistical analysis. A new initiative, PRISM, is underway to coordinate and expand on existing shorebird survey efforts, including the ISS, the Western Shorebird Survey (WSS) and the Canadian Maritimes Shorebird Survey (MSS). The closer coordination and expanded survey effort will increase the power of statistical analyses and more clearly define shorebird conservation issues on a continental scale. (http://www.manomet.org/programs/shorebirds/).

Volunteer participation in the ISS has declined since 2000 (B. A. Harrington, unpubl. data) and the level of effort from year to year and state to state is highly variable. Concerted effort should be made by state and federal agencies to reinvigorate survey efforts through PRISM.

DELAWARE BAY — INCREASED AVAILABILITY OF
HORSESHOE CRAB EGGS

Management in the Delaware Bay aims primarily at the protection of horseshoe crabs and spawning beaches which increases the availability of horseshoe crab eggs the Red Knot's prime food resource. Central to the protection of horseshoe crabs is the ASMFC Management Plan for the horseshoe crab. The plan adopted in 1998, along with subsequent addenda in 2000, 2001, 2004, and 2006 has provided the coast-wide framework for the protection of horseshoe crabs. The protection of horseshoe crabs has been achieved through tighter restrictions on the harvest of crabs as bait. This is covered in the section on history of regulations. However, past restrictions on the harvest have not created a substantial increase in the spawning population or crab egg numbers to date, partially because it takes nine years for crabs to reach breeding age. Thus other options have been explored to improve egg availability in the short- and mid-term periods.

Management efforts to increase the availability of horseshoe crab eggs have taken several forms. The first is protecting beaches important for crabs and birds from repeated disturbances by people and dogs. The first part of the protection is the Shorebird Steward Program conducted by NJDFW, USFWS, NJAS, TNC, and other groups, and the former Shorebird Ambassador Program conducted by the DDFW, where volunteers form a corps of stewards, educating beach users about the effects of disturbance on shorebirds and warn them of regulations that protect shorebirds. This effort is supported by agency staff providing logistical support in the form of outreach materials, signs, and post-and-string symbolic fencing. The second part of protection is conservation law enforcement, which has become necessary to obtain full compliance at the protected beaches. In New Jersey, the Red Knot is a state threatened species and conservation officers have authority to issue summonses for disturbance. In three spring seasons, only a small number of warnings and one summons have been issued. Conservation officers have become the backup for shorebird beach stewards who may encounter difficulties with the public. Finally, the ASMFC approved addendum III to the horseshoe crab management plan. In addition to reducing the Delaware Bay harvest to 300,000 crabs annually, it prohibits the collection of horseshoe crabs during the shorebird migratory period of 1 May through 7 June. By prohibiting the collection of crabs during the spawning period, females are free to spawn providing much needed eggs, and disturbance to foraging and roosting shorebirds due to beach harvesting is eliminated.

The second effort to increase the availability of horseshoe crab eggs is to develop management solutions to the high gull numbers along the New Jersey and Delaware Bay shore. The impact of gull numbers is greatest on bayshore beaches that are closest to gull colonies on the Atlantic coast, namely those along the shore of the Cape May peninsula. These beaches, including Norbury's Landing, Kimbles Beach, and Gandys Beach were among those where shorebird numbers were the greatest (B. A. Harrington, unpubl. data; K. Clark, unpubl. data; Clark et al. 1993). In 2003–2004, shorebirds shifted to beaches most distant from gull colonies on the Atlantic coast — Fortescue Beach and Gandy Beach. Birds returned to Reeds Beach in 2005 coinciding with the introduction of an experimental gull exclosure. Created by the NJDFW Shorebird Team, the exclosure consisted of metal conduit supporting strands of 200-lb test monofilament approximately 1–3 m high (C. D. T. Minton, unpubl. data). The team applied a number of variations that prevented gull predation on eggs but also restricted shorebird use. However, flocks of up to 3,000 Red Knots roosted and foraged in areas adjacent to and within the exclosure for most of the latter half of May. Further experimentation is planned for 2006.

The gull exclosure is considered to be only a short-term solution to the low density of horseshoe crab eggs in New Jersey. A longer-term solution is the control of gulls. Although the killing of gulls would provide an immediate solution, the control of gull productivity presents a more publicly acceptable management alternative.

DELAWARE BAY — PROTECTION OF ROOSTING SITES

The fourth management focus on Delaware Bay is to create secure day and nighttime high-tide roosts. Shorebirds at stopover sites require not only an adequate food supply but also safe and disturbance-free sites that are close to their feeding grounds where they can roost when not feeding and be relatively free from ground predators (Rogers 2003, Sitters et al. 2001). As is typical worldwide the main roosting sites used in New Jersey have always been the sand-spits and sand islands in Hereford Inlet on the Atlantic coast between Stone Harbor and Wildwood. In contrast, the bay shore of Delaware has no similar roosting site so birds tend to roost in areas of open marshland about

1.7 km inland near Mispillion River (H. P. Sitters, unpubl. data). Presently, this is the only place in the world where Red Knots have been recorded as roosting inland at night.

In 2004, radio tracking showed birds commuting from diurnal feeding areas on the Delaware coast to roost at Hereford Inlet, New Jersey, at night, a 94-km round trip. In 2005, perhaps because of tidal flooding just before the main arrival of Red Knots, most, if not all, Red Knots that fed in Delaware commuted to Hereford Inlet every night. On some nights, when high water occurred in the evening, the whole of the Delaware Bay stopover population of up to 20,000 birds roosted at Hereford Inlet.

In response to the increasing numbers of shorebirds roosting on the Atlantic coast at Stone Harbor Point, NJDFW created protection zones in 2005 on two areas covering approximately 125 ha. By the end of May >20,000 Red Knots and thousands of Dunlin and Sanderlings were using the protected area as a night time roost, and as many as 2,000 Red Knots were roosting in the same area during daytime high tides. In 2006, NJDFW partnered with the municipality of Stone Harbor to create year-round protection of Stone Harbor Point with emphasis on spring, fall and winter populations of all shorebirds, and spring and fall populations of Red Knots. Protection efforts include physical barriers to disturbance, outreach materials, a full time naturalist on duty at critical periods, and the development of plans for long-term protection.

On the southbound journey the same consideration for safe and secure roosts and foraging areas also apply. In a study conducted on the Two Mile Beach Unit of the Cape May NWR, which is closed to beachgoers during the period of the southbound migration, Red Knots and other shorebird species occurred ten times more often than on beaches open to the public (Mizrahi 2002).

DELAWARE BAY — REDUCE DISTURBANCE BY MINIMIZING RESEARCH ACTIVITIES

Research efforts on Delaware Bay, including trapping, banding, and resighting efforts have been minimized to reduce disturbance to foraging shorebirds. Trapping and banding effort was reduced to the minimum necessary to monitor weight gains of Red Knots, Ruddy Turnstones, and Sanderlings during the migratory stopover period, and individually mark enough birds to perform survival analyses via resightings of marked individuals. Catch effort is limited to six catches of 50–75 individuals of each species spread throughout the migratory stopover

period (approximately 10 May–7 June), and catches are spaced 3–5 d apart. On any one day, catching activities take place at no more than one site on each side of the bay and catching effort is spread out over various locations to avoid frequent disturbance to individual beaches. Where catching takes place, disturbance is mostly limited to around 100 m of shoreline and, except for around 20 min when a catch is made, is much less than that caused by typical recreation use. Optimally, all three species are caught in one attempt to reduce disturbance and catch frequency. The effects on migratory shorebirds of disturbance by researchers were quantified and no difference was found between either the frequency or flight duration of researcher-caused disturbance as compared to control periods (B. A. Harrington, unpubl. data). Most birds are weighed, measured, and banded within 2 hr of capture, and banding activities take place away from foraging beaches to allow shorebirds to return to forage.

Researchers carrying out systematic resighting surveys for individually marked shorebirds are restricted to hidden or distant viewing areas including viewing platforms constructed for shorebird viewing, roads, and occasionally from beachfront property with the permission of the landowner.

Shorebird banding teams are led by biologists from NJDFW and DDFW and are comprised of professional local and foreign shorebird biologists as well as experienced local and foreign bird banders. The Delaware Bay Shorebird Project began in 1997 and employed cannon netting, a method widely used in Europe and Australia. Because this method is not widely used in the U.S., biologists requested the aid of certified cannon netters from the United Kingdom and Australia, all with decades of experience, to train U.S. teams in this trapping technique. This dedicated corps of experienced cannon netters, many of whom are professional shorebird biologists in their respective countries, have returned each year since 1997 to help carry out this project.

DELAWARE BAY — MONITOR NUMBERS OF MIGRATORY SHOREBIRDS ON THE DELAWARE BAY STOPOVER

In 1986, the NJDFW and DDFW commenced weekly aerial surveys of the Delaware Bay coastline to document shorebird abundance during the migratory stopover (May through early June). This long-term survey has tracked the decline of the migratory stopover in terms of shorebird abundance and has been used to track changes in shorebird distribution relative to horseshoe crab egg densities on bayshore beaches. This survey has been conducted by the same observers throughout its nearly 20-yr duration and continues to be one of the most valuable long-term monitoring programs in place on the Delaware Bay stopover.

DELAWARE BAY—PAST AND CURRENT MANAGEMENT ACTIONS FOR SHOREBIRD POPULATIONS

1. 1986—Delaware Governor Michael Castle and New Jersey Governor Thomas Kean designated the bayshore as a sister reserve, the first such commitment under WHSRN. The WHSRN ties together critical shorebird stopovers in North, Central and South America.
2. 1986—NJENSP with DDFW conducted bay-wide aerial surveys of shorebirds. This survey has been conducted every year since 1987.
3. 1992—NJDFW contracted a study of shorebird and shorebird habitat vulnerability to oil spills in the bay. This study projected the likely impact areas of spills from different locations under different weather conditions to provide information necessary for response planning.
4. 1993—In May 1993, the NJENSP convened a 2-d Delaware Bay shorebird workshop, which resulted in the Comprehensive Management Plan for Shorebirds on Delaware Bay. The workshop included over 100 people representing 22 organizations, and aimed to improve communication and develop a framework for conservation actions across two states and multiple government and non-governmental organizations.
5. 1994—In May 1994 the NJENSP convened a single day Delaware Bay meeting to finalize the management plan drafted after the 1993 workshop. The final plan was printed and distributed to regulatory agencies and conservation groups in the region. NJENSP completed mapping of shorebird distribution and suitable habitats, and made it available to emergency response and planning agencies.
6. 1994—New Jersey convened a shorebird outreach team as a result of the 1993 planning meeting, including representatives from NJENSP, DDFW Nongame and Endangered Species Program (NGES), NJAS, Bay Shore landowners TNC, New Jersey Natural Lands Trust (NLT), New Jersey Conservation Foundation (NJCF), USFWS, and the Wetlands Institute. This team developed educational materials

including fact sheets on shorebirds and safe viewing locations.
7. 1995—New Jersey hosted a 2-d Delaware River and Bay Oil Spill Emergency Workshop, assembling all agencies responsible for spill response on the bay. The results of this workshop were incorporated into the Area Contingency Plan, the chief reference document in the case of a spill.
8. 1997—Delaware Coastal Management Program (DECMP) and WHSRN host a shorebird management workshop for Delaware Bay. The goal of the workshop was to provide information that can be used to integrate shorebird management into traditional environmental practices and programs in the Delaware Bay region such as wetlands management, public access management, and the beneficial use of dredged material.
9. 2003—NJENSP and DDFW Natural Heritage and Endangered Species Program (NHESP) conducted bay-wide aerial shorebird surveys during the fall migratory period.
10. 2005—NJENSP, Richard Stockton University in New Jersey, and DDFW-NHESP carried out the first year of bay-wide horseshoe crab egg surveys using a standardized sampling protocol developed by the U.S. Geological Survey.
11. 2004—ASMFC approved addendum III of the horseshoe crab management plan. The addendum limits Delaware Bay harvest to 300,000 crabs annually and prohibits the harvest of crabs during the shorebird migratory period (1 May–7 June). This closure decreases the number of gravid females collected and limits the disturbance to shorebirds caused by beach harvesting.
12. 2006—ASMFC approves addendum IV of the horseshoe crab management plan. In relation to New Jersey and Delaware for the 2 yr from 1 October 2006, this prohibits the directed harvest and landing of all horseshoe crabs between 1 January and 7 June and female horseshoe crabs between 8 June and 31 December and limits the harvest to 100,000 (male) crabs per state per year. In relation to Maryland and for the same 2-yr period, it prohibits the directed harvest and landing of horseshoe crabs between 1 January and 7 June. It also prohibits the landing of horseshoe crabs in Virginia from federal waters between 1 January and 7 June.

DELAWARE BAY — PAST AND CURRENT MANAGEMENT ACTIONS FOR THE HORSESHOE CRAB POPULATIONS

1. 1991 — DDFW was given authority to regulate horseshoe crabs. Collecting permits were required and mandatory reporting regulations were established and horseshoe crab dredge licenses were capped at five.

2. 1992 — DDFW prohibited horseshoe crab harvesting within 300 m of all state and federal lands from 1 May — 7 June (except Port Mahon on Wednesday, Thursday, and Friday). A personal possession limit of six horseshoe crabs was established for non-permitees (i.e., people can have up to six to bait a minnow trap or eel pot to catch fish bait).

3. 1993 — New Jersey passed regulations that prohibited harvest of horseshoe crabs on New Jersey Delaware Bay beaches during daylight hours. Reporting of harvest was voluntary.

4. 1994 — New Jersey passed regulations that prohibited harvest of horseshoe crabs on New Jersey Delaware Bay beaches or within 300 m of beaches. Reporting of harvest was mandatory.

5. 1995 — Regulations limited harvest of horseshoe crabs on New Jersey Delaware Bay beaches to nighttime hours on Mondays, Wednesdays, and Fridays only during the period 1 May–7 June.

6. 1996 — An amendment to N.J.A.C. 7: 25-18.16 to provide added protection to spawning horseshoe crabs and reduce the disturbance to the migratory shorebirds feeding on the Delaware Bay waterfront beaches. Regulations prohibited harvest of horseshoe crabs on Delaware Bay waterfront at any time; hand harvest permitted only in back bays and tidal creeks of the state (minimum of 300 m from bay front) on Tuesdays and Thursdays commenting 1 hr after sunset until 1 hr before sunrise. Harvest and landing of crabs was prohibited during May unless by hand.

7. 1997 — DDFW instituted an emergency closure of the horseshoe crab fishery in May and closed the dredge fishery and hand harvest (state and federal lands) through 30 June.

8. 1998 — The ASMFC approved the Interstate Fishery Management Plan for Horseshoe Crabs. DDFW closed horseshoe crab fishery 1 May–30 June except Tuesday and Thursday hand harvest at Port Mahon and Monday, Wednesday, and Friday hand harvest on private lands.

An 8.5 m³ containment limit on hand harvest fishery was established. The dredge fishery was closed from 1 May — 30 June and a 1,500 horseshoe crab limit on dredge harvest was imposed. Hand harvest permit eligibility criteria were established (had to have secured two permits prior to July 1997). Requirements for timelier reporting were established. Landings from the Exclusive Economic Zone (EEZ, 3.2-485 km) were prohibited. Nighttime harvest was prohibited.

9. 2000 — The ASMFC approved addendum I to the Fishery Management Plan for Horseshoe Crab. The addendum caps bait landings to 25% below reference-period landings and recommends a closure of horseshoe crab harvest in federal waters within 56 km of the mouth of the Delaware Bay.

10. 2001 — The NMFS established the Carl N. Shuster, Jr. Horseshoe Crab Reserve. The establishment of this reserve prohibits the harvest of horseshoe crabs in nearly 3,800 km² of federal waters off the mouth of the Delaware Bay.

11. 2004 — (March). The ASMFC Horseshoe Crab Management Board agreed to adopt new conservation measures for the horseshoe crab. Specifically, the Addendum capped annual harvest in New Jersey and Delaware at 150,000 crabs per state and set Maryland's annual quota at its 2001 landings level (170,653 crabs). Further, it required the three states to prohibit the harvest and landings of horseshoe crab for bait from 1 May–7 June. Addendum III also encouraged states with both bait and biomedical fisheries to allow biomedical companies to bleed harvested crabs prior to their use as bait. This would eliminate mortality associated with the process of bleeding and returning crabs to the waters from which they were harvested.

12. 2003 for the 2004 season — New Jersey and Delaware quota reduced to 150,000 horseshoe crabs. Season established to be 1 April through 30 April and 8 June through 15 August. No harvest allowed during the period 1 May through 7 June. Permit holders must report their harvest each Friday by telephone. The dredge fishery was limited to 35% of total quota prior to 1 May. The use of bait savings devices required. DDFW bans the personal exemption of six horseshoe crabs.

13. 2006 — ASMFC approves addendum IV of the horseshoe crab management plan. In relation to New Jersey and Delaware for

the 2 yr from 1 October 2006, this prohibits the directed harvest and landing of all horseshoe crabs between 1 January and 7 June and female horseshoe crabs between 8 June and 31 December and limits the harvest to 100,000 (male) crabs per state per year. In relation to Maryland and for the same 2-yr period, it prohibits the directed harvest and landing of horseshoe crabs between 1 January and 7 June. It also prohibits the landing of horseshoe crabs in Virginia from federal waters between 1 January and 7 June.

DELAWARE BAY—MANAGEMENT PLANS

1. 1998—(Dec). The ASMFC Fisheries Management Plan for Horseshoe Crab was approved requiring a suite of monitoring requirements—Delaware, New Jersey, and Maryland required to keep current regulations in place.
2. Late 1999—ASMFC Horseshoe Crab Management Board approved Addendum I to the Interstate Fishery Management Plan for Horseshoe Crab, which implemented harvest reduction measures along the Atlantic coast for the commercial horseshoe crab bait fishery. Specifically, the Addendum established a state-by-state cap at 25% below 1995–1997 levels of 2,999,491 horseshoe crabs for all states.
3. 2000 (May)—Addendum I of the Fishery Management Plan approved requiring a cap on the fishery at 361,801 horseshoe crabs.
4. 2001—Atlantic States Marine Fisheries Commission (2001) approved addendum II to the FMP for horseshoe crabs allowing interstate transfer of harvest quotas.
5. 2004—ASMFC approved addendum III to the FMP for horseshoe crabs. addendum III further limits harvest of Delaware Bay horseshoe crabs to 300,000. It also closes harvest from 1 May through 7 June to limit harvesting of spawning crabs and to limit disturbance of shorebirds from harvesters.
6. 2006—ASMFC approved addendum IV of the Horseshoe Crab management Plan. In relation to New Jersey and Delaware for the 2-yr from 1 October 2006, this prohibits the directed harvest and landing of all horseshoe crabs between 1 January and 7 June and female horseshoe crabs between 8 June and 31 December and limits the harvest to 100,000 (male) crabs per state per year. In relation to Maryland and for the same 2-yr period, it prohibits the

directed harvest and landing of horseshoe crabs between 1 January and 7 June. It also prohibits the landing of horseshoe crabs in Virginia from federal waters between 1 January and 7 June.

DELAWARE BAY—HABITAT PROTECTION

1. 1999—The Ecological Research Development Group (ERDG) launched its community-based horseshoe crab sanctuary program. The program works with private landowners and communities to establish sanctuaries where crabs cannot be harvested.
2. 2000—ERDG works with the community of Broadkill Beach, Delaware, to become the first horseshoe crab sanctuary restricting the harvest of horseshoe crabs along a 4-km section of beach.
3. 2005—Currently, approximately 32 km are registered as designated horseshoe crab sanctuaries with DDFW.

DELAWARE BAY—BAIT BAGS

1. 1999—ERDG initiated phase I of its bait bag initiative dispersing 500 bait bags to Virginia conch fishermen. Bait bags were found to reduce the amount of horseshoe crab bait needed by 25–50%.
2. 2000—ERDG completes phase II of its bait-bag initiative by manufacturing and distributing 6,000 bait bags to commercial fishermen in Maryland, Delaware, and New Jersey free of charge.

NON-BREEDING AND STOPOVER AREA MANAGEMENT AND CONSERVATION

South America

Monitoring winter population of Red Knots in South America:
1. 2000–2005. NJENSP and CWS instituted a winter survey of Red Knots in South America following the protocol of Morrison and Ross (1989). Continuation of this survey is dependent on availability of funding.
2. 2000–2005. NJENSP and biologists from Chile and Argentina captured and individually marked Red Knots wintering on Bahía Lomas, Chile, to augment adult survival analyses and assess proportion of immature birds in the wintering population.

In Chile, no special protection measures exist for Bahía Lomas. In 1996, the Corporación

Nacional Forestal (Muñoz et al. 1996) recommended Bahía Lomas as one of the 21 sites in the urgent category stated in the priority sites for the conservation of the biodiversity in Chile (Muñoz et al. 1996). No activities were associated with this conservation status. Due to its world importance, Bahía Lomas was recently declared a Ramsar site in December 2004, the second southern most after the neighboring Atlantic coastal reserve of Tierra del Fuego in Argentina. Thus far, the Ramsar designation is the only unique conservation measurement that Bahía Lomas has received. The Red Knot is protected by the hunting law No. 19.473.

Argentina is a signatory party of the Convention on the Conservation of Migratory Species of Wild Animals. Migratory species that need or would benefit significantly from international co-operation are listed in appendix II of the convention. The family Scolopacidae is listed in appendix II. Migratory species threatened with extinction are listed on appendix I of the convention. The *C. c. rufa* subspecies of the Red Knot was added to appendix I at a meeting of the Parties to the Convention that took place in November 2005. Under the terms of the convention, the parties agree to strive towards strictly protecting the animals listed in appendix I, conserving or restoring the places where they live, mitigating obstacles to migration, and controlling other factors that might endanger them.

Besides the Bonn Convention, different levels of government provide legal protection status to key Red Knot critical areas as described below. International recognition from the WHSRN and IBA from Birdlife International are also included:

1. Reserva Costa Atlántica de Tierra del Fuego (1992) — provincial natural area protected.
   a. Ramsar site (1995).
   b. WHSRN hemispheric site.
   c. IBA area (Bahía San Sebastián is a priority IBA area).
2. Reserva Provincial de Río Chico para Aves Playeras Migratorias (2001) and Reserva Urbana Costera del Río Chico (2004) — provincial natural area protected and urban natural area protected.
   a. Potential WHSRN site.
   b. IBA area.
3. Bahía Bustamante — no conservation status.
4. Península Valdés — reserva natural integral provincial.
   a. Patrimony of the Humanity.
   b. Potential Ramsar and WHSRN site.
   c. IBA area.
5. Bahía Samborombón (1979) — integral natural reserve.

   a. Provincial integral natural reserve with restricted access (9,311 ha).
   b. Provincial integral natural reserve, Rincón de Ajó (2,311).
   c. Campos del Tuyú Private Reserve, Fundación Vida Silvestre Argentina.
   d. Punta Rasa Biological Station, agreement between the Naval Hydrography Service (Argentinian Navy) and the Fundación Vida Silvestre Argentina.
   e. Punta Rasa Traveled Municipal Ecological Reserve (1991).
   f. Ramsar site (1997).
   g. Priority IBA area.
   h. Potential WHSRN site.
6. Bahía San Antonio Natural Protected Area.
   a. Potential Ramsar site.
   b. Priority IBA area.
   c. WHSRN site.

Management plans are being developed for Reserva Costa de Tierra del Fuego, Provincial de Río Chico para Aves Playeras Migratorias, Reserva Urbana Costera del Río Chico, in conjunction with ongoing shorebird research and public education. Shorebird research is also ongoing at Península Valdés, which has a current management plan and is used as a camp by artesanal fishermen, and Bahía Samborombón where an Environmental Ordering Plan is implemented. No research or management is being done at Bahía Bustamante.

The Bahía San Antonio Natural Protected Area has an urban management plan which restricts land use near key shorebird areas and actively protects shorebird roosting sites. Besides the CMS national and inter-government agreement, this area has international recognition from the WHSRN, is designated as a priority IBA by Birdlife International, and is a potential Ramsar site.

The Brazilian government through CEMAVE-IBAMA has been developing conservation projects on migratory Nearctic species since the beginning of the 1980s. In addition to the Brazilian legislation that protects fauna, the conservation of these species has been given impetus by the government entering into international agreements, such as the Washington Convention in 1948, and the Ramsar Convention in 1993. Projects aimed at monitoring and developing strategies for the conservation of Pan-American migrants have been developed, particularly in coastal areas.

Over the years, Brazil has entered into various international, technical cooperation agreements in relation to nature conservation. The first was in 1981 with the US government through the USDIFWS. This led to training in the technique of cannon-netting at Salinas, in the state of Pará. In the same year, a project with CWS resulted in an aerial survey of Nearctic shorebirds along the Brazilian coastline. This was carried out between 1982 and 1986, and the results were published in Morrison and Ross (1989).

In 1984, a workshop was held in Porto Alegre, in cooperation with Manomet Bird Observatory and Worldwide Fund for Nature, to teach and discuss techniques for monitoring migratory birds. This particularly involved the participation of teachers and researchers from the University of the Valley of the Sinos River and the Zoo-botanical Foundation of Río Grande do Sul. At the same time, field activities commenced at Lagoa do Peixe including bird banding. Subsequently CEMAVE started an annual bird monitoring program at Lagoa do Peixe during northward migration in April and May. This included catching birds with mist-nets and cannon-nets, banding, collecting biometric data, and bird surveys in the region of the Park.

Since 1992, CEMAVE has carried out surveys along several parts of the coast to study the ecological characteristics of the areas preferred by Nearctic shorebirds. It has also carried out studies along several other parts of the coasts of the states of Amapá, Pará, Maranhão, Ceará, Río Grande do Norte, Pernambuco, Alagoas, and Bahía. These have involved trained banders registered with the Brazilian National Banding Scheme.

Between 1996 and 1998, CEMAVE in partnership with CWS and with support from the Interamerican Development Bank, and WWF Canada, developed the project *Surveys of the Nearctic and Neotropical avifauna in the Marshland of the state of Mato Grosso*. These surveys were carried out in the states of Mato Grosso and Mato Grosso do Sul with the aim of identifying the main sites for passage migrant shorebirds in September and October. The results have not yet been published.

Since 1997, CEMAVE has participated in an international cooperative research project called *Migration of Red Knots in South America: ecological research to support the conservation of the longest bird flights on earth*. The aim of this project is to study the migration strategies of the species, integrating monitoring activities in the states of Maranhão and Río Grande do Sul with those carried out in others countries that share the same Red Knot population, such as Argentina and the US.

The monitoring of birds for transmittable diseases started in 2001 under an executive committee that includes representatives of the Ministers of Health, Agriculture and Environment, the National Health Foundation, IBAMA, the Office of the Secretary of Agricultural Defense in the Department of Agriculture, Livestock Farming and Supply, and the Zoological Society of Brazil. The main purpose is to achieve early detection of infected birds, and to take steps to prevent infections from spreading. Already eight serological investigations have been carried out at various sites including the coastline of the States of Amapá, Maranhão, Río Grande do Norte, Pernambuco, and Río Grande do Sul, and at other places in the states of Amazon, Mato Grosso do Sul, and Paraná. The results to date can be accessed through the epidemiology bulletins produced by the National Health Foundation, FUNASA.

In terms of shorebird conservation in Brazil, the main achievements include the designation in 1991 of the Lagoa do Peixe National Park, and the Reentrâncias Maranhenses as significant international and regional reserves, respectively, as part of the Western Hemispheric Shorebirds Reserve Network. These areas were also designated Ramsar sites at the time that Brazil joined the Ramsar Convention. Other significant achievements are the presentation of the results of shorebird studies at international and national conferences, the publication of articles in scientific journals; and participation in writing the management plan for the Lagoa do Park National Park between 1997 and 1999.

CEMAVE has promoted the training and qualification of personnel in the techniques of shorebird studies including capture, marking, and censuses. Trainees have also come from other countries including Argentina, Uruguay, Paraguay, Peru, Chile, Colombia, Venezuela, and Panama. Already, in six courses of short to medium duration, 45 professionals and biology students have been trained in shorebird study techniques.

It is noteworthy that the activities describe above received 95% financing from the Brazilian federal government, which has subsidized the monitoring of migratory birds over the years, despite of the economic instability of the country.

No current management activities in Maranhão. However, CEMAVE has organized scientific expeditions to Maranhão for banding and collection of biological data during northward migration in May, and also in November. CEMAVE have also undertaken outreach in Maranhão with the object of integrating local communities in conservation activities, as well as promoting banding and the collection of biological data. This has included talks to groups, such as schoolchildren and fishermen's associations.

United States — Florida

1. Shell Key — portions of the island are closed to entry.
2. Caladesi Island, Hurricane Pass — limited posting of signs on a roosting site.
3. Passage Key — closed to entry but poorly enforced.
4. Merritt Island NWR, Black Point Drive — restricted access.
5. Ding Darling NWR, tower stop — restricted access.
6. Kennedy Space Center — limited access.

United States — Georgia

1. Little Tybee Island — heritage preserve-natural area.
2. Ogeeche River Bar — not managed.
3. Wassaw Island — wildlife refuge.
4. Ossabaw Island — heritage preserve-natural area.
5. St. Catherines Island — undeveloped, conservation intent.
6. St. Catherines Bar — closed natural area.
7. Grass Island — not managed.
8. Blackbeard Island — wildlife refuge.
9. Sapelo Island — national estuarine research reserve-wildlife management area.
10. Wolf Island — wildlife refuge-wilderness.
11. Little Egg Island Bar — closed natural area.
12. Little St. Simons Island — undeveloped, conservation intent.
13. Sea Island — developed.
14. St. Simons Island, Gould's Inlet — developed.
15. Jekyll Island — developed.
16. Little Cumberland Island–partially developed.
17. Cumberland Island — national seashore, some private residences.

United States — South Carolina

Presently no protection efforts are specifically designed for Red Knots. Complete closures of important Red Knot roosting areas in Cape Romain NWR are planned for winter 2005–2006. Motions to completely close SCDNRs seabird nesting islands, which are also Red Knot roosting areas, will begin winter 2005–2006. SCDNR has begun tagging horseshoe crabs, identifying their critical spawning and nursery habitat, and working with harvesters to estimate and minimize fishery mortality.

United States — North Carolina

The following is a list of key sites with current management for wintering shorebirds:

1. Cape Lookout National Seashore — posting to protect breeding birds (April–August) also benefits migrants.
2. Cape Hatteras National Seashore — posting to protect breeding birds (April–August) also benefits migrants.
3. Pea Island — posting to protect breeding birds (April–August) also benefits migrants.

United States — Virginia

Previous Red Knot aerial surveys conducted in late May and/or early June indicate that the barrier islands located along the seaward margin of Virginia's Eastern Shore harbor the state's greatest densities and abundance of spring migrants and serve as important stopover locations. In addition, most of the islands are remote, free of development, and have for the most part been allowed to revert back to their natural state following periods of settlement by humans and livestock over the past several centuries.

Today, most management measures are directed toward minimizing human disturbance, reducing predator populations, and removal and/or control of invasive species. Organizations that own and manage the islands already have in place seasonal and year round public use policies designed to protect breeding waterbird populations. They include confining recreational activities to areas of the beach below the high-tide line, prohibiting dogs and other pets on the islands, temporarily closing portions of the islands that are particularly vulnerable to disturbance, and for a few of the islands, seasonal and year round closures. It should be noted a few private inholdings remain on two of the barrier islands. Owners of these private land parcels work cooperatively with conservation organizations to ensure their activities do not impact the islands' natural resources. Many of the seasonal closures and public use policies cover the peak Red Knot spring migration period.

Other sites where Red Knots have been observed during spring migration in substantially fewer numbers include Plum Tree Island NWR and Goodwin Island; both are located on the western shore of the lower Chesapeake Bay. Very little is known about the extent of use of these sites by Red Knots. Moreover, they receive very little human disturbance because they are remote and difficult to access (Plum Tree Island NWR is largely off limits to the public because of unexploded ordinances), therefore will likely not require much in the form of management.

United States – Maryland

The state of Maryland does not conduct or sponsor any organized surveys that include Red Knots. No research, monitoring, or management efforts regarding Red Knots occur in the state. Suitable habitats do exist within the state, however, these include: Hart Miller Island, Assateague Island, and Poplar Island. Hart Miller Island is owned and managed by the state of Maryland. Assateague Island is divided into three areas: Assateague Island National Seashore managed by the National Park Service, Chincoteague NWR managed by the USFWS, and Assateague State Park managed by Maryland Department of Natural Resources. Current management of Assateague Island consists of managed areas at the northern end of the island for Piping Plovers (*Charadrius melodus*) and tidal flats on the landward shore of the island managed as part of a coastal management program. Poplar Island is located off the Chesapeake Bay coastline, about 55 km south of Baltimore in Talbot County. It is currently being managed by the U.S. Army Corps of Engineers, the Maryland Port Administration, and other federal and state agencies as a site for habitat restoration and beneficial use of dredged materials.

United States – New Jersey

The principle shorebird conservation issues in the Delaware Bay stopover are human disturbance to birds and their habitats and the availability of abundant food in the form of horseshoe crab eggs. While recognition of the shorebird migration was improved with the reporting of bay wide surveys beginning in 1981 (Wander and Dunne 1981), management began in 1989 with the first shorebird wardens on three New Jersey beaches.

Outreach and protection:
1. 1989. NJENSP contracted NJAS to train and supervise shorebird wardens at three New Jersey beaches (Norbury's Landing, Reed's Beach, and Fortescue) to reduce disturbance. Educational signs were created and placed at two of those beaches (Reed's and Fortescue), and a brochure was distributed by the wardens.
2. 1990. The first year that NJENSP provided a viewing platform at Reed's Beach, to limit disturbance of that beach by encouraging use of a single viewing point. NJENSP contracted NJAS to train and supervise shorebird wardens at four New Jersey beaches (Sunray, Norbury's Landing, Reed's Beach, and Fortescue) on

weekends in May. Wardens distributed an informative brochure to 1,000 people.
3. 1992. Viewing areas were put in place at Norbury's Landing, Reed's Beach (2), and Fortescue. A map was created that identified all designated viewing areas
4. NJENSP trained and supervised 12 shorebird wardens who monitored four beaches on May weekends
5. 1994. Viewing areas were set up at Norbury's Landing, Reed's Beach, and Fortescue, and other accessible beach access points were posted with information signs warning of the problems of disturbance to feeding and resting shorebirds. A new brochure that included a viewing area map was distributed at all viewing areas and through local nature centers and businesses. New Jersey fielded shorebird wardens at viewing areas on May weekends.
6. 1995. The New Jersey Shorebird Outreach Team continued to work together on educational materials for the public. This team developed educational materials including a map of viewing areas with a local business listing on the back. Viewing areas were set up at Norbury's Landing, Reed's Beach, and Fortescue, and other accessible beach access points were posted with a new sign designed to clearly indicate the safe viewing point to prevent disturbance to feeding and resting shorebirds. New Jersey fielded shorebird wardens at viewing areas on May weekends. A new brochure that included a viewing area map was distributed at all viewing areas and through local nature centers and businesses.

Human use and disturbance:
1. 1985. NJENSP began research and survey actions initiating surveys of human use (K. E. Clark and L. J. Niles, unpubl. data).
2. 1987. NJDFW conducted human use surveys on New Jersey bayshore beaches.
3. 1988. NJDFW conducted human use surveys on New Jersey bayshore beaches.

Habitat restoration:
1. 1991. Fishing Creek marsh was managed to promote shorebird habitat by controlling *Phragmites* and restore tidal flow to its western section.
2. 2006. NJDFW received funding to remove rubble from Moore's and Thompson's Beach to improve spawning conditions for horseshoe crabs

Radio telemetry of shorebirds:
1. 1989. NJENSP initiated a shorebird telemetry study to determine habitat use patterns.

2. 1990. A limited telemetry study continued (seven Red Knots) to determine habitat use patterns.
3. 2003–2005. NJENSP, in cooperation with DDFW and the USFWS, initiated a bay-wide Red Knot telemetry study using stationary receivers to monitor bay wide bird movements and identify critical foraging and roosting sites.

Aerial and ground surveys:

1. 1990. NJENSP conducted aerial transect surveys across New Jersey Atlantic and Delaware Bay habitats three times per day, once a week for 3 wk, continued in 1991.
2. 1991. This year saw increased demand for (and harvest of) horseshoe crabs as bait.
3. NJENSP conducted aerial transect surveys across New Jersey Atlantic and Delaware Bay habitats three times per day, once a week for 3 wk, similar to those done in 1990. Ground surveys of shorebirds in marsh and beach habitats were conducted in 1991 and 1992, resulting in Burger et al. (1997).
4. 2004. NJENSP and NJAS began fall shorebird surveys using a modified ISS methodology. Trained volunteers count/estimate flock size of individual species, determine the ratio of juvenile/adult Red Knots in flocks, collect data on individually marked shorebirds, record sources of disturbance.
5. 2005. NJENSP and NJAS conduct spring shorebird surveys using modified ISS methodology. Trained volunteers count/estimate flock size of individual species, collect data on individually marked shorebirds, record sources of disturbance.

Monitoring horseshoe crab egg densities:

1. 1985. NJENSP began research and survey actions initiating surveys of horseshoe crab egg density (K. E. Clark and L. J. Niles, unpubl. data). In 1985 and 1986 egg density was measured at selected bayshore beaches (Botton et al. 1988).
2. 2000–2005. NJENSP took over horseshoe crab egg sampling following a protocol established by Robert Loveland, Rutgers University, and Mark Botton, Fordham University. This survey will be replaced in 2006 with a method developed by the U.S. Geological Survey to be implemented both in New Jersey and Delaware.

Monitoring shorebird mass gains and adult survival:

1. 1997–present. NJENSP began an intensive shorebird trapping and banding program in New Jersey and Delaware to monitor weight gains of shorebirds stopping over on Delaware Bay and color mark individuals for survival analyses and population estimation. In 1998, the DECMP took over the trapping effort on the Delaware side of the Bay. These studies are ongoing and continue to the present under the direction of DDFW-NHESP.

United States – Delaware

Outreach and Protection:

1. 1995. DDFW-NGES established shorebird interpretive signs and viewing platforms at key shorebird viewing areas including Ted Harvey Wildlife Area and Little Creek Wildlife Area at Port Mahon Road.
2. 1995. DDFW-NGES launched the Shorebird Ambassador Program that placed volunteers at key shorebird stopover sites in Delaware during the weekends. The shorebird ambassadors were to provide outreach and education to Delaware Bayshore visitors.
3. 1998. DDFW-NGES developed a shorebird viewing guide to promote shorebird conservation and viewing opportunities in Delaware.
4. 1998. DDFW closed horseshoe crab fishery 1 May–30 June except for limited hand-harvest; landowners were allowed to have their beaches declared sanctuaries.

Horseshoe crab radio telemetry:

1. 2003–2005. DDFW and DECMP, in partnership with the USGS have used an array of stationary telemetry receivers located throughout Delaware Bay to track horseshoe crab movement patterns and spawning frequency. In 2004 and 2005 shorebirds were added to the system to simultaneously track horseshoe crabs and shorebirds providing insight into the spatial and temporal overlap of beach use by these species.

Aerial and ground surveys:

1. 1992. DDFW coordinates ISS in Delaware during spring migrations. The ISS surveys were largely conducted by volunteers from the Delmarva Ornithological Society and continued through 1997.
2. 2003. DDFW-NHESP began coordinating fall shorebird surveys for the Program for Regional and International Shorebird Monitoring program.

Monitoring shorebird mass gains and adult survival:

1. 1998. DECMP initiated a shorebird-monitoring program that including intensive survey and banding operations that continues to this day.

Horseshoe crab egg densities:

1. 1997–2005. DECMP began studying horseshoe crab egg densities for a variety

of objectives related to coastal management activities and permitting issues.

2. 2005. DDFW initiated the Delaware portion of a bay-wide horseshoe crab egg survey.

Land acquisition:

1. Acquisition of former Lighthouse Restaurant facility in Mispillion Harbor to create the DuPont Nature Center, an interpretive and research center for horseshoe crab and shorebird outreach, education and viewing opportunities. Facility opened spring 2007.

2. Acquisition of approximately 28 ha of marsh and dunes in Mispillion Harbor, purchased by DNREC from the Conservation Fund in July 2006 for the purpose of protecting prime horseshoe spawning and shorebird feeding areas. This acquisition, along with the DuPont Nature Center and additional surrounding state wildlife area lands, comprise the Mispillion Harbor Reserve.

United States — New York

Jamaica Bay has been designated and mapped as an otherwise protected beach unit pursuant to the federal Coastal Barrier Resources Act, prohibiting incompatible federal financial assistance or flood insurance within the unit. The New York State Natural Heritage Program, in conjunction with TNC, recognizes two priority sites for biodiversity within the Jamaica Bay and Breezy Point habitat complex — Breezy Point (B2, very high biodiversity significance) and Fountain Avenue landfill (B3, high biodiversity significance). Jamaica Bay and Breezy Point have been designated as significant coastal fish and wildlife habitats by the New York State Department of State, and the bay up to the high-tide line was designated as a critical environmental area by the New York State Department of Environmental Conservation. Jamaica Bay was also designated as one of three special natural waterfront areas by New York City's Department of City Planning. A comprehensive watershed management plan for the bay was completed in 1993 by the New York City Department of Environmental Protection in order to better protect and restore habitats and improve water quality. Wetlands are regulated in New York under the state's Freshwater Wetlands Act of 1975 and Tidal Wetlands Act of 1977; these statutes are in addition to federal regulation under section 10 of the Rivers and Harbors Act of 1899, section 404 of the Clean Water Act of 1977, and various executive orders. (http://training.fws.gov/library/pubs5/web_link/text/jb_form.htm).

United States — Connecticut

Connecticut Department of Environmental Protection, Wildlife Division completed a shorebird use assessment as part of the Wildlife Conservation and Restoration Program. This project helped in identifying priority sites for protection.

United States — Rhode Island

Rhode Island has monitored spring and fall passage of shorebirds annually and all important shorebird stopovers are known.

United States — Massachusetts

Currently management and protection plans are in place for some of the important stopover areas in Massachusett federally owned areas, Plum Island (southern three fourths only), Nasuset Coast Guard Beach, South Beach Island (portions) and Monomoy NWR, are currently managed by their respective agencies. Portions of Sandy Neck are managed by TNC. The remainder of the important areas is municipal and/or private land and may or may not be managed. Information on the management and protection status of private and/or municipal-owned important stopover areas was not available at the time of writing.

United States — New Hampshire

No known management of shorebird stopover locations at the time of this writing.

United States — Maine

During the period 1989–1995, the state of Maine began intensive shorebird surveys to locate and designate critical staging areas. These locations have been designated as shorebird areas of management concern and are candidate areas under Maine's Natural Resource Protection Act, which allows the Maine Division of Inland Fisheries and Wildlife to review permits relating to development and dock placement.

Panama

The total number of shorebirds using the upper Panama Bay at some time during the year has been estimated at well over 500,000 qualifying it as a hemispheric reserve of the Western Hemisphere Shorebird Reserve Network (Morrison et al. 1998). Despite this, the site remains unprotected and unmonitored, and only recently the westernmost part (Watts' main study area (Watts 1998) was lost to housing (Buehler 2002).

Canada

Migration staging areas are along coastal areas in Canada and are either federally or provincially owned. The federal government has many tools and programs for nature conservation. These range from outright ownership and management of various types of formal protected areas to the negotiation of voluntary agreements with private landowners. The federal approach to conservation and protection is to combine this range of approaches and partners, using each tool when and where appropriate.

Within the federal government, Environment Canada, the Parks Canada Agency, and Fisheries and Oceans Canada have the mandate to protect critical habitats by managing complementary protected area programs:

1. Environment Canada, directly and/or through partnership arrangements, establishes and manages national wildlife areas, migratory bird sanctuaries and marine wildlife areas to protect wildlife habitat, and unique and productive ecosystems. The first two designations also allow Environment Canada to set up marine protected areas off Canada's shores and along the coasts of inland waters.
2. Fisheries and Oceans Canada has the authority to establish marine protected areas for a variety of purposes, including the conservation and protection of species at risk and their habitats, the conservation and protection of unique habitats, and the conservation and protection of marine areas of high biodiversity or high biological productivity.
3. Parks Canada establishes and manages national parks and national marine conservation areas, which are intended to protect a representative sample of the features of the country's natural regions and marine natural heritage and to provide opportunities for public education and enjoyment.

Finally, the federal government plays a lead role in managing the implementation of international protected areas programs in Canada, including UNESCO biosphere reserves, UNESCO world heritage sites.

Breeding Habitat Management

Nunavut Tunngavik Incorporated (NTI) was set up as a private corporation in 1993 to ensure that promises made in the Nunavut Land Claims Agreement are carried out. The operations of NTI are managed through offices in Iqaluit, Rankin Inlet, Cambridge Bay, and Ottawa. Features of the Nunavut Land Claims agreement include some to the more outstanding of its 41 articles include the title to approximately 350,000 km^2 of land of which about 35,000 km^2 include mineral rights.

Monitoring breeding densities on Arctic breeding area:
1. 1999–2004. NJENSP, the ROM, and Rutgers University instituted a study to relocate Red Knots (outfitted with radio transmitters on the Delaware Bay) on Arctic breeding grounds in 2000, 2001, and 2003, develop a model of potential breeding habitat, and monitor breeding densities on a 10 km^2 study site in Nunavut, Canada. Breeding densities were monitored during June–July of 2000–2004; limited funding in 2005 was dedicated to aerial survey of winter Red Knot population in South America.

Other Management Considerations and Opportunities

Recent research conducted by NJENSP has demonstrated the importance of roosts for migratory shorebirds on Delaware Bay. One series of high tides in late May flooded all available roosting sites on the bay and the entire population of shorebirds moved elsewhere to find safe roosts. NJDFW and DDFW biologists plan to investigate the creation of new roosts sites in Delaware Bay marshes and state and USFWS impoundments.

The biomedical industry could play a major role in supporting survey and monitoring of the horseshoe crab population, and identifying ways to reduce crab mortality through improved monitoring (pre- and post-bleeding) to identifying sources of mortality, subsidize improvements to transport and holding facilities, bleeding methods, and reduction of holding time to reduce mortality.

Long-term research to improve/lower cost of a synthetic test for contaminants in injectable drugs would eliminate the need for horseshoe crabs altogether.

MONITORING EFFECTS AND MANAGEMENT ACTIVITIES

Several very robust methods exist for monitoring the efficacy of conservation action because of the significant amount of work that has already been accomplished by scientists throughout the western Atlantic flyway. In Delaware Bay, the departure mass of Red Knots has been linked to survival rates and would serve as a key indicator of the vitality of the stopover. Weight gain achieved is primarily influenced by the availability of food resources (horseshoe crab eggs) and weight on any particular date is a function of that as well as arrival date and arrival condition. Therefore, these interrelated effects need to be monitored carefully.

A bay-wide survey of crab eggs was implemented in 2004 after 5 yr of similar surveys conducted on the New Jersey side of the bay. Moreover a bay-wide survey of spawning crabs has also been conducted since 1999 and could serve as a useful counterpart to the egg survey. Finally, a count of shorebirds on the bay has been conducted by New Jersey Fish and Wildlife since 1986. The best monitoring tool for the long term is a model based on four main parameters: shorebird numbers, egg densities, crab numbers and departure-weight profiles.

Survival rate is a critical input into long-term modeling of the population. Banding with individually identifiable flags allows for yearly assessment of the survival of birds coming through the Delaware Bay. Ultimately, banding in each of the three major wintering areas, Tierra del Fuego, Maranhão and the southeastern U.S., coupled with stable isotope studies will help distinguish survival rates related to each. A continued focus on resighting flagged birds must be a key element of monitoring, at least until recovery is assured.

With populations of shorebirds and crabs in Delaware Bay at such low levels, departure weights may also be influenced by competition for eggs from other species, particular Laughing Gulls, as well as disturbance especially in areas of high egg density. Therefore, in the short term it will be necessary to monitor disturbance and gull populations as inputs into the model based primarily on the four parameters mentioned above. Ultimately, the model could help decide the size of the horseshoe crab harvest for bait or as a source for lystate that is consistent with maintaining the shorebird population. The goals of management in Delaware Bay should be: (1) that the majority of the Red Knots (>80%) reach a departure weight of at least 185 g by the end of May, and (2) the peak stopover population of Red Knots increase to at least 100,000 as it was in the 1980s.

More comprehensive monitoring of the effect of management on the Red Knot population will come from the continuation of yearly counts in the primary wintering areas. The Patagonia counts have been carried out every year since 2000 allowing direct comparison with the population size at the time of the first comprehensive survey in the mid-1980s. A new count was carried out along the coast of Maranhão, northern Brazil, in February 2005 and if this can be repeated regularly, it too may serve as a useful measure of recovery. The wintering population in the southeastern U.S. must also be monitored with the same intensity as in Patagonia. The Florida Division of Fish and Wildlife intends to restart a coast-wide survey of shorebirds, first conducted in 1996. This survey, or at least that part that relates directly to Red Knots, should be conducted every year.

The population of Red Knots breeding in a study area of 9.2 km^2 on Southampton Island in arctic Canada was surveyed from 2000 to 2004. During this time it fell from about 1–0.3 nests/km^2. No survey was possible in 2005 due to lack of funds. These surveys are logistically challenging and costly and this means that it is difficult to expand them to an area of sufficient size to make year-to-year comparisons statistically robust. However, they would be a useful means of measuring recovery. Therefore, if at all possible they should be continued in order to monitor future change. The nest densities of Red Knots can be compared with those of other species to determine whether population change is likely to be the effect of arctic breeding conditions or factors affecting them elsewhere.

CONSERVATION GOALS AND THE SURVEYS, MONITORING, RESEARCH, AND MANAGEMENT NEEDED TO SUPPORT THEM

Brown et al. (2001) proposes a tentative target for restoration of the C. c. rufa population to 240,000. Though we agree that this would be desirable and would ensure C. c. rufa's future, it does not now seem to be realistic. Moreover, no evidence exists that the population was ever that large. Overall the goal of conservation activities throughout the flyway should be to increase the C. c. rufa population to at least the figure of 25 yr ago of 100,000–150,000 by 2015. Given the uncertain genetic relationships between the three main wintering populations, there should also be a target for each. The following are suggested: (1) Tierra del Fuego wintering population increased to 70,000–80,000 birds, (2) Brazilian wintering population increased to 20,000–25,000, (3) Florida wintering population increased to 20,000–25,000, and (4) other sites increased to 15,000–20,000.

The means whereby such population increases might be achieved include:

1. Recovery and maintenance of Delaware Bay horseshoe crab egg densities at levels sufficient to sustain stopover populations of all shorebirds including 100,000 Red Knots.
   a. Continuation of all current yearly studies of shorebird numbers, weight distribution and rate of mass gain, horseshoe crab numbers, and egg densities.
   b. Development and testing of a predictive model for use by managers to determine the egg densities appropriate to support the existing stopover population and the gradual increase necessary as shorebird numbers recover.
2. By 2008, development of a system for the yearly determination of population demographic status based on survey results, capture data, and re-sightings of banded individuals.
   a. Create a survival and population status model using existing data and updated annually with new data.
   b. Develop annual estimates of productivity and juvenile survival as inputs for population models using the framework established for waterfowl population assessments.
   c. Distinguish the population parameters of each wintering population (Tierra del Fuego, Maranhão, and Florida) based on site-specific banding, re-sightings of marked individuals, and stable isotope analyses.
3. By 2008, determine the genetic and breeding status of the three main wintering populations (Tierra del Fuego, Maranhão, and Florida).
   a. Identify the arctic breeding area associated with each wintering subpopulation.
   b. Determine sub-specific status of each wintering population.
   c. Determine the migration routes used by each wintering population.
4. By 2011, create a hemisphere-wide system of protected areas for each significant wintering, stopover and breeding area.
5. By 2009, complete site assessment, using Western Hemisphere Shorebird Reserve Network (WHSRN) site assessment tools, for Bahia Lomas, Rio Grande, San Antonio Oeste, Lagoa do Piexe, Maranhão, the west coast of Florida, the Altamaha Region of Georgia, the Virginia Barrier Islands, Delaware Bay, Stone Harbor Point, James Bay, Southampton Island, and King William Island.

   a. Development management plans and integrate them into local and national conservation systems.
   b. Identify survey and research needs for each site.
6. By 2008, identify all important breeding locations in Canada, and recommend protection needs for the top ten sites.
   a. Use radio telemetry to determine the arctic breeding areas of each winter populations (Florida, northern Brazil, and Tierra del Fuego).
   b. Use GIS to determine suitable breeding habitat and extent of important breeding areas.
   c. Formulate recommendations to national governments on protection designations for most important breeding areas.
7. By 2009, delineate and propose protection measures for key habitats within the main wintering areas of Maranhão, Tierra del Fuego, and Florida, and develop management plans to guide protection.
   a. Conduct intensive surveys and determine areas of greatest importance within each site.
   b. Create maps of each site and determine chief threats and management needs using WHSRN site-assessment tools.
   c. In conjunction with national and local government agencies, create management plans for each wintering area that identify actions necessary to improve conditions and protect sites.
   d. Conduct site-specific research necessary to determine important-use areas as well as existing and emerging threats.
8. Carry out studies of food resources and studies of habitat use using radio telemetry.
9. Determine key southbound and northbound stopovers that account for at least 80% of stopover areas supporting at least 100 Red Knots, and develop coastwide surveillance of birds as they migrate.
   a. Set up survey, re-sighting, and banding programs to determine importance of individual stopovers relevant to associated wintering and breeding areas in places other than the Delaware Bay, including James Bay, the Mingan Islands in the Gulf of St Lawrence, at least two sites each in New Jersey, Virginia, South Carolina, Georgia, Maranhão, Brazil, and Patagonia, Argentina.
   b. Use WHSRN site-assessment tools to determine threats and management

needs at each site and develop a plan to meet them.

10. Control impact of disturbance at all stop-overs and wintering areas, particularly in high-importance, high-disturbance areas like Delaware Bay and the west coast of Florida
   a. Identify, through site-assessment tools, all sites where human use is impacting birds by preventing access to key resources and/or roost sites
   b. Restrict access to all beaches using methods developed in Delaware Bay as outlined in this report.

SURVEY NEEDS

To effectively manage the Red Knot population, it is necessary to undertake regular assessment of numbers, demographic rates and conditions in wintering, and staging and breeding areas. A comprehensive and integrated monitoring program is necessary, not only to monitor the status of the populations but also for the objective assessment of the results of any management actions undertaken as a result of this review and further research.

South America – overall

Red Knots use South America both for locations to spend the northern winter and for stopover sites to and from the breeding areas. During northward migration, passage through Peninsula Valdés, Patagonia, Argentina, has become later since year 2000 (Bala et al. 2005). This may have led the number of Tierra del Fuego birds arriving late into Delaware Bay to have increased and some evidence shows this for 2000, 2001, and 2003 (Baker et al. 2004; K. Clark, unpubl. data). Any such late arriving birds will be at a lower weight compared with those that arrived earlier and Baker et al. (2004) has shown that low mass birds in Delaware Bay subsequently have a lower resighting rate throughout the flyway, implying lower survival. Therefore, further investigation is required to determine the reasons why northward passage has become later. This should focus particularly on the food resources used in South America, especially in Chile, Argentina, and Brazil. More specific needs are detailed below.

Very little is known about the distribution of juvenile Red Knots during their first northern winter apart from the fact that most do not go as far south as the main wintering area of the adults in Tierra del Fuego. It should be a priority to determine their distribution and

monitor their survival as well as year-to-year changes in their numbers as a measure of breeding productivity.

South America – Argentina

Counts of and resighting of individually marked Red Knots at Rio Grande, Tierra del Fuego to increase the precision of annual survival and recruitment estimates specifically of the *C. c. rufa* population, and to allow the estimation of specific locality-survival-resighting parameters with multi-state models are needed. Training of more local biologists and shorebird rangers at key sites is needed.

South America – Chile

Aerial surveys of Bahia Lomas and surrounding areas have provided the best estimate of the change in the *C. c. rufa* population and these should continue. Studies on population dynamics of the wintering population (i.e., monitoring survival and recruitment through marking and subsequent resighting of individually marked birds) are needed because this area represents the largest known wintering concentration of *C. c. rufa*. Given the delayed northward migration through Patagonia and its implications, studies of any interactions of Red Knots with other migrant and non-migrant species, and use of the Bahia Lomas by all these birds as a foraging ground will determine whether this is caused by lack of food supplies on the non-breeding grounds.

South America – Brazil

How Red Knots use Brazil as a wintering and staging area is one of the largest unknowns in their life cycle. Basic count and distribution information is needed before more detailed studies can be designed:

1. Aerial surveys on the Amazon coast, especially the coast of the state of Maranhão, during migration (boreal and austral), as well as during wintering seasons.
2. Ground surveys on the Río Grande do Sul coast during the migrations.
3. Aerial survey on the Amapá and Pará coast when Red Knots are wintering in Maranhão.
4. Establish to what extent the Pantanal is used as a stopover site during northward and southward migration using aerial and/or ground surveys (April and end of September to first week of October).

Caribbean countries and northern South America

Because feather isotope studies suggest that a substantial number of birds winter in an unidentified area, clarification of the status and numbers wintering around the Caribbean and less known parts of northern South America is necessary. This unidentified area may be within Brazil but other likely areas include the Gulf of Maricaibo where high hundreds were found during an early March survey in the early 1980s.

Mexico

Confirmation of numbers and subspecific status of Red Knots wintering and staging on both the east and west coasts is needed. Birds wintering on the east coast may be *C. c. rufa,* those on the west coast, *C. c. roselaari*

United States — Delaware Bay

Cross-bay commuting for the whole 12–14 d stopover is equivalent in distance to almost half of the flight to the arctic breeding grounds. This is an energetic cost the birds can ill afford at a time when they are under pressure to reach the breeding grounds. Continued surveys of the Hereford Inlet roosting site are warranted to help evaluate roost site management and improvement. Roost sites in Delaware should be identified and surveyed to monitor management actions.

United States — Virginia

Systematic resighting survey efforts should be conducted in conjunction with daily counts of Red Knots using the barrier islands during spring migration, April through early June.

United States — North Carolina, South Carolina, Georgia, and Florida

1. The survey of wintering Red Knot numbers in southeastern U.S. needs to be expanded with an annual winter aerial survey of appropriate coasts including the west coast of Florida, and the Atlantic coasts of Georgia, South Carolina, and Florida. Early January would be best because that is when annual ground-based counts are traditionally carried out in Georgia. Determining the size of the population wintering in the southeastern U.S. is seen as a high priority. It is particularly important that surveys aimed at achieving this are coordinated, time-constricted, and wide-ranging in view of the apparent mobility of this population.

Ideally aerial counts should be combined with ground counts.

2. Statewide surveys of Red Knots are needed to document important areas, habitats and timing of migration. Surveys would include color-band resightings. These states should participate in ISS surveys that have long-term data sets.

United States — Alaska

Spring aerial or ground surveys are needed in the major spring staging areas to compare with previous counts which may no longer reflect the current situation. Ground-based searching for color-marked birds to determine which wintering populations these birds come from is a major objective. This could be particularly productive in view of the large numbers of Red Knots that are currently marked in the western Atlantic and east Asian–Australasian flyways.

United States — California

Statewide surveys need to be carried out to update counts of wintering and staging Red Knots in California.

United States — Washington

Regular monitoring of the Red Knot is needed on spring passage through areas such as Westport and Gray's Harbor.

MONITORING — NEEDS

Overall

1. Monitoring is essential to objectively determine trends in numbers, survival and recruitment to the Red Knot population on an annual basis. Because several separate, apparently isolated populations exist, it is important to focus attention on wintering areas (i.e., the discrete wintering populations) as well as staging sites such as Delaware Bay.

2. It is important to continue to individually color-mark samples from all populations (Florida, Georgia, Carolinas, Northern Brazil, and Tierra del Fuego). Comparison of the proportions of birds from each wintering and migration site will facilitate a clear understanding of the migration routes and breeding areas of each population. Without this information it will be impossible to monitor the success

of conservation actions throughout the flyway.

3. Considerable effort is needed in all major sites to locate individually marked birds to determine which populations use which sites.

4. Other wintering sites need to be investigated to locate the wintering location of the group identified by their isotope signatures as being from an unknown wintering area.

5. To ensure that conservation action is focused on reversing the declines observed, it is vital that we identify all migration stopover sites that are used by the species on a regular basis. Identification of individually marked birds will enable conservation effort to be focused on those sites that hold the highest proportion of birds from groups that are known to be in greatest decline. Catching samples at these sites and individually marking (and taking a feather for isotope analyses) may also help in identifying the location of the unknown group.

6. Autumn monitoring of return rates and juvenile abundance should be developed further to increase our understanding of breeding success and how it feeds through into recruitment into the breeding population monitored in spring in Delaware Bay.

South America – Argentina

1. Continue the long-term monitoring programs and management plan development already in place.

2. Continue to catch and mark Red Knots as individuals. Collect blood samples from a sample of birds to monitor parasite levels, collect a feather from a sample of birds to maintain a current up-to-date isotopic signature for wintering areas.

3. Resight individually marked Red Knots to increase the precision of annual survival and recruitment estimates, and to allow the estimation of specific locality-survival-resighting parameters.

4. Monitor food sources at Argentinian wintering and staging areas to investigate the cause behind the delayed northward migration reported by Bala et al. (2005).

South America – Chile

1. Constantly monitor abundance, both aerial and terrestrial, during every season of the year, especially during the key arrival and departure periods.

2. Continue to catch and mark Red Knots as individuals. Collect blood samples from a sample of birds to monitor parasite levels, collect a feather from a sample of birds to maintain a current up-to-date isotopic signature for wintering areas.

3. Resight individually marked Red Knots to increase the precision of annual survival and recruitment estimates, and to allow the estimation of specific locality-survival-resighting parameters.

4. Continue with, and develop, the benthic invertebrate sampling program at Bahía Lomas to investigate the cause behind the delayed northward migration reported by Bala et al. (2005).

South America – Brazil

1. Monitor Red Knots on the coast of Maranhão during passage and winter (September to May).
   a. Capture Red Knots using cannon and mist nets and individually mark them.
   b. Attach radio transmitters in May to determine date of arrival in Delaware Bay.
   c. Gather biometric data (molt, age, sex, ectoparasites load, feathers for stable isotope analysis, blood samples for studies of genetic variability, and disease data such as West Nile virus, avian influenza, etc.).
   d. Search for individually marked birds to increase the precision of annual survival and recruitment estimates, and to allow the estimation of specific locality-survival-resighting parameters.
   e. Initiate a benthic invertebrate sampling program to determine whether the later northward passage is due to poor food supplies farther south.

2. Create a field station in the municipality of Cururupu for supporting field work in Maranhão.

3. Monitor Red Knots and their food supplies in Lagoa do Peixe National Park during September, October, April, and May using the same methods as described above.

4. Publish literature and give talks about the conservation importance of the Red Knot and the activities mentioned above for local communities and the authorities responsible for land management (IBAMA, Government of the States of Maranhão and Río Grande do Sul).

5. Monitor shorebird species in the Pantanal (Río Negro) during northward and southward migration.

United States—Delaware Bay

1. Monitor survival and recruitment of different sub-populations of Red Knots. In order to fill in the gaps in knowledge that have been identified in this status review, regular samples of Red Knots need to be caught throughout the spring season at a range of locations. Each bird should be individually color-marked, a primary covert taken (for isotope analysis to identify wintering area) along with full biometrics including weight. The level of the catching should be minimized, consistent with keeping enough individually color-marked birds in the population to assess survival rates of the different populations coming through the bay and sufficient to allow Pradel modeling of recruitment rates.

2. Undertake a program of daily counts and resightings each spring in Delaware Bay to estimate the total number of birds of each wintering population passing through the bay.

3. Continue the aerial survey during May and early June using consistent methods to ensure the long-term data set is maintained.

4. Continue the various horseshoe crab monitoring programs, specifically the Delaware Bay spawner survey and Delaware Bay egg abundance survey, both of which need support and provide critical data.

5. Continue fall ground-based shorebird counts, especially in the Atlantic coast of New Jersey.

6. Monitor site use through aerial and ground surveys. Bay-wide radio tracking should be further evaluated for its application to monitor and track changes in site use patterns. These data in combination with other site-specific data should be used to determine site-specific management actions.

United States—Virginia

1. Regularly count and resight banded birds to investigate arrival date, departure date, and residence time of Red Knots using the barrier islands during spring migration.

2. Assess the body condition of Red Knots upon arrival and also at the time of departure in order to determine whether they are able to fly direct to the Arctic or may need to stop over further north, such as in Delaware Bay.

3. Determine food supplies available at the main staging sites.

United States—North Carolina and South Carolina

Cannon net flocks and mark individuals during winter and passage periods to determine how these birds use the Florida and Georgia wintering areas and Delaware Bay in spring.

United States—Florida and Georgia

1. Catch birds using cannon and/or mist nets and mark as individuals using coded flags in winter.

2. Collect biometric data and details of molt, age, sex, and ectoparasites; collect feathers for stable isotopic analysis and blood samples for studies of genetic variability.

3. Resight individually marked Red Knots to increase the precision of annual survival and recruitment estimates, and to allow the estimation of specific locality-survival-resighting parameters.

United States—other sites on the United States East Coast

Search for and monitor other potentially important stopover sites for Red Knots along the U.S. East Coast, such as Jamaica Bay, New York.

Arctic—Canada and Alaska

Marking Red Knots in the Arctic will be incredibly valuable for understanding the migration routes. Feather samples need to be taken to obtain isotope signatures of their wintering areas. This is extremely difficult as the birds are highly dispersed but even small samples of individually marked birds can be extremely valuable as resighting rates are >50%.

If sites are located where adults congregate even in small numbers on arrival in the Arctic or before departure, effort should be put into increasing the samples of birds from the Arctic. It would be of particular value to mark samples of birds in Alaska in order to identify their wintering areas, as resighting effort in some known wintering areas is quite high.

RESEARCH NEEDS

Several key gaps exist in our knowledge of the Red Knot's life cycle in the Americas. Some relate to specific sites or countries while others can only be addressed by broad-scale coordinated research throughout one or more of the major flyways.

Broad-scale research topics

1. Good evidence from feather isotope studies shows that birds from different wintering areas use the foraging resources of Delaware Bay in different ways. New Jersey-banded Red Knots (based on resightings and isotope signatures) are being found in the southeastern U.S. more frequently than Delaware-banded Red Knots, particularly those feeding on mussel spat on the Atlantic coast of New Jersey adjacent to Delaware Bay. Collection of these data should be amplified by expansion of individual marking efforts in Tierra del Fuego and in the northern Brazil and southeastern U.S. migration and wintering areas and intensified searches for them on Delaware Bay. In addition, a well designed radio-tracking program could be used to establish whether Red Knots from the various wintering areas use Delaware Bay in the same way with respect to foraging activities. The focus for radio tracking of Red Knots from the U.S. wintering areas should be on migrants during April in South Carolina. In view of this apparent difference in usage, efforts should be made to improve conditions across the Delaware Bay, rather than just in a few hotspots.

2. About 20% of the Red Knots passing through Delaware Bay have isotope signatures not compatible with known molting areas—where do these birds molt? Currently, the non-breeding distribution of northern wintering Red Knots is not well known. The group of Red Knots that winters in the Northern Hemisphere may now comprise as much as half of the Red Knots passing through Delaware Bay during northward migration. This is a dramatically higher proportion than was estimated to have been the case in the middle 1980s. One possible cause of this change is that the Patagonian-wintering Red Knots have shown a major decline since the 1980s, whereas the northern-wintering group has not declined. If so, the health of the Red Knot population passing through Delaware Bay may substantially depend on the continued well-being of the northern wintering group.

3. Although it is clear that some of this group winters in the southeastern U.S. (coasts of South Carolina, Georgia, and the gulf coast of Florida), it is possible that substantial numbers also use other major wintering areas. The individual

marking and scanning of Red Knots from this group will be valuable at key migration staging sites during southward migration, especially at Cape Cod, Massachusetts, and the Altamaha River Estuary, Georgia, as well as during winter and in March and April on the coasts of South Carolina, Georgia, and the gulf coast of Florida. In combination with counts, such a banding-scanning effort should yield a much better idea of the size of the northern-wintering group, an improved understanding of its migration strategies as well as a clearer understanding of the relationships between the U.S.-wintering Red Knots and those that spend winter on the coast of northern Brazil.

4. There is a need for a better understanding of Patagonian-wintering Red Knots and their food supplies. Numbers at Bahía Lomas have declined dramatically since 2000, whereas those at Río Grande have not. This suggests that the cause of the recent decline may originate at Bahía Lomas. Birds from both wintering sites pass through Delaware Bay, so both populations should have decreased if the environment of Delaware Bay is the root cause of the overall decline in the Red Knot population. Evidence also shows that the northerly wintering populations (southeastern U.S. and northen Brazil), of which some birds pass through Delaware Bay, have not undergone the catastrophic decline observed in Tierra del Fuego. Individual color marking and resighting can be used to determine whether there is any difference between the survival of birds from Bahía Lomas and Río Grande. Consistent monitoring of Red Knots and their food resources at Bahía Lomas and other wintering areas is also required. This should include regular (e.g., monthly) counts to determine whether Red Knot numbers change during the season, monitoring body condition (e.g., plumage oiling, ectoparasites and general health, molt, and mass), and regular sampling of food resources. This work might be promoted through the formation and funding of a Chile–Argentina working group.

5. Feather isotope studies indicated that in 2003–2005, a third to a half of the Red Knots passing through Delaware Bay were from northerly wintering areas. As far as it is possible to ascertain, a dramatic decline amongst these birds has not occurred since 2000. In spring

2004, turnover and isotope studies indicated that 24,000 birds passed through Delaware Bay, 12,000 from each population (Gillings et al. 2007).

6. Although 31,568 birds were counted in southern South America in January 2004 (Fig. 31), it is apparent that many did not pass through Delaware Bay on northward migration that year. In January 2005, the southern wintering count dropped to 17,653, indicating a major decline. If this dramatic population change was due to mortality solely caused by changes in conditions in Delaware Bay then most if not all of the 12,000 southern South American Red Knots passing through Delaware Bay in May 2004 must have died. Annual survival rates of the Tierra del Fuego population averaged only 56% during 1999–2001 (Baker et al. 2004), and little different at around 60% in 2004 and 2005. This indicates that major problems may be occurring for Red Knots in the wintering or staging grounds, and this may be a reason for some of the later arriving birds into Delaware Bay. Studies aimed at understanding why numbers have dropped at Bahía Lomas and at other traditional wintering sites in southern South America are urgently needed. Although the decline in Bahía Lomas suggests problems in the wintering areas, an alternative explanation is that birds are facing problems at staging areas farther north in South America. One possibility is that they are affected by ectoparasite infestation as found in the Maranhão, Brazil, wintering area in February 2005 (Baker et al. 2005a) and among birds from each of the three wintering areas passing through Delaware Bay in the springs of 2004 and 2005. Because very little is known about conditions at several staging sites in South America, exploration of this part of the life cycle is a priority.

7. As discussed in the taxonomy section of this review, a great deal of uncertainty exists about the subspecific status of Red Knots wintering in southern South America, in comparison with those in Maranhão, in the southeastern U.S., on the Northern Hemisphere Pacific coast (San Francisco Bay, Mexico (Baja California, and Sonora-Sinaloa), and on the Pacific coast of Chile. Genetic and isotopic studies need to be continued and expanded. In view of numbers claimed for Alaska, it is possible that populations wintering in Mexico and on the west coast of South America are higher than currently thought. Surveys of Mexican Red Knot populations should be expanded. This might be achieved as part of the annual January winter waterfowl surveys conducted jointly by the U.S. and Mexico.

8. Breeding productivity is a major unknown — monitoring it might help with understanding the impact of depleted food resources in Delaware Bay as well as allowing full demographic modeling. It is argued that Red Knots unable to secure adequate resources on Delaware Bay have lower survival. It should follow that they also have lower breeding productivity. Given the difficulty of measuring breeding success in sufficient representative areas of the nesting grounds, the most practical option would seem to be counting juveniles during southward migration and possibly also in the wintering areas. This might be achieved using volunteer surveys. Participation in the collection of juvenile/adult ratios during the ISS has been low, but appropriate training could change this and increase participation in age-monitoring.

Country-specific research needs — Argentina

1. Conduct trophic ecology studies at San Antonio Oeste, the key site hosting highest numbers of Red Knots in Argentina, to determine whether food supplies at this site limit the pace or timing of migration.
2. Monitor food supplies at Río Grande and movements between nearby Bahía Lomas.
3. Continue individually marking birds with coded flags and resighting individually marked birds to allow analyses of site and population specific survival and recruitment rates.
4. Collect a sample of primary covert feathers each year to maintain a current isotopic signature for each major wintering site.

Country-specific research needs — Chile

1. Study geomorphology of the intertidal ecosystem, floristic analysis of the palustrine and steppe communities, and ecosystem ecology.
2. Study population dynamics of the wintering Red Knot population and interaction with local species and other Nearctic visitors, and use of the bay by all these birds as a foraging ground including regular surveys of benthic invertebrates.

3. Continue individually marking birds with coded flags and resighting individually marked birds to allow analyses of site and population specific survival and recruitment rates.
4. Collect a sample of primary covert feathers each year to maintain a current isotopic signature for each major wintering site.

Country-specific research needs – Brazil

1. Study how birds use staging sites in Brazil—one of the greatest unknowns in the life cycle of the Red Knot wintering in Chile and Argentina. Research into this aspect is urgently needed to determine whether problems affecting sites in Brazil are the cause of birds arriving late into Delaware Bay. This will require the development of studies on foraging ecology and food availability in Maranhão and Lagoa do Peixe National Park.
2. Study potential impact of disease (West Nile virus, avian influenza, Newcastle virus, etc.).
3. Study ectoparasite infection during winter and also during different stages of migration, especially in Maranhão.

Country-specific research needs Mexico

1. Clarify the status and number of Red Knots wintering in Baja California, and Sonora-Sinaloa.
2. Collect a sample of primary covert feathers to obtain a current isotopic signature for comparison with passage birds in Delaware and also other wintering sites.
3. Initiate marking programs in conjunction with other Red Knot biologists.
4. Collect genetic material to determine affinity of these populations with others.

Country-specific research needs – United States

New Jersey and Delaware:
1. Horseshoe crab egg data and shorebird behavior need to be integrated into a model that can predict the numbers of eggs needed by shorebirds. From this, an estimate of the density of eggs required to support present and future numbers of shorebirds can be calculated. This can be used as one benchmark against which to determine whether Delaware Bay is in a satisfactory condition for shorebirds and provides an easily collected metric against which to assess the impacts of

management actions. The changes in food supply are thought to be the main reason for the decline in birds in Delaware Bay, but it is also important to determine the importance of changes in gull numbers and human disturbance (including at roost sites) on the stopover birds. The behavior-based individuals models (Stillman et al. 2003) are suitable for this situation, and steps need to be taken to integrate the existing egg density and bird-behavioral data into a comprehensive model. Much of the data required for the models exist, but they still need to be integrated.
2. Modeling food availability to Red Knots in Delaware Bay will need bay-wide egg data and an understanding of the conditions under which the egg supply in the top 5 cm of sand (and therefore potentially available to Red Knots) increases and decreases. These data can then be used for determining the minimum level of the crab population necessary to produce a sustainable food resource for the birds. These data are also needed to fully parameterize the CEH individual based population model and use it to predict the quantity of eggs that need to be on the beaches for current shorebird populations and for future populations if they recover from the declines of the last two decades.
3. Studies that determine the level of harvest that will ensure enough eggs for migratory shorebirds are essential. Horseshoe crabs do not breed until they are about 8 yr old and the demographic structure of the population, especially immature survival, is only partly understood.
Virginia:
1. Investigation of which prey Red Knots are targeting on the Virginia barrier islands is needed with specific attention paid to identifying the availability of prey on peat banks versus high energy beaches and the relative importance of each to migrating Red Knots.
North Carolina:
1. Conduct research on impacts of beach stabilization and impacts of human disturbance.
South Carolina:
1. Develop a South Carolina Department of Natural Resources web site with information on the status, management, and natural history of Red Knots in South Carolina. Work with public and private land managers to protect areas identified as important Red Knot roost sites. Obtain

travel money to participate in Red Knot working groups.

Massachusetts:

1. Conduct research and monitoring of human disturbance in shorebird habitats, particularly those disturbances associated with commercial and recreational fishing and public access to beaches.
2. Monitor recruitment through observations of juveniles during fall migration.

MANAGEMENT NEEDS

The management needs presented in this section are preliminary and largely based on work described in more detail in previous sections. As nearly all management work focused on Red Knot occurs in the area of the Delaware Bay, management needs in other locations will only be determined after preliminary survey and research is complete. However, the experiences of conserving the Delaware Bay stopover, as well as work in Patagonian wintering areas, provide general management needs:

1. On the Delaware Bay, recover and maintain horseshoe crab egg densities at levels sufficient to maintain a stopover population of Red Knots of >100,000 birds.
2. Control impacts of disturbance at all stopovers and wintering areas where appropriate. This is especially important at key stopovers like Delaware Bay, but applies to the many Atlantic coast stopovers that occur in both spring and fall. This would include use restrictions and outreach programs.
3. Create an oil-spill response plan for key stopovers and wintering areas.
4. Maintain precise GIS maps of important use areas in each stopover and on wintering areas.
5. Ensure that all major stopover and wintering areas are recognized in protection initiatives such as WHSRN, International Association of Fish and Wildlife Agency's expanded flyway system, and Ramsar.
6. Avoid impacts of beach replenishment through timing restrictions, and specifications on beach fill to ensure quick recovery of beach invertebrates and horseshoe crab spawning in the Delaware Bay.
7. Clean up and restore all beaches on the Delaware Bay that include any structures impeding crab spawning such as bulkheads, homes, or rip rap. Avoid the placement of any new structures. The cross-bay commuting of Red Knots from feeding sites in Delaware to roosting sites on the Atlantic coast of New Jersey for the whole 14-d stopover is equivalent in distance to almost half the flight to the arctic breeding grounds. In energetic terms, the daily flight involves expenditure of about 83 kJ, which would require the ingestion of about 6,000 horseshoe crab eggs (H. P. Sitters, unpubl. data). Conservation management prescriptions should therefore include ensuring the existence of suitable roosting sites for Red Knots at various locations throughout the bay, especially in Delaware where steps should be taken to conserve the known inland roosting site near Mispillion Harbor. Coastal impoundments should be managed to maximize their potential use as Red Knot roosting sites, or sites created by building isolated sandbars or islands along the shore (such as beside the jetty protecting Mispillion Harbor where suitable high water roosting islands once existed but have since eroded away).

UPDATE TO THE STATUS OF THE RED KNOT (*CALIDRIS CANUTUS*) IN THE WESTERN HEMISPHERE, FEBRUARY 2008

Previous sections of this volume (referred to below as the original review) were based on data available as of June 2006. Since then important new information has become available and is presented in this section based on data and analyses available in February 2008.

Recent information suggests that the population of *Calidris canutus roselaari*, which breeds in Alaska and on Wrangel Island and migrates along the American Pacific coast, may be even more threatened than *C. c. rufa*. Therefore, in this update we give equal emphasis to both subspecies.

TAXONOMIC STATUS

According to the original review, Red Knots wintering in Tierra del Fuego are *C. c. rufa*, but the subspecific status of those wintering in Florida and in Maranhão (Brazil) is uncertain and either or both could be partly or wholly *C. c. rufa* or *C. c. roselaari*.

The original review includes the following statement which has been misinterpreted as meaning that the wintering populations of Florida and Tierra del Fuego are genetically distinct: "Despite the lack of fixed genetic differences among subspecies, the population divergence time of the Red Knots that winter in the southeast of the U.S. (presumed to be *C. c. roselaari*) and those that winter in Tierra del Fuego (*C. c. rufa*) is estimated to be about 1,200 yr ago (Buehler and Baker 2005). Therefore, these populations have not been exchanging a significant number of individuals per generation for a long time, and clearly are independent units for conservation." That statement was made on the assumption that the Red Knots that winter in the southeastern U.S. <u>are</u> *C. c. roselaari*. Therefore, the genetic distinction refers to that between known *C. c. roselaari* from Alaska and known *C. c. rufa* from Tierra del Fuego. To date, no evidence exists of any genetic distinction between Red Knots from the wintering populations of the southeastern U.S., Maranhão, and Tierra del Fuego. Considerable evidence does show little or no interchange between these populations, that they have distinct migrations and ecological scheduling, and they behave as distinct biogeographic populations.

In October 2007, a Red Knot was seen at Guerrero Negro, Baja California, Mexico that had been marked as a breeding adult on Wrangel Island, Russia, during the summer of 2007 (P. S. Tomkovich et al., pers. comm.) and two Red Knots were seen at Guerrero Negro that had been marked on migration through the Yukon-Kuskokwim Delta, Alaska, in May 2006 (P. S. Tomkovich et al., pers. comm.) These observations confirm that Red Knots found on the Pacific coast of North America are of the *C. c. roselaari* subspecies which breeds in Alaska and on Wrangel Island (Tomkovich 1992).

In October 2006, 162 Red Knots were caught and measured at Guerrero Negro (R. Carmona, unpubl. data). These birds, which have not yet been sexed, had longer bill-lengths ($\bar{x}$ = 37.07 mm, 95% CI = 0.27) than males from the winter populations of Maranhão, Florida, and Tierra del Fuego, and also longer than Tierra del Fuego females (Fig. 4). So, unless most or all of the Mexican birds were females (which would seem unlikely), it would appear that *C. c. roselaari* are larger than the Red Knots wintering in Florida, Maranhão, and Tierra del Fuego and therefore larger than *C. c. rufa*.

Current scientific opinion, as expressed in a paper submitted to *Bioscience* on 23 December 2007 by L. J. Niles et al. (including most of the authors of this volume) is that the Florida and Maranhão populations are believed to be *C. c. rufa* (as well as the population of Tierra del Fuego). However, the three wintering populations do show morphological, particularly size, differences, with Tierra del Fuego birds being significantly smaller than those from Maranhão or Florida (Fig. 4). This may suggest that they have discrete breeding areas. However, as yet no proof of this exists (despite unsuccessful efforts to determine the status of Red Knots that breed on Victoria Island during summer 2007). While breeding areas may not currently be clearly delineated, it is important to recognize that the three populations are biogeographically distinct.

POPULATION STATUS OF *CALIDRIS CANUTUS ROSELAARI*

According to Brown et al. (2001), the *C. c. roselaari* population was about 150,000 in 2001. This estimate, however, was based on information for 1975–1980 and was, therefore, out of date when the conservation plan was written. Moreover all attempts to assess the size of the *C. c. roselaari* population have been bedeviled by uncertainty as to which passage or wintering population belongs to which subspecies.

C. c. roselaari breeds in west Alaska and on Wrangel Island (Tomkovich 1992) and several population estimates are based on numbers counted in May on Alaskan estuaries, just before the birds disperse to the breeding grounds. These include 110,000 on the Yukon-Kuskokwim Delta (on the west coast of Alaska) in May 1980 and 40,000 on the Copper River Delta (on the south coast) in May 1975 where up to 100,000 have been thought to occur (Morrison et al. 2006). No records of such large numbers are available before 1975–1980 or since or of similar numbers in the passage-winter sites of *C. c. roselaari* further south along the Pacific coast. Morrison et al. (2006) therefore suggest that at least some of the large numbers seen in Alaska are likely to have been *C. c. rogersi* which breeds in east Siberia (more or less due south of Wrangel Island) and winters in east Australia and New Zealand and whose population has been estimated recently at about 90,000 (C. D. T. Minton, unpubl. data). Precisely why *C. c. rogersi* would migrate from Australasia to Siberia via Alaska in 1975–1980 and why they do not appear to do so now (or do so less) is not clear but the possibility cannot be rejected.

The only recent evidence that moderately large numbers may still pass through Alaska is an unpublished report by Pavel Tomkovich and Maksim Dementyev on observations they made in May 2006 on the Tutakoke River in the Yukon-Kuskokwim Delta (Tomkovich and Dementyev 2006). Most of the Red Knots they saw arrived daily from the south and departed northward. The sum of their counts—5,780—was therefore considered to give a reasonably accurate measure of numbers passing through the area. Since they were unable to cover the entire estuary, they were quite sure that not less than 10,000 Red Knots come through the lower Tutakoke River area. Bearing in mind that the Tutakoke River is only one site among several on the Yukon-Kuskokwim Delta, the total passage population could still be quite large.

Evidence of numbers farther south along the American Pacific coast is fragmentary and difficult to interpret but suggests that the population that has never exceeded about 10,000. Page et al. (1999) present summed maximum counts for all sites on the U.S. Pacific coast (except Alaska) for 1988–1995 (fall 7,981; winter 4,813; spring 9,035). However, as these are summed peak counts without reference to date, it is highly likely that many individual birds were counted several times over.

In Washington, passage numbers have declined from a few thousand in the 1980s to peaks of 248 in spring 2006 and 446 in spring 2007 (Buchanan 2006, 2007).

In Baja California, 1,053 were counted at Guerrero Negro in January 1994 (Page et al. 1997), but it was not until recently that relatively larger numbers were recorded there. Carmona et al. (2006) working in the Guerrero Negro area counted 2,907 Red Knots in the saltworks alone in October 2005. Subsequently, 6,458 were counted in the saltworks and the adjoining Guerrero Negro and Ojo de Liebre lagoons in September 2006, 4,595 in December 2006 and 4,647 in April 2007 (R. Carmona, unpubl. data). Whether the recent observations represent a real increase in the population is not clear. It is a remote area and this population could have been overlooked in the past.

Summary

1. *C. c. roselaari* might have declined from 100,000+ to <10,000 if the large numbers reported in Alaska in 1975–1980 were *C. c. roselaari* and did not include substantial numbers of *C. c. rogersi*.
2. Alternatively, *C. c. roselaari* has always had a small population, probably <10,000, and has shown no clear long-term trend. Nevertheless, as a small population (probably less than half that of *C. c. rufa*), it is vulnerable and deserves protection.

POPULATION STATUS OF *CALIDRIS CANUTUS RUFA*

All three of the main wintering populations of *C. c. rufa* have shown substantial declines compared with the numbers reported in the original review (Table 39). From 2004–2005 to 2007–2008, counts were conducted each winter in Tierra del Fuego, Maranhão, and on the west coast of Florida, apart from 2005–2006 and 2007–2008 in Maranhão and 2004–2005 in Florida. If the previous years' counts are used for the missing counts in Maranhão and the succeeding year's count is used for the missing count in Florida (which is the most conservative approach in terms of estimating the scale of the decline), the total wintering population declined from 27,728 to 18,350 (33% or 11% per annum) over the four winters. However, since these wintering groups behave as separate populations, it would be more appropriate from the conservation point of view to consider their status individually.

Tierra del Fuego population

In April 2007, approximately 1,300 dead Red Knots were found on the coast of Uruguay, as described in the following report posted on BirdLife International's website (http://www.birdlife.org/).

Recent unexplained Red Knot die-offs have highlighted further the need for research into the variety of threats afflicting the already declining *C. c. rufa* population. In April 2007, 312 dead *C. c. rufa* were discovered at Playa La Coronilla in southeastern Uruguay and the same day over 1,000 birds were found dead at a second site nearby. Joaquín Aldabe (pers. comm.) suggested a possible connection between harmful algal blooms and the deaths, although additional studies are required in order to fully understand this unexpected event. Aves Uruguay, in connection with other national and international organizations, is already working in the area to establish the possible causes of the casualties and the role

TABLE 39. COUNTS OF RED KNOTS DURING THE NORTHERN WINTERS OF 2004–2005 TO 2007–2008 IN TIERRA DEL FUEGO (ARGENTINA AND CHILE), MARANHÃO (BRAZIL), AND ON THE WEST COAST OF FLORIDA (NC = NO COUNT). WHERE NO COUNT OCCURRED, THE TOTALS ROW USES THE PREVIOUS YEARS' COUNT FOR MARANHÃO AND THE SUCCEEDING YEAR'S COUNT FOR FLORIDA (SEE TEXT).

	2004–2005	2005–2006	2006–2007	2007–2008	Observers
Tierra del Fuego	17,653[a]	17,211[a]	17,316	14,800	R. I. G. Morrison and R. K. Ross
Maranhão	7,575[a]	NC	3,000	NC	I. Serrano
Florida west coast	NC	2,500[a]	1,200	550	L. Niles, A. D. Dey, and R. I. G. Morrison
Total	27,728	26,286	21,516	18,350	

[a] Numbers reported in the original review.

of Uruguay as stopover for the species. The death of more than 1,300 Red Knots in Uruguay is of particular concern because this number represents >6% of the *C. c. rufa* population, all of which winter in southern South America (R. Clay, pers. commun.). The discovery underlines the need to better understand factors which may be affecting the species during migration and on its wintering grounds.

Subsequently, PMG and AB interviewed the people who had found the dead knots and it was established that the count of 312 was accurate but the statement that over 1,000 were found dead at a second site was only a very rough estimate. Therefore, there is some doubt as to the total number of birds affected. However, whatever the number seen, it is likely that more died and were lost (e.g., in the sea or to scavengers).

This appears to have been a one-off event but has similarities to a smaller one mentioned in the Status Review that occurred at Lagoa do Peixe in southern Brazil in 1997.

The January 2008 Tierra del Fuego count of 14,800 was 2,516 or 15% lower than the previous year.

Maranhão population

Baker et al. (2005) counted 7,575 Red Knots from the air along 150 km of the shore of Maranhão, Brazil, in February 2005. A repeat count in December 2006 could only find 3,000 (I. Serrano, unpubl. data).

Florida population

The original review made a very tentative estimate of the size of the Florida population as 7,500 and found no clear evidence of a trend. Counts in the winter of 2005–2006 showed a minimum population of about 4,000 plus another 1,500 scattered along the coasts of Georgia, North and South Carolina, and Virginia (Niles et al. 2006). Of the 4,000 in Florida, 2,500 were found along 300 km of the west coast between Anclote Key and Cape Romano where an estimated 10,000 occurred in the 1980s (Morrison and Harrington 1992) indicating a substantial decline in what used to be the main Florida stronghold. Further counts along this coast show that the numbers wintering in this area declined to 1,200 in 2006–2007 and only 550 in 2007–2008.

Are the counts accurate?

The aerial counting of shorebirds requires skill and rapid assessment. Those involved in

the counts reported here are all highly qualified counters, particularly R. I. G. Morrison and R. K. Ross who are probably the most experienced aerial counters of shorebirds in the world. Morrison and Ross have conducted all of the Tierra del Fuego counts, so the data have all been collected in a consistent manner by the same observers, and Morrison took part in the last Florida count. The remaining counts were conducted by people who have very considerable experience of counting shorebirds on the ground as well as some experience of counting from the air.

In Tierra del Fuego, all potential Red Knot habitat consists of simple linear shorelines leaving little likelihood that any birds will have been overlooked. In comparison, the shores of west Florida and Maranhão are complex and highly fragmented making accurate counting more difficult. To allow for this, aerial coverage in both areas was more extensive and included not only the ocean shore but also a great variety of back bays and channels where Red Knots might possibly occur.

In all three areas when fewer birds were found than in earlier years, searching was intensified. In some cases, repeat flights were made in case birds had been missed; in others the search was extended to marginal habitats to ensure that all locations where knots might possibly be found were covered. Intensified coverage revealed virtually no additional knots.

It is concluded that all of the counts were of sufficient accuracy giving confidence that the trends shown are true and the scale of the declines is correct.

Could the birds have moved elsewhere?

Generally, arctic-breeding shorebirds, including Red Knots, have been found to be highly site-faithful to their wintering grounds. However, changes in wintering site have not infrequently been recorded and have variously been attributed to changes in the availability of food, changes in the risk of predation, loss of habitat, and improved conditions closer to breeding grounds arising from climate change.

We are not aware of any changes to the habitats used by Red Knots in Maranhão or Tierra del Fuego that could have led the birds to winter elsewhere. In Florida, recreational use of the beaches has increased in recent years to such an extent that it could be a factor that has led birds to change site. However, the main sites occupied in 2005–2006 are well within or towards the middle of the 300 km of coast surveyed each year. Therefore if the birds have moved elsewhere, they must have moved a considerable distance. It should be noted that the population of the remainder of the south coast of the U.S. has not been surveyed since 2005 so its recent trend is unknown.

In Tierra del Fuego, all coastlines that have supported Red Knots in the past, and especially the core sites supporting the bulk of the population (Bahia Lomas, Bahia San Sebastian, and Rio Grande) have been surveyed from the air in January in the years 2000–2008. Previously occupied areas on the coast of Patagonia were also surveyed in three separate years, but were found to support few Red Knots (2% of the wintering count) compared to the 1980s (14%), indicating the population is now found almost entirely in the core sites, with few in the more peripheral areas, and with no evidence for any redistribution outside the core region. Moreover, we are in regular contact with shorebird observers in Patagonia and there have been no reports of significant numbers of Red Knots wintering north of Tierra del Fuego in Argentina in 2007–2008, again indicating that no significant redistribution has occurred. With consistent declines observed at all migration areas as well, it is considered extremely unlikely that redistribution could account for the declines observed since 2000.

MASS GAIN IN DELAWARE BAY

At the time the original review was written, it was well understood that the decrease in the food supply of Red Knots in Delaware Bay—horseshoe crab eggs—was strongly implicated in the decline of the *C. c. rufa* population. Baker et al. (2004) showed that Red Knots unable to gain adequate weight in Delaware Bay for onward migration to the arctic breeding grounds had significantly lower survival. Morrison et al. (2007) also showed that body stores were important indicators of survival in *C. c. islandica* populations of Red Knots breeding in the high Arctic. However, the precise impact of reduced numbers of eggs was not clear. In a study of birds trapped twice during a single spring stopover, Atkinson et al. (2006) showed that the earliest arrivals accumulate mass at a relatively low rate (~4 g/day) but later arrivals can catch up lost time and achieve a much higher rate of mass gain (up to 10–15 g/day). New analyses led by Robert A. Robinson (British Trust for Ornithology, presented to a joint meeting of the Horseshoe Crab and Shorebird Technical Committees of the Atlantic States Marine Fisheries Commission in October 2007) have shown that the earliest arrivals have not suffered reduced rates of mass gain. However, the later arrivals that try to catch up lost time, comprising approximately three quarters of the entire stopover population, have

shown a significant year-on-year decline in the rate of mass gain they have achieved over 1998 to 2007. Because lower weight birds have lower survival (Baker et al. 2004), it can be concluded that the reduced availability of crab eggs in Delaware Bay has been a critical factor in the decline of *C. c. rufa* .

As reported in the original review, there has been a tendency for northward passage of knots to be about a week later at three sites in South America. To date no clear evidence has been found (e.g., from the aerial counts) that this has led to later arrival in Delaware Bay. However, if this does occur it will merely exacerbate an already bad situation (more birds will be arriving late and trying to gain mass rapidly on inadequate food supplies).

HORSESHOE CRABS AND THEIR EGGS IN DELAWARE BAY

Current evidence suggests that the horseshoe crab population of Delaware Bay has stabilized following the major decline documented in the original review. From the birds' perspective, the key factor in being able to acquire adequate body reserves for onward migration is the density of available eggs. This has shown no significant change over 2000–2007 (though over 2005–2007 it declined; Table 40). Similarly, the number of spawning female crabs has shown no significant trend over 1999–2007; however, the number of breeding males has increased (Table 2). The increase in males might be an indication that the population is on the brink of recovery; however, it is females that lay eggs, so an increase in male crabs is largely irrelevant to the birds. More encouraging however, is a sharp 7–10-fold increase in 2006 and 2007 in the number of crabs recorded by the Delaware Division of Fish and Wildlife's trawl survey (Table 40; Michels et al. 2008). Presumably the increase relates largely to males and/or immature individuals because the number of spawning females has not yet increased. Nevertheless, this might be a welcome indication that the population is starting to recover. However, this evidence should be treated with great caution because the sharp increase recorded by the Delaware trawl in 2006 was not corroborated by the offshore trawl survey conducted by the Horseshoe Crab Research Center (D. Hata, unpubl. data) which recorded a much lower and non-significant increase (2.5–3.0; Table 40).

In summary, recovery in the horseshoe crab population might possibly be starting in response to harvest restrictions, but the evidence is far from clear and, even if it is starting

TABLE 40. POPULATION PARAMETERS OF HORSESHOE CRABS IN DELAWARE BAY FOR 2004–2007.

	2004	2005	2006	2007	Trend	Source
Spawning female (index)	0.77	0.82	0.99	0.89	None[c]	S. Michels et al. (unpubl. data).
Spawning males (index)	2.93	3.23	3.99	4.22	Increase[c]	Michels et al. (unpubl data).
Egg density New Jersey (index)[a]	61	100	49	29	None[d]	NJDFW (unpubl. data.)
Egg density Delaware (index)[a]	No survey	100	73	76	None	DDFW (unpubl. data).
Delaware Trawl Survey (geometric mean)[b]	0.059	0.203	1.372	1.617[e]	Increase	S.F. Michels (pers. comm.).
Offshore trawl core area multiparous females (stratified mean catch/tow)	8.2	10.7	24.6	29.1	Increase	D. Hata (unpubl. data).
Offshore trawl peripheral area multiparous females (stratified mean catch/tow)	3.2	2.8	5.5	2.8	None	D. Hata (unpubl. data)

[a] In top 5 cm of sand, 2005 = 100 .
[b] Data relate to trawls during April–July.
[c] Trend relates to 1999–2007.
[d] Trend relates to 2000–2007; over 2005–2007, the trend is a decline.
[e] The Delaware trawl figure for 2007 is provisional.

it has not yet led to an increase in the number of spawning female crabs or eggs for the birds.

We emphasize that the scale of recovery of the horseshoe crab population needed to sustain the Delaware Bay shorebird stopover is an order of magnitude increase to the levels of the early 1990s, not just an improvement in current numbers.

In the course of preparing this update we realized that from 2005 to 2007, surveys of horseshoe crab eggs have shown much higher densities in Delaware than in New Jersey, though percentage change from year to year is not dissimilar (Table 41; compare with index in Table 40). This is thought to be a sampling problem which does not reflect a systematic difference in egg densities between the two states.

All egg surveys have shown considerable heterogeneity with especially high densities in protected bays and creek mouths. One New Jersey data set avoids samples from known hot-spots (Table 41), another includes such sites, but both show much lower densities than the main Delaware data set. The Delaware data include a known hot-spot, Mispillion Harbor, but even if that site is excluded the difference in mean density between New Jersey and Delaware is still very large.

In principle, there is no reason why egg densities in New Jersey and Delaware should be very different because the density of spawning females in the same years has been quite similar with even higher numbers in New Jersey than in Delaware in 2005 and 2006 (Table 41; Michels et al. 2008). We therefore assumed a systematic difference in habitat quality for spawning crabs occurred between the sites sampled in each state. Discussion is currently under way between the New Jersey and Delaware Divisions of Fish and Wildlife with a view to designing a new survey protocol that will facilitate a better comparison of egg densities across Delaware Bay.

RECOMMENDATIONS

1. In 2006, the USFWS decided that listing *C. c. rufa* as threatened or endangered under the Endangered Species Act was justified but was precluded by species with higher conservation priority. That decision was made on the basis of the information contained in the original review. Since then all three of the main wintering populations have shown significant further decline. Therefore, the

TABLE 41. DENSITY OF HORSESHOE CRAB EGGS IN THE TOP 5 CM OF SAND IN THE BEACHES OF DELAWARE BAY DURING MAY AND JUNE 2004–2007 IN NEW JERSEY AND DELAWARE (SURVEYS CONDUCTED RESPECTIVELY BY THE NEW JERSEY AND DELAWARE DIVISIONS OF FISH AND WILDLIFE).

Mean egg density[a] (eggs /m², top 5 cm sand)	2004	2005	2006	2007
New Jersey (no hot-spots)	3,175	5,237	2,551	1,502
New Jersey (with hot-spots)	No survey	7,469	3,772	2,006
Delaware (all sites)	No survey	49,933	36,687	38,131
Delaware (all except Mispillion Harbor)	No survey	33,534	16,357	20,664
New Jersey index of female crab spawning	0.78	0.99	1.17	0.82
Delaware index of female crab spawning	0.76	0.65	0.81	0.96

[a] Data from Michels et al. (unpubl. data); the index is the mean number of female crabs per square meter per night.

priority for listing *C. c. rufa* has increased. Accordingly we recommend that the USFWS reconsider listing *C. c. rufa*. It may be noted that the *C. c. rufa* population has been designated as endangered by the Committee on the Status of Endangered Wildlife in Canada (COSEWIC 2007).

2. Although the status of *C. c. roselaari* may be uncertain because of the lack of comprehensive surveys, it is probable that its population is <10,000, which is considerably less than current estimates for *C. c. rufa*. As a small population, it is particularly vulnerable to stochastic events, harmful genetic mutation, and habitat loss. Therefore we recommend that the USFWS consider listing *C. c. roselaari* as well as *C. c. rufa*.

3. The original review showed that the Delaware Bay population of horseshoe crabs declined by around 90% between 1990 and 2006 as a result of excessive harvest. This has been shown to be strongly implicated in the decline of *C. c. rufa*, a finding now further reinforced by the demonstration that the majority of knots stopping over in Delaware Bay have suffered reduced rates of mass gain over 1998–2007. The suggestion that the crab population might have started to recover in 2006 as a result of harvest management is therefore welcome. However, the recovery needs to be toward the levels of the early 1990s—an order of magnitude increase—before it can be expected to have a beneficial effect on the survival of the Red Knot population. Therefore, we recommend that the Atlantic States Marine Fisheries Commission and the individual states involved further restricts the harvest of adult crabs until such time as there is unequivocal evidence of a strong recovery in the number of spawning crabs and the density of their eggs towards the levels of the early 1990s.

ACKNOWLEDGMENTS

We wish to acknowledge and thank the New Jersey Natural Lands Trust for 20 years of support for shorebird protection and research on the Delaware Bay, including the Arctic and Chile. This assessment, which embodies our cumulative understanding of Red Knot ecology and the factors affecting population decline, would not have been possible without the trust's commitment to protection and long-term support. We also wish to thank the Wildlife Conservation Society for supporting the first five years of research in the Canadian Arctic and Chile. We wish to thank all of the authors who contributed to this document—Olivia Blank, Ruth Boettcher, Susan Cameron, Sharon DeFalco, Pamela Denmon, Jenny Dickson, Nancy Douglass, William Haglan, Michael Haramis, Stephanie Koch, Scott Melvin, David Mizrahi, Nellie Nunez, Tom Penn, Christopher Raithel, Susan Rice, Felicia Sanders, Becky Suomala, Glen Therres, Kim Tripp, Barry Truitt, Lindsay Tudor, Dennis Varza, Julia Victoria, Bryan Watts, Alexandra Wilkie, and Brad Winn. This was a monumental task that could not have been completed without each of them. We also wish to thank Joe Jehl and thirteen anonymous reviewers for commenting on an earlier draft of this review. Additionally, we thank the NJENSP technical staff: Sharon DeFalco, Kim Korth, Pete Winkler, Gretchen Fowles, Patrick Woerner, Mike Davenport and Brian Henderson. We especially express our gratitude to Annette Scherer of the USFWS New Jersey Field Office (NJFO). Not only did she give generously of her time and advice throughout the preparation and revision of this document, but she also commented in detail on each of its various drafts and organized a thorough peer review. The final product owes much to her care, expertise and effort. We wish to thank the following people for their expertise, assistance and/or use of data for preparing this assessment: David Allen, North Carolina Wildlife Resources Commission, Nongame and Endangered Wildlife Program; Joseílson de Assis Costa, CEMAVE, Brazil; John Arvin, Gulf Coast Bird Observatory, Lake Jackson, TX; Luis Bala, CenPat, Argentina; Daniel Blanco, Wetlands International; Milan Bull, Connecticut Audubon Society and Connecticut Ornithological Society; Winnie Burkett, Houston Audubon Society; CEMAVE-IBAMA; Luis A. Espinosa G., Censo de Aves Acuticas Chile, UNORCH; Silvia Ferrari, University Patagonia Austral, John Fussell, North Carolina; Bob Gill, U.S. Geological Survey, Alaska Science Center, Anchorage, AK; William Howe, USFWS, TX; Sid Maddock, Audubon North Carolina; Brian McCaffery, USFWS, Yukon Delta NWR, Bethel, AK; Katy McWilliams, TNC, Charleston, VA; Brent Ortego, Texas Parks and Wildlife Department; Sergio Luis Pereira, Brazil; Don Reipe, American Littoral Society, NY; Wallace Rodrigues Telino-Júnior, Brazil; Ken Ross, Canadian Wildlife Service, National Wildlife Research Center, Ottawa, Canada; and Craig Watson, USFWS, South Carolina. We are grateful to Pavel Tomkovich for providing a copy of the unpublished report on the studies he and Maxim Dementyev carried out in Alaska in May 2006. We also thank S.F. Michels for providing details of the 2007 Delaware horseshoe crab trawl and spawning surveys.

LITERATURE CITED

ALBRIEU, C., S. IMBERTI, AND S. FERRARI. 2004. Las aves de la Patagonia Sur, el estuario del Río Gallegos y zonas aledañas. Universidad Nacional de la Patagonia Austral, Rio Gallegos, Argentina.

ALERSTAM, T., G. A. GUDMUNDSSON, AND K. JOHANNESSON. 1992. Resources for long distance migration: intertidal exploitation of Littorina and Mytilus by Red Knots Calidris canutus in Iceland. Oikos 65:179–189.

ALLEN, A. S. 1995. Tidepool value as foraging patches for breeding and migrating birds in tidal salt marshes in the lower Chesapeake Bay. M. A. thesis, College of William and Mary, Williamsburg, VA.

ANTAS, P. T. Z., AND I. L. S. NASCIMENTO. 1996. Analysis of Red Knot Calidris canutus rufa banding data in Brazil. International Wader Studies 8:63–70.

ARAÚJO, F. A. A., M. Y. WADA, E. V. DA SILVA, G. C. CAVALACANTE, V. S. MAGALHAES, G. V. FILHO, S. G. RODRIGUES, L. C. MARTINS, C. E. FEDRIZZI, A. SCHERER, L. V. MORH, M. A. B. DE ALMEIDA, B. S. BUNA, L. R. O. CSOTA, S. B. SCHERER, R. S. VIANNA, AND V. L. GATAS. 2003. Primeiro inquérito sorológico em aves migratórias no Parque Nacional da Lagoa do Peixe para detecção do vírus da febre do Nilo Ocidental. Secretaria de Vigilância em Saúde. Ministério da Saúde. <http://www.ibama.gov.br/cemave/index.php?id_menu=297> (10 January 2008).

ARAYA, B., AND G. MILLIE. 1996. Guía de campo de las aves de Chile. Séptima edición. Editorial Universitaria, Santiago, Chile.

ATLANTIC STATES MARINE FISHERIES COMMISSION. 2001. Addendum II to the interstate fishery management plan for horseshoe crab. Atlantic State Marine Fisheries Commission, Washington, DC.

ATKINSON, P. W., G. F. APPLETON, J. A. CLARK, N. A. CLARK, S. GILLINGS, I. G. HENDERSON, R. A. ROBINSON, AND R. A. STILLMAN. 2003. Red Knots Calidris canutus in Delaware Bay 2002. Survival, foraging and marking strategy. British Trust for Ornithology Research Report 308, Thetford, UK.

ATKINSON, P. W., A. J. BAKER, R. M. BEVAN, N. A. CLARK, K. B. COLE, P. M. GONZÁLEZ, J. NEWTON, L. J. NILES, AND R. A. ROBINSON. 2005. Unravelling the migratory strategies of a long-distance migrant using stable isotopes: Red Knot Calidris canutus movements in the Americas. Ibis 147:738–749.

ATKINSON, P. W., A. J. BAKER, K. A. BENNETT, N. A. CLARK, J. A. CLARK, K. B. COLE, A. DEKINGA, A. DEY, S. GILLINGS, P. M. GONZÁLEZ, K. KALASZ, C. D. T. MINTON, L. J. NILES, R. A. ROBINSON, AND H. P. SITTERS. 2007. Rates of mass gain and energy deposition in Red Knot on their final spring staging site is both time- and condition-dependent. Journal of Applied Ecology 44:885–895.

AUBRY, Y., AND R. COTTER. 2001. Using trend information to develop the Quebec Shorebird Conservation Plan. Bird Trends 8:21–24.

AVISE, J. C. 1989. A role for molecular genetics in the recognition and conservation of endangered species. Trends in Ecology and Evolution 4:279–281.

BAKER, A. J., T. PIERSMA, AND A. GREENSLADE. 1999a. Molecular versus phenotypic sexing in Red Knots. Condor 101:887–893.

BAKER, A. J., T. PIERSMA, AND L. ROSENMEIER. 1994. Unraveling the intraspecific phylogeography of Red Knots (Calidris canutus) – a progress report on the search for genetic markers. Journal für Ornithologie 135:599–608.

BAKER, A. J., P. M. GONZÁLEZ, L. BENEGAS, S. RICE, V. L. D'AMICO, M. ABRIL, A. FARMER, AND M. PECK. 2005b Annual international shorebird expeditions to Río Grande in Tierra del Fuego 2000–2004. Wader Study Group Bulletin 107:19–23.

BAKER, A. J., P. M. GONZÁLEZ, I. L. SERRANO, W. R. T. JÚNIOR, M. EFE, S. RICE, V. L. D'AMICO, M. ROCHA, AND M. A. ECHAVE. 2005a. Assessment of the wintering area of Red Knots in Maranhão, northern Brazil, in February 2005. Wader Study Group Bulletin 107:10–18.

BAKER, A. J., P. M. GONZÁLEZ, T. PIERSMA, L. J. NILES, I. L. S. DO NASCIMENTO, P. W. ATKINSON, N. A. CLARK, C. D. T. MINTON, M. K. PECK, AND G. AARTS. 2004. Rapid population decline in Red Knot: fitness consequences of decreased refueling rates and late arrival in Delaware Bay. Proceedings of the Royal Society B 25:125–129.

BAKER, A. J., P. M. GONZÁLEZ, T. PIERSMA, C. D. T. MINTON, J. R. WILSON, H. SITTERS, D. GRAHAM, R. JESSOP, P. COLLINS, P. DE GOEIJ, M. PECK, R. LINI, L. BALA, G. PAGNONI, A. VILA, E. BREMER, R. BASTIDA, E. IENO, D. BLANCO, Y DE LIMA S. DO NASCIMIENTO, S. S. SCHERER, M. P. SCHNEIDER, A. SILVA, AND A. A. F. RODRIGUES. 1999b. Northbound migration of Red Knots Calidris canutus rufa in Argentina and Brazil: report on results obtained by an international expedition in March–April 1997. Wader Study Group Bulletin 88:64–75.

BALA, L. O., V. L. D'AMICO, AND P. STOYANOFF. 2002. Migrating shorebirds at Península

Valdés, Argentina: report for the year 2000. Wader Study Group Bulletin 98:6–9.

BALA, L. O., M. A. HERNÁNDEZ, AND V. L. D´AMICO. 2001. Shorebirds present on Fracasso Beach (San José Gulf, Península Valdés, Argentina): report of the 1999 migrating season. Wader Study Group Bulletin 94:27–30.

BALA, L. O., M. A. HERNÁNDEZ, AND L. R. MUSMECI. 2005. Phenology of northward migration of Red Knots at Peninsula Valdés, Argentina, 1994–2005. Wader Study Group Bulletin 108:23.

BELTON, W. 1994. Aves do Río Grande do Sul: distribuição e biologia. Editora UNISINOS, São Leopoldo, Brazil.

BLANCO, D. E., AND M. CARBONELL (EDITORS). 2001. The Neotropical waterbird census. The first 10 years: 1990–1999. Wetlands International, Buenos Aires, Argentina and Ducks Unlimited, Inc. Memphis, TN.

BLANCO, D. E., G. D. PUGNALI, AND H. RODRÍGUEZ GOÑI. 1992. La importancia de Punta Rasa, Prov. de Buenos Aires, en la migración del Chorlo rojizo *Calidris canutus*. Hornero 13: 203–206.

BOTTON, M. L., R. E. LOVELAND, AND T. R. JACOBSEN. 1988. Beach erosion and geochemical factors: influence on spawning success of horseshoe crabs (*Limulus polyphemus*) in Delaware Bay. Marine Biology 99:325–332.

BOTTON, M. L., R. E. LOVELAND, AND T. R. JACOBSEN. 1992. Overwintering trilobite larvae of the horseshoe crab, *Limulus polyphemus*, on a sandy beach of Delaware Bay (New Jersey, USA). Marine Ecology Progress Series 88: 289–292.

BOTTON, M. L., R. E. LOVELAND, AND T. R. JACOBSEN. 1994. Site selection by migratory shorebirds in Delaware Bay, and its relationship to beach characteristics and abundance of horseshoe crab (*Limulus polyphemus*) eggs. Auk 111:605–616.

BOYD, H., AND T. PIERSMA. 2001. Changing balance between survival and recruitment explains population trends in Red Knots *Calidris canutus islandica* wintering in Britain, 1969–1995. Ardea 89:301–317.

BROWN, S., C. HICKEY, B. HARRINGTON, AND R. GILL (EDITORS). 2001. The U.S. shorebird conservation plan, 2nd ed. Manomet Center for Conservation Sciences, Manomet, MA.

BUCHANAN, J. B. 2006. A census of spring migrant Red Knots *Calidris canutus* in coastal Washington, USA: results from 2006. Wader Study Group Bulletin 111:64–66.

BUCHANAN, J. B. 2007. Observations of Red Knots *Calidris canutus* in coastal Washington, USA: the 2007 spring migration. Wader Study Group Bulletin 114:65–66.

BUEHLER, D. M. 2002. Shorebird counts in Panama in 2002 emphasize the need to monitor and protect the upper Panama Bay. Wader Study Group Bulletin 99: 41–44.

BUEHLER, D. M., AND A. J. BAKER. 2005. Population divergence times and historical demography in Red Knots and Dunlins. Condor 107: 497–513.

BURGER, J. 1986. The effect of human activity on shorebirds in two coastal bays in northeastern United States. Environmental Conservation 13:123–130.

BURGER, J., M. GOCHFELD, AND L. NILES. 1995. Ecotourism and birds in coastal New Jersey: contrasting responses of birds, tourists, and managers. Environmental Conservation 22: 56–65.

BURGER, J., L. NILES, AND K. E. CLARK. 1997. Importance of beach, mudflat and marsh habitats to migrant shorebirds on Delaware Bay. Biological Conservation 79:283–292.

BURGER, J., S. A. CARLUCCI, C. W. JEITNER, AND L. NILES. 2007. Habitat choice, disturbance, and management of foraging shorebirds and gulls at a migratory stopover. Journal of Coastal Research 25:1159–1166.

BURGER, J., C. JEITNER, K. CLARK, AND L. NILES. 2004. The effect of human activities on migrant shorebirds: successful adaptive management. Environmental Conservation 31:283–288.

BUTLER, R. W., R. C. YDENBERG, AND D. B. LANK. 2003. Wader migration on the changing predator landscape. Wader Study Group Bulletin 100:130–133.

CANEVARI, P., D. E. BLANCO, E. H. BUCHER, G. CASTRO, AND I. DAVIDSON (EDITORS). 1998. Los humedales de la Argentina: clasificación, situación actual, conservación y legislación. Wetlands International Publication 46, Buenos Aires, Argentina.

CARMONA, R., V. AYALA-PÉREZ, N. ARCE, AND L. MORALES-GOPAR. 2006. Use of saltworks by Red Knots at Guerrero Negro, Mexico. Wader Study Group Bulletin 111:46–49.

CASTRO, G., AND J. P. MYERS. 1993. Shorebird predation on eggs of horseshoe crabs during spring stopover on Delaware Bay. Auk 110: 927–930.

CASTRO, G., J. P. MYERS, AND A. R. PLACE. 1989. Assimilation efficiency of Sanderlings (*Calidris alba*) feeding on horseshoe crab (*Limulus polyphemus*) eggs. Physiological Zoology 62:716–731.

CLARK, K., L. NILES, AND J. BURGER. 1993. Abundance and distribution of shorebirds migrating on Delaware Bay, 1986–1992. Condor 95:694–705.

CLARK, N. A., P. W ATKINSON, J. A. CLARK, S. GILLINGS, AND R. ROBINSON. 2004. Report on the migration of Red Knots *Calidris canutus rufa* and Turnstone *Arenaria interpres* passing through Delaware Bay in 2003. British Trust for Ornithology Research Report 351, Thetford, UK.

COSEWIC. 2006. Status report on Red Knot *Calidris canutus*. Revised draft. Canadian Wildlife Service, Ottawa, ON, Canada.

COSEWIC. 2007. COSEWIC assessment and status report on the Red Knot *Calidris canutus* in Canada. Committee on the Status of Endangered Wildlife in Canada, Ottawa, ON, Canada.

COUVE, E., AND C. VIDAL. 2003. Birds of Patagonia, Tierra del Fuego and Antarctic Peninsula. Fantastico Sur, Chile.

CRAMER, W. 1997. Modeling the possible impact of climate change on broad-scale vegetation structure: examples from northern Europe. Pp. 312–329 *in* W. C. Oechel, T. Callaghan, T. Gilmanov, J. I. Holten, B. Maxwell, U. Molau, and B. Sveinbjornsson (editors). Global change and arctic terrestrial ecosystems. Springer-Verlag, New York, NY.

DAVIDSON, N., AND P. ROTHWELL. 1993. Disturbance to waterfowl on estuaries. Wader Study Group Bulletin, (Special Issue) 68. Royal Society for the Protection of Birds, Bedfordshire, UK.

DELHEY, K. V., AND P. F. PETRACCI. 2004. Aves marinas y costeras en: el ecosistema del estuario de Bahía Blanca. Pp. 203-220 *in* M. C. Píccolo, and M. S. Hoffmeyer (editors). Instituto Argentino de Oceanografía (CONICET-UNS), Bahía Blanca, Argentina.

DEKINGA, A., AND T. PIERSMA. 1993. Reconstructing diet composition on the basis of faeces in a mollusc-eating wader, the Red Knot *Calidris canutus*. Bird Study 40:44–156.

DEVILLERS, P., AND J. A. TERSCHUREN. 1976. Some distributional records of migrant North American Charadriiformes in coastal South America (Continental Argentina, Falkland, Tierra del Fuego, Chile and Ecuador). Gerfaut 66:107–125.

DINSMORE, S. J., J. A. COLLAZO, AND J. R WALTERS. 1998. Seasonal numbers and distribution of shorebirds on North Carolina's Outer Banks. Wilson Bulletin 110:171–181.

DUNNE, P., D. SIBLEY, C. SUTTON, AND W. WANDER. 1982. 1982 aerial shorebird survey of Delaware Bay. Records of New Jersey Birds 8:68–75.

ERWIN, R. M. 1996. Dependence of waterbirds and shorebirds on shallow-water habitats in the mid-Atlantic coastal region: an ecological profile and management recommendations. Estuaries 19:213–219.

ESCUDERO, G., M. ABRIL, M. G. MURGA, AND N. HERNÁNDEZ. 2003. Red Knots wintering in Bahía Bustamante, Argentina: are they lost? Wader Study Group Bulletin 101/102: 59–61.

ESPOZ, C., A. PONCE, R. MATUS, O. BLANK, N. ROZBACZYLO, H. P. SITTERS, S. RODRÍGUEZ, AND L. J. NILES. 2008. Trophic ecology of the Red Knot *Calidris canutus rufa* at Bahía Lomas, Tierra del Fuego, Chile. Wader Study Group Bulletin 115:69–75.

FERRARI, S., C. ALBRIEU, AND P. GANDINI. 2002. Importance of the Río Gallegos estuary, Santa Cruz, Argentina, for migratory shorebirds. Wader Study Group Bulletin 99:35–40.

GALBRAITH, H., R. JONES, R. PARK, J. CLOUGH, S. HERROD-JULIUS, B. HARRINGTON, AND G. PAGE. 2002. Global climate change and sea level rise: potential losses of intertidal habitat for shorebirds. Waterbirds 25:173–183.

GILLINGS, S., P. W. ATKINSON, S. L. BARDSLEY, N. A. CLARK, S. E. LOVE, R. A. ROBINSON, R. A. STILLMAN, AND R. G. WEBER. 2007. Shorebird predation of horseshoe crab eggs in Delaware Bay: species contrasts and availability constraints. Journal of Animal Ecology 76:503–514.

GONZÁLEZ, P. 1991. Importancia de las Bahía de San Antonio y zona de influencia en el Golfo San Matías para la comunidades de aves costeras. Legislatura de la Provincia de Río Negro (Mayo 1991). Centro Provincial de Documentacion e Información, Gobierno de la Provincia de Río Negro, Viedma, Argentina.

GONZÁLEZ, P. M., T. PIERSMA, AND Y. VERKUIL. 1996. Food, feeding, and refueling of Red Knots during northward migration at San Antonio Oeste, Río Negro, Argentina. Journal of Field Ornithology 67:575–591.

GONZÁLEZ, P. M., M. CARBAJAL, R. I. G. MORRISON, AND A. J. BAKER. 2004. Tendencias poblacionales del playero rojizo (*Calidris canutus rufa*). en el sur de sudamérica. Ornithologia Neotropical (Supplement) 15:357–365.

GONZÁLEZ, P. M., M. CARBAJAL, A. J. BAKER, M. E. ECHAVE, R. PISSACO, AND L. BENEGAS. 2003. Migración austral en relación al tiempo de llegada de *Calidris canutus rufa* al Hemisferio Norte. P. 98 *in* Programa y libro de resúmenes. VII Congreso de Ornitología Neotropical, Puyehue, Chile.

HARAMIS, G. M., W. A. LINK, P. C. OSENTON, D. B. CARTER, R. G. WEBER, N. A. CLARK, M. A. TEECE, AND D. S. MIZRAHI. 2007. Stable isotope and pen feeding trial studies confirm the value of horseshoe crab *Limulus polyphemus* eggs to spring migrant shorebirds in Delaware Bay. Journal of Avian Biology 38:367–376.

HARRINGTON, B. A. 2001. Red Knot (*Calidris canutus*). *In* The Birds of North America online. A. Poole (editor). Ithaca, Cornell Laboratory of Ornithology; Retrieved from The Birds of North American Online database: <http://bna.birds.cornell.edu/BNA/account/Red_Knot/> (3 December 2007).

HARRINGTON, B., AND C. FLOWERS. 1996. The flight of the Red Knot. W. W. Norton and Company, New York, NY.

HARRINGTON, B. A., AND L. LEDDY. 1982. Sightings of Red Knots banded and color-marked in Massachusetts in August 1980. Journal of Field Ornithology 53:55–57.

HARRINGTON, B. A., AND R. I. G. MORRISON. 1980. An investigation of wintering areas of Red Knots (*Calidris canutus*) and Hudsonian Godwits (*Limosa haemastica*) in Argentina. Report to World Wildlife Federation, Washington, DC. and Toronto, ON, Canada.

HARRINGTON, B. A., P. T. Z. ANTAS, AND F. SILVA. 1986. Northward shorebird migration on the Atlantic coast of southern Brazil. Vida Silvestre Neotropical 1:45–54.

HARRINGTON, B. A., J. M. HAGAN, AND L. E. LEDDY. 1988. Site fidelity and survival differences between two groups of New World Red Knots *Calidris canutus*. Auk 105:439–445.

HATA, D. 2008. A Report to the Atlantic States Marine Fisheries Commission, Horseshoe Crab Management Board. Horseshoe Crab Research Center, Virginia Polytechnic Institute and State University, Blacksburg, VA.

HAYMAN, P., J. MARCHANT, AND T. PRATER. 1986. Shorebirds: an identification guide. Houghton Mifflin Co., Boston, MA.

HERNÁNDEZ, D. 2005. Conservation and foraging dynamics of migratory shorebirds. Ph.D. dissertation, Rutgers University, New Brunswick, NJ.

HERNÁNDEZ, M. A., V. D'AMICO, AND L. BALA. 2004. Presas consumidas por el playero rojizo *Calidris canutus* en Bahía San Julián, Santa Cruz, Argentina. Hornero 19:7–11.

HICKLIN, P. W. 1987. The migration of shorebirds in the Bay of Fundy. Wilson Bulletin 99:540–570.

HOBSON, W. 1972. The breeding biology of the Knot. Proceedings of the Western Foundation of Vertebrate Zoology 2:1–29.

HOPE, C. E., AND T. M. SHORTT. 1944. Southward migration of adult shorebirds on the west coast of James Bay, Ontario. Auk 61:572–576.

IBAMA. 1999. Plano de manejo do Parque Nacional da Lagoa do Peixe. Ministério do Meio Ambiente, Instituto Brasileiro do Meio Ambiente e dos Recursos Naturais Renováveis, Fase 2. Brasília, Brazil.

IENO, E., D. ALEMANY, D. BLANCO, AND R. BASTIDA. 2004. Prey size selection by Red Knot feeding on mud snails at Punta Rasa (Argentina) during migration. Waterbirds 27:493–498.

INTERNATIONAL WADER STUDY GROUP. 2003. Waders are declining worldwide: conclusions from the 2003 International Wader Study Group Conference, Cadiz, Spain. Wader Study Group Bulletin 101/102:8–12.

KOCHENBERGER, R. 1983. Survey of shorebird concentrations along the Delaware bayshore, spring 1983. Peregrine Observer (Fall):3–4.

LARA-RESENDE, S. M., AND F. LEUWEMBERG. 1987. Ecological studies of Lagoa do Peixe. Final Report to World Wildlife Federation, Washington, DC.

LATHROP, R. G., AND M. ALLEN. 2005. Mapping the critical horseshoe crab spawning habitats of Delaware Bay. Rutgers University Center for Remote Sensing and Spatial Analysis. <http://www.crssa.rutgers.edu/projects/delbay/hcrab/ALS_DelBay_hcrab_report_20060718.pdf>(3 December 2007).

MANNING, T. H. 1952. Birds of the west James Bay and southern Hudson Bay coasts. Natural Museum of Canada, Bulletin No. 125.

MCLEAN, E. F. 1993. Human impacts on beach use by wintering and migrating birds in lower Chesapeake Bay. M.A. thesis, College of William and Mary, Williamsburg, VA.

MENDES, L., T. PIERSMA, M. LECOQ, B. SPAANS, AND R. E. RICKLEFS. 2005. Disease-limited distributions? Contrasts in the prevalence of avian malaria in shorebird species using marine and freshwater habitats. Oikos 109:396–404.

MICHELS, S., AND D. SMITH, 2006. Horseshoe crab spawning activity in Delaware Bay: 1999–2005. Report to the Atlantic States Marine Fish Comission's Horseshoe Crab Technical Committee. Delaware Division of Fish and Wildlife, Little Creek, DE.

MINTON, C. D. T., T. PIERSMA, D. BLANCO, A. J. BAKER, L. BENEGAS, P. DE GOEIJ, R. E. MANRIQUEZ, M. PECK, AND M. S. RAMÍREZ. 1996. Wader numbers and the use of high tide roost at the Hemispheric Reserve "Costa Atlántica de Tierra del Fuego," Argentina, January and February 1995. Wader Study Group Bulletin 79:109–114.

MIZRAHI, D.S. 2002. Shorebird distribution along New Jersey's southern Atlantic coast: temporal patterns and effects of human disturbance. Final report, USDI Fish and Wildlife Service, Cape May National Wildlife Refuge, Cape May Court House, NJ.

MORRISON, R. I. G., AND B. A. HARRINGTON. 1992. The migration system of the Red Knot *Calidris canutus rufa* in the New World. Wader Study Group Bulletin 64 (Supplement):71–84.

MORRISON, R. I. G., AND R. K. ROSS. 1989. Atlas of Nearctic shorebirds on the coast of South America. Special Publication, Canadian Wildlife Service, Ottawa, ON, Canada.

MORRISON, R. I. G., P. T. Z. ANTAS, AND R. K. ROSS. 1987. Migratory routes in the Amazon coast. Pp. 159–199 *in* Anais do seminario sobre desenvolvimento economico e impacto ambiental em areas de tropico umido Brasileiro, a experiencia da CVRD. Companhia Vale do Rio Doce, Rio de Janeiro, Brazil.

MORRISON, R. I. G., N. C. DAVIDSON, AND T. PIERSMA. 2005. Transformations at high latitudes: why do Red Knots *Calidris canutus* bring body stores to the breeding grounds? Condor 107:449–457.

MORRISON, R. I. G., R. K. ROSS, AND L. J. NILES. 2004. Declines in wintering populations of Red Knots in southern South America. Condor 106:60–70.

MORRISON, R. I. G., N. C. DAVIDSON, AND J. R. WILSON. 2007. Survival of the fattest: body stores on migration and survival in Red Knots *Calidris canutus islandica*. Journal of Avian Biology 38:479–487.

MORRISON, R. I. G., R. K. ROSS, AND M. S. TORRES. 1992. Aerial surveys of Nearctic shorebirds wintering in Mexico: Some preliminary results. Canadian Wildlife Service Progress Notes No. 201, Canadian Wildlife Service, Ottawa, ON, Canada.

MORRISON, R. I. G., R. W. BUTLER, F. S. DELGADO, AND R. K. ROSS. 1998. Atlas of Nearctic shorebirds and other waterbirds on the coast of Panama. Canadian Wildlife Service Special Publication. Canadian Wildlife Service, Ottawa, ON, Canada.

MORRISON, R. I. G., R. GILL, B. HARRINGTON, S. SKAGEN, G. W. PAGE, C. L. GRATTO-TREVOR, AND S. M. HAIG. 2001. Estimates of shorebird populations in North America. Occasional Paper No. 104, Canadian Wildlife Service, Ottawa, ON, Canada.

MORRISON, R. I. G., B. J. MCCAFFERY, R. E. GILL, S. K. SKAGEN, S. L. JONES, G. W. PAGE, C. L. GRATTO-TREVOR, AND B. A. ANDRES. 2006. Population estimates of North American shorebirds. Wader Study Group Bulletin 111:67–85.

MUÑOZ, M., H. NÚÑEZ, AND J. YÁÑEZ (EDITORS). 1996. Libro rojo de los sitios prioritarios para la conservación de la diversidad biológica en Chile. Ministerio de Agricultura, Corporación Nacional Forestal, Santiago, Chile.

MUSMECI, L. R. 2005. Evaluación de Playa Colombo (Golfo Nuevo, Chubut) como sitio de parada utilizado por aves playeras. Tesis de Licenciatura. Facultad de Ciencias Naturales, Universidad Nacional de la Patagonia, Chubut, Chile.

MYERS, J. P., AND L. P. MYERS. 1979. Shorebirds of coastal Buenos Aires Province, Argentina. Ibis 121:186–200.

MYERS, J. P., P. D. MCLAIN, R. I. G. MORISON, P. Z. ANTAS, P. CANEVARI, B. HARRINGTON, T. E. LOVEJOY, V. PULIDO, M. SALLABERRY, AND S. E. SENNER. 1987. The Western Hemisphere Shorebird Reserve Network. Wader Study Group Bulletin 49, Supplement IWRB Special Publication 7:122–124.

NAJJAR, R. G., H. A. WALKER, P. J. ANDERSON, E. J. BARRO, R. J. BORD, J. R. GIBSON, V. S. KENNEDY, C. G. KNIGHT, J. P. MEGONIGAL, R. E. O'CONNOR, C. D. POLSKY, N. P. PSUTY, B. A. RICHARDS, L. G. SORENSON, E. M. STEELE, AND R. S. SWANSON. 2000. The potential impacts of climate change on the mid-Atlantic coastal region. Climate Research 14:219–233.

NASCIMENTO, I. L. S. 1995. As aves do Parque Nacional da Lagoa do Peixe. Instituto Brasileiro do Meio Ambiente e dos Recursos Naturais Renovaveis, Brasília, Brazil.

NASCIMENTO, J. L. X. 1998. Muda de Charadriidae e Scolopacidae (Charadriiformes) no norte do Brasil. Ararajuba 6:141–144.

NILES, L. J., A. D. DEY, N. J. DOUGLASS, J. A. CLARK, N. A. CLARK, A. S. GATES, B. A. HARRINGTON, M. K. PECK, AND H. P. SITTERS. 2006. Red Knots wintering in Florida: 2005/6 Expedition. Wader Study Group Bulletin 111:86–99.

OBERHOLSER, H. C. 1974. Bird life of Texas. University of Texas Press, Austin, TX.

PAGE, G. W., E. PALACIOS, L. ALFARO, S. GONZÁLEZ, L. E. STENZEL, AND M. JUNGERS. 1997. Numbers of wintering shorebirds in coastal wetlands of Baja California, Mexico. Journal of Field Ornithology 68:572–574.

PAGE, G. W., L. E. STENZEL, AND J. E. KJELMYR. 1999. Overview of shorebird abundance and distribution in wetlands of the Pacific coast of the contiguous United States. Condor 101:461–471.

PAULSON, D. 1993. Shorebirds of the Pacific Northwest. University of Washington Press, Seattle, WA.

PÉREZ, F., P. SUTTON, AND A. VILA. 1995. Aves y mamíferos marinos de Santa Cruz. Recopilación e integración de relevamientos realizados entre 1986 y 1992. Boletin Técnico No. 26. Fundación Vida Silvestre Argentina. Buenos Aires, Argentina.

PHILLIPS, J. D. 1986a. Coastal submergence and marsh fringe erosion. Journal of Coastal Research 2:427–436.

PHILLIPS, J. D. 1986b. Spatial analysis of shoreline erosion, Delaware Bay, New Jersey. Annals of the Association of American Geographers 76:50–62.

PHILLIPS, J. D. 1987. Shoreline processes and establishment of *Phragmites australis* in a coastal plain estuary. Vegetatio 71: 139–144.

PIERSMA, T. 1994. Close to the edge: energetic bottlenecks and the evolution of migratory pathways in Red Knots. Ph.D. dissertation, University of Groningen, Groningen, The Netherlands.

PIERSMA, T., AND A. J. BAKER. 2000. Life history characteristics and the conservation of migratory shorebirds. Pp. 105–124 *in* L. M. Gosling, and W. J. Sutherland (editors). Behaviour and conservation. Cambridge University Press, Cambridge, MA.

PIERSMA, T., AND N. C. DAVIDSON. 1992. The migrations and annual cycles of five subspecies of Red Knots in perspective. Wader Study Group Bulletin 64 (Supplement):187–197.

PIERSMA, T., AND R. E. GILL, JR. 1998. Guts don't fly: small digestive organs in obese Bartailed Godwits. Auk 115:196–203.

PIERSMA, T., G. A. GUDMUNDSSON, AND K. LILLIENDAHL. 1999. Rapid changes in the size of different functional organ and muscle groups during refueling in a long-distance migrating shorebird. Physiological and Biochemical Zoology 72:405–415.

PIERSMA, T., R. HOEKSTRA, A. DEKINGA, A. KOOLHAAS, P. WOLF, P. BATTLEY, P. WIERSMA. 1993. Scale and intensity of intertidal habitat use by Red Knots *Calidris canutus* in the western Wadden Sea in relation to food, friends and foes. Netherlands Journal of Sea Research 31:31–357.

PIERSMA, T., D. I. ROGERS, P. M. GONZÁLEZ, L. ZWARTS, L. J. NILES, I. DE LIMA DO NASCIMENTO, C. D. T. MINTON, AND A. J. BAKER. 2005. Fuel storage rates before northward flights in Red Knots worldwide: facing the severest constraint in tropical intertidal environments? Pp. 262–273 *in* R. Greenberg, and P. P. Marra (editors). Birds of two worlds. Smithsonian Institution Press, Washington, DC.

REHFISCH, M. M., AND H. Q. P. CRICK. 2003. Predicting the impact of climatic change on arctic-breeding waders. Wader Study Group Bulletin 100:86–95.

ROBINSON, R. A., P. W. ATKINSON, AND N. A. CLARK. 2003. Arrival and weight gain of Red Knot *Calidris canutus*, Ruddy Turnstone *Arenaria interpres* and Sanderling *Calidris alba* staging in Delaware Bay in spring. British Trust for Ornithology Research Report 307, Thetford, UK.

ROGERS, D. I. 2003. High-tide roost choice by coastal waders. Wader Study Group Bulletin 100:73–79.

ROSELAAR, C. S. 1983. Subspecies recognition in Red Knot *Calidris canutus* and occurrence of races in western Europe. Beaufortia 33: 97–109.

ROSS, K., K. ABRAHAM, R. CLAY, B. COLLINS, J. IRON, R. JAMES, D. MCLACHLIN, AND R. WEEBER. 2003. Ontario shorebird conservation plan. Environment Canada, Toronto, Canada.

ROTTENBORN, S. C. 1992. Cover utilization and flocking behavior of shorebirds foraging in agricultural fields in Northampton County, Virginia. Undergraduate honors thesis, College of William and Mary, Williamsburg, VA.

SANDERCOCK, B. K. 2003. Estimation of survival rates for wader populations: a review of mark–recapture methods. Wader Study Group Bulletin 100:163–174.

SHOPLAND, J. M. 1975. Foraging strategies of a shorebird community in a manmade habitat. Undergraduate honors thesis. College of William and Mary, Williamsburg, VA.

SHUSTER, C. N., JR., AND M. L. BOTTON. 1985. A contribution to the population biology of horseshoe crabs, *Limulus polyphemus* (L.), in Delaware Bay. Estuaries 8:363–372.

SHUSTER, C. N., JR, R. B. BARLOW, AND H. J. BROCKMANN. 2003. The American horseshoe crab. Harvard University Press, Cambridge, MA.

SIBLEY, D. A. 2000. The Sibley guide to birds. Alfred A Knopf, Inc., New York, NY.

SITTERS, H. P., P. M. GONZÁLEZ, T. PIERSMA, A. J. BAKER, AND D. J. PRICE. 2001. Day and night feeding habitat of Red Knot in Patagonia: profitability versus safety? Journal of Field Ornithology 72:86–95.

SITTERS, H. P. 2004. Time budgets in stopover Red Knots at Mispillion, Delaware, in May 2003. Unpublished report to the Endangered and Nongame Species Program, New Jersey Division of Fish and Wildlife, Trenton, NJ.

SKAGEN, S. K., P. B. SHARPE, R. G. WALTERMIRE, AND M. B. DILLON, 1999. Biogeographical profiles of shorebird migration in mid-continental North America. Biological Science Report USGS/BRD/BSR-2000-0003. U.S. Government Printing Office, Denver, CO.

SMITH, D. R., P. S. POOLER, B. J. SWAN, S. F. MICHELS, W. R. HALL, P. J. HIMCHAK, AND M. J. MILLARD. 2002a. Spatial and temporal distribution of horseshoe crab spawning in

Delaware Bay: implications for monitoring. Estuaries 25:115–125.

SMITH, D. R., P. S. POOLER, R. E. LOVELAND, M. L. BOTTON, S. F. MICHELS, R. G. WEBER, AND D. B. CARTER. 2002b. Horseshoe crab (*Limulus polyphemus*) reproductive activity on Delaware Bay beaches: implications for monitoring. Journal of Coastal Research 18:730–750.

SMITH, D., N. JACKSON, S. LOVE, K. NORDSTROM, R. WEBER, AND D. CARTER. 2002c. Beach nourishment on Delaware Bay beaches to restore habitat for horseshoe crab spawning and shorebird foraging. Report to The Nature Conservancy, Delaware Bayshores Office, Delmont, NJ.

SPAANS, A. L. 1978. Status and numerical fluctuations of some North American waders along the Surinam coast. Wilson Bulletin 90:60–83.

SPRANDEL, G. L., J. A. GORE, AND D. T. COBB. 1997. Winter shorebird survey. Final performance report, Florida Game and Fresh Water Fish Commission. Tallahassee, FL.

STILLMAN, R. A., A. D. WEST, J. D. GOSS-CUSTARD, R. W. G. CALDOW, S. MCGRORTY, S. E. A. LE V. DIT DURELL, M. G. YATES, P. W. ATKINSON, N. A. CLARK, M. C. BELL, P. J. DARE, AND M. MANDER. 2003. An individual behaviour-based model can predict shorebird mortality using routinely collected shellfishery data. Journal of Applied Ecology 40:1090–1101.

SUMMERS, R. W., AND L. G. UNDERHILL. 1987. Factors related to breeding production of Brent Geese *Branta b. bernicula* and waders (Charadrii) on the Taimyr Peninsula. Bird Study 34:161–171.

SUTTON, C., AND J. DOWDELL. 2002. Survey of gull populations along New Jersey's Delaware Bay beaches spring, 2002 with comparisons to identical surveys conducted in spring 1990-1992. Report to the Endangered and Nongame Species Program, New Jersey Division of Fish and Wildlife, Trenton, NJ.

THOMAS, G. H., T. SZÉKELY, AND W. J. SUTHERLAND. 2003. Publication bias in waders. Wader Study Group Bulletin 100:216–223.

TOMKOVICH, P. S. 1992. An analysis of the geographic variability in Red Knots *Calidris canutus* based on museum skins. Wader Study Group Bulletin 64 (Supplement):17–23.

TOMKOVICH, P. S. 2001. A new subspecies of Red Knot *Calidris canutus* from the New Siberian Islands. Bulletin of the British Ornithologists' Club 121:257–263

TRUITT, B. R., B. D. WATTS, B. L. BROWN, AND W. DUNSTAN. 2001. Red knot densities and invertebrate prey availability on the Virginia barrier islands. Wader Study Group Bulletin 95:12.

TRUITT, B. R., B. D. WATTS, B. L. BROWN, AND W. DUNSTAN. 2001. Red knot densities and invertebrate prey availability on the Virginia barrier islands. Wader Study Group Bulletin 95:12.

TSIPOURA, N., AND J. BURGER. 1999. Shorebird diet during spring migration stopover on Delaware Bay. Condor 101:633–644.

UNDERHILL, L. G., R. P. PRYS-JONES, E. E. JR. SYROECHKOVSKI, N. M. GROEN, V. KARPOV, H. G. LAPPO, M. W. J. VAN ROOMEN, A. RYBKIN, AND H. SCHEKKERMAN. 1993. Breeding of waders (Charadrii) and Brant geese *Branta bernicla bernicla* at Pronchishcheva Lake, northeastern Taimyr, Russia, in a peak and a decreasing lemming year. Ibis 135:277–292.

VAN DE KAM, J., B. ENS, T. PIERSMA, AND L. ZWARTS. 2004. Shorebirds: an illustrated behavioural ecology. KNNV Publishers, Utrecht, The Netherlands.

VARZA, D. 2004. Wildlife conservation restoration program shorebird use assessment. Unpublished report. Connecticut Department of Environemntal Protection, Wildlife Division, Hartford, CT.

VILA, A. R., E. R. BREMER, AND M. S. BEADE. 1994. Censos de chorlos y playeros migratorios en la Bahía de Samborombón, Provincia de Buenos Aires, Argentina. Boletin Técnico No. 22. Fundación Vida Silvestre, Buenos Aires, Argentina.

VOOREN, C. M., AND A. CHIARADIA. 1990. Seasonal abundance and behaviour of coastal birds of Csasino Beach, Brazil. Ornithologia Neotropical 1:9–24.

WANDER, W., AND P. DUNNE. 1981. Species and numbers of shorebirds on the Delaware Bayshore of New Jersey—spring 1981. Occasional Paper No. 140. Records of New Jersey Birds 7:59–64.

WASH WADER RINGING GROUP. 2004. Wash Wader Ringing Group 2002–2003 Report. Wash Wader Ringing Group, Thetford, UK.

WATTS, B. D. 1992. The influence of marsh size on marsh value for bird communities of the lower Chesapeake Bay. Center for Conservation Biology Technical Report series CCBTR-92 01. Center for Conservation Biology, College of William and Mary, Williamsburg, VA.

WATTS, B. 1998. An investigation of waterbirds within the Panama Canal Zone and the upper Bay of Panama. Center for conservation Biology, College of William and Mary, Williamsburg, VA.

WEBER, R. G. 2003. Horseshoe crab egg densities observed on six Delaware beaches, Final Report to Delaware Coastal Management Program, Dover, DE.

WEBER, R. G. 2004. Horseshoe crab egg densities observed on six Delaware beaches, Final Report to Delaware Coastal Management Program, Dover, DE.

WEBER, T. P., AND A. I. HOUSTON. 1997. Flight costs, flight range and the stopover ecology of migrating birds. Journal of Animal Ecology 66:297–306.

WETLANDS INTERNATIONAL. 2006. Waterbird population estimates, 4th ed. Wetlands International Global Series, Wageningen, The Netherlands.

WHITLOCK, M. C. 2000. Fixation of new alleles and the extinction of small populations: drift load, beneficial alleles, and sexual selection. Evolution 54:1855–1861.

APPENDIX 1. REGIONAL MAPS OF RED KNOT CRITICAL HABITAT (MIGRATORY STOPOVER AND WINTERING-NONBREEDING AREAS).

These important habitats are classified on the following maps as critical or suitable according to the following criteria:

Critical habitats (dark gray) are: (1) sites of known importance for Red Knots and are documented by survey, (2) sites of known importance by expert opinion, and may or may not have survey data available, and (3) sites of known importance that are occupied intermittently (because of naturally fluctuating food resources, human disturbance, beach replenishment, etc.), and may or may not have survey data.

Suitable habitats (light gray) are: (1) sites of known importance that are occupied intermittently, may or may not have survey data, and are deemed by expert opinion as secondary sites not critical to the persistence of the Red Knot population at its current population level. These sites may become critical if the Red Knot population increases, and (2) sites that were historically used by Red Knot but are now unused although the habitat has not been altered. These sites may become critical if the red knot population increases.

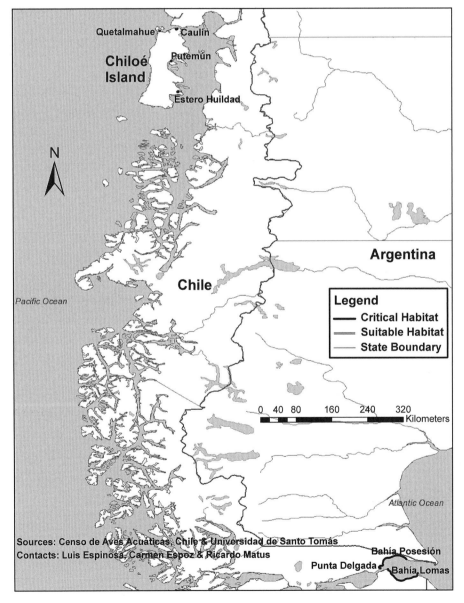

MAP 1. Critical habitat in Chile.

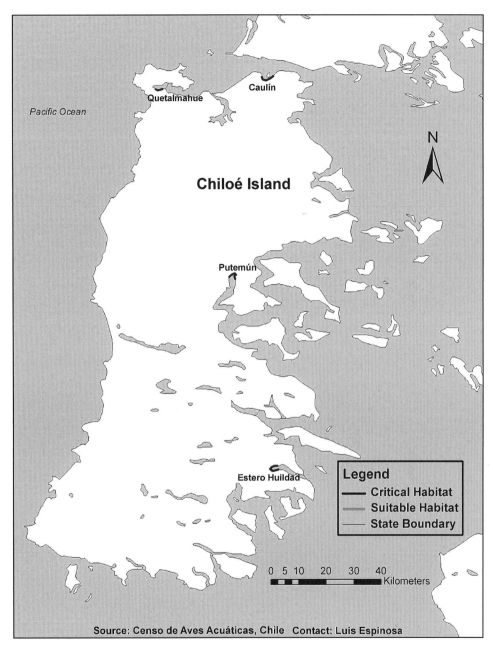

MAP 2. Critical habitat in Chiloé Island.

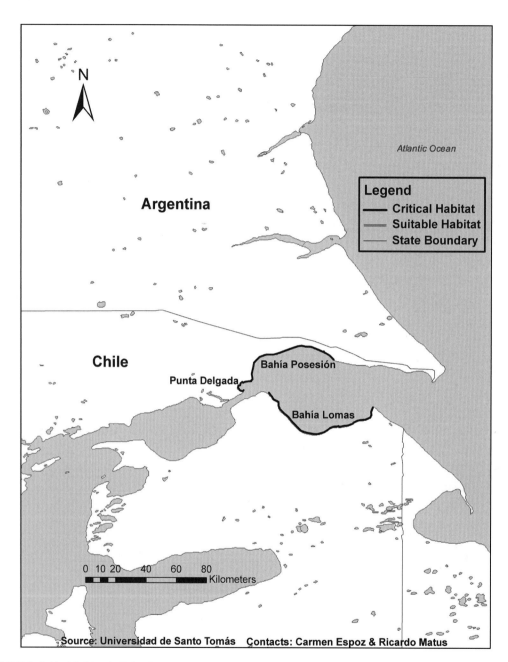

MAP 3. Critical habitat in Bahía Lomas.

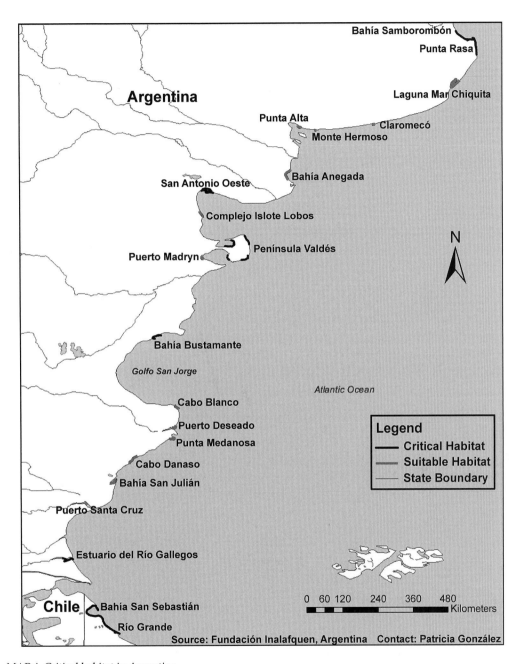

MAP 4. Critical habitat in Argentina.

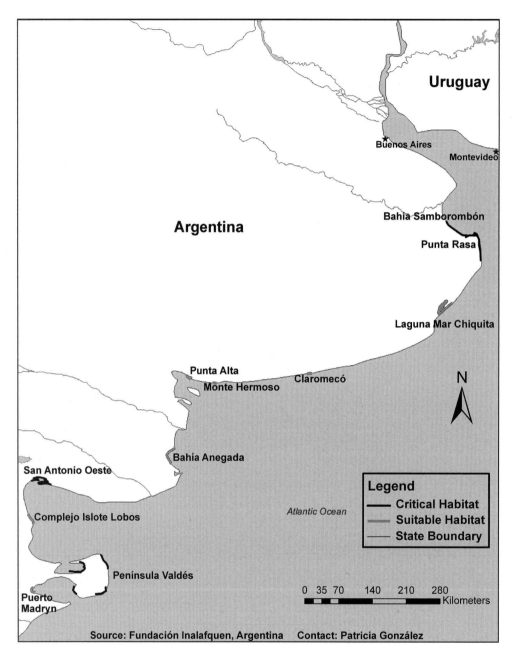

MAP 5. Critical habitat in northern Argentina.

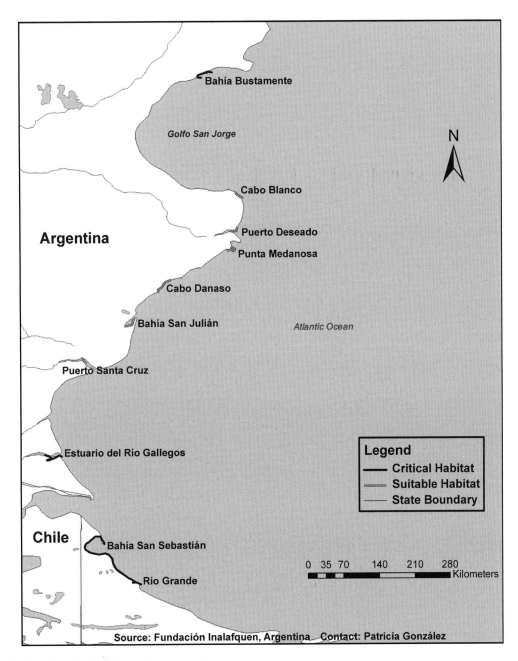

MAP 6. Critical habitat in southern Argentina.

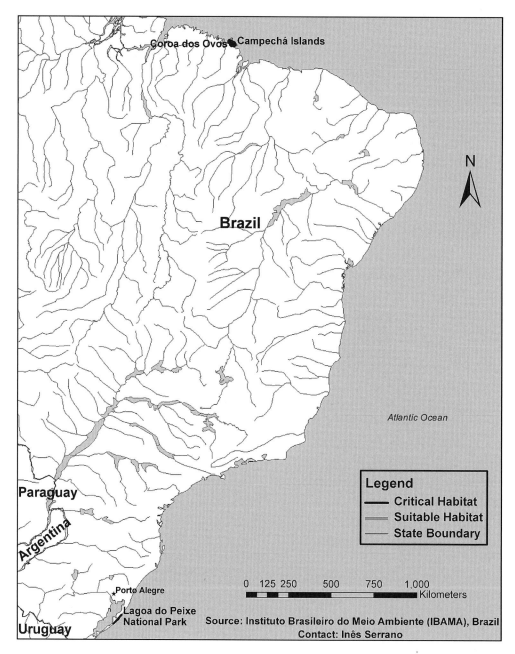

MAP. 7. Critical habitat in Brazil.

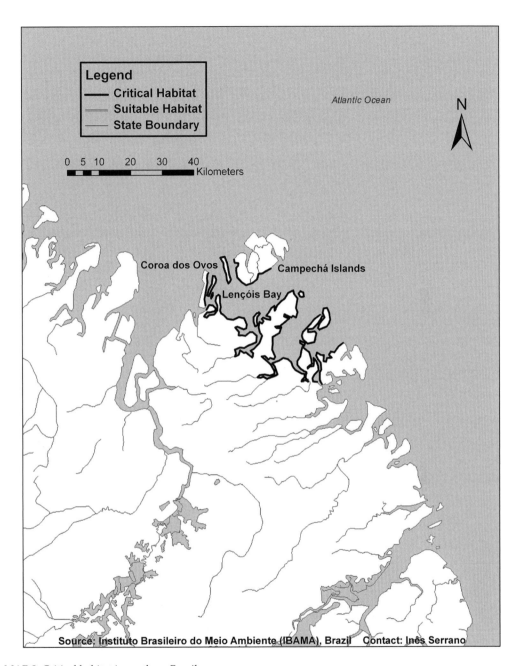

MAP 8. Critical habitat in northern Brazil.

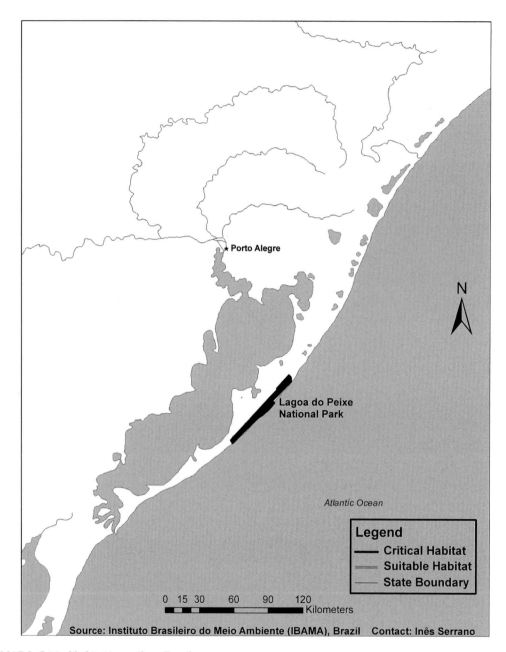

MAP 9. Critical habitat in southern Brazil.

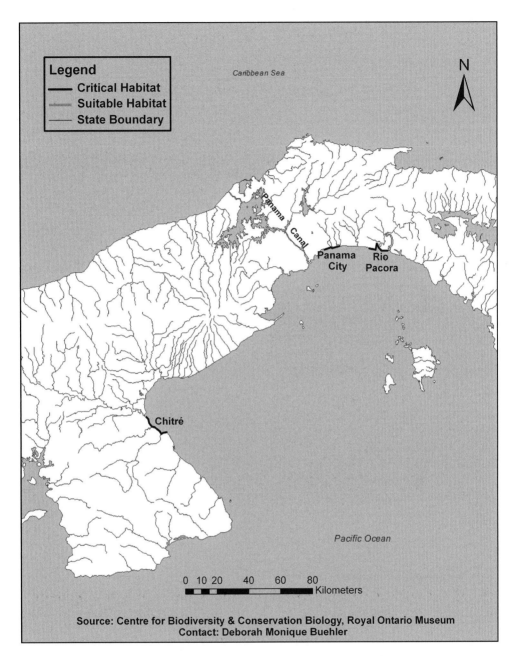

MAP. 10. Critical habitat in Panama.

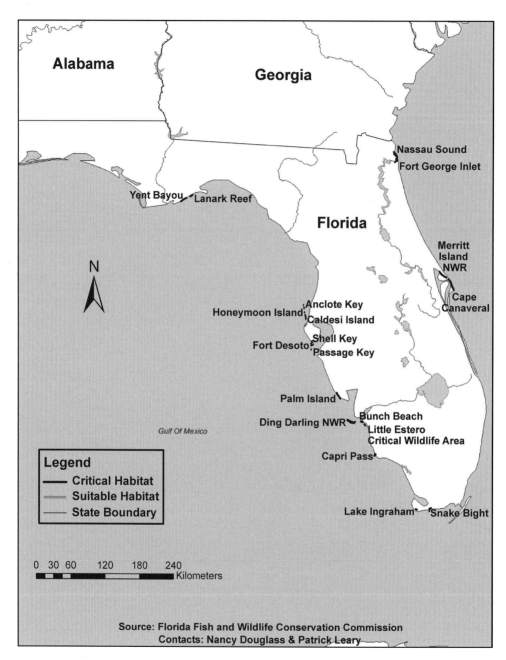

MAP 11. Critical habitat in Florida.

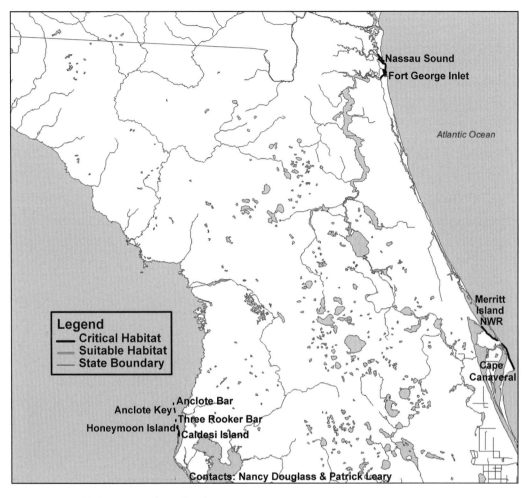

MAP 12. Critical habitat in northern Florida.

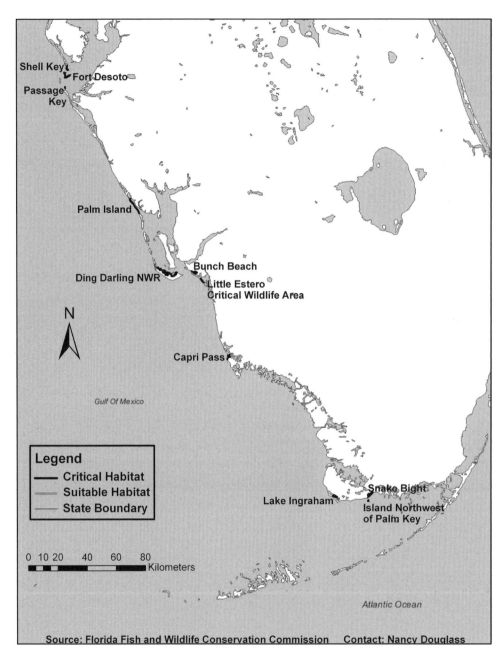

MAP 13. Critical habitat in southern Florida.

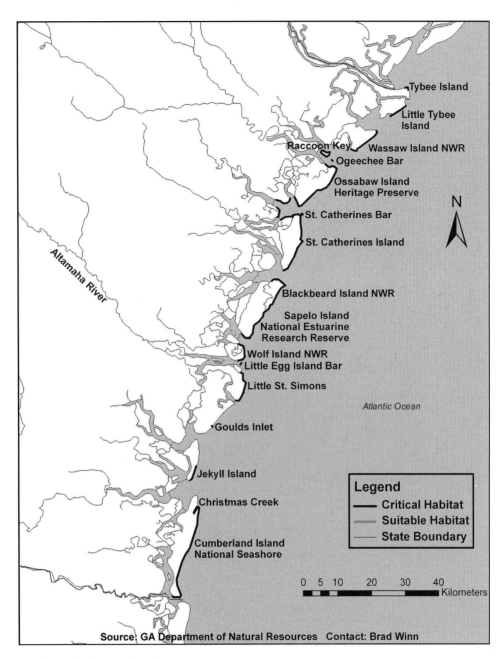

MAP 14. Critical habitat in Georgia.

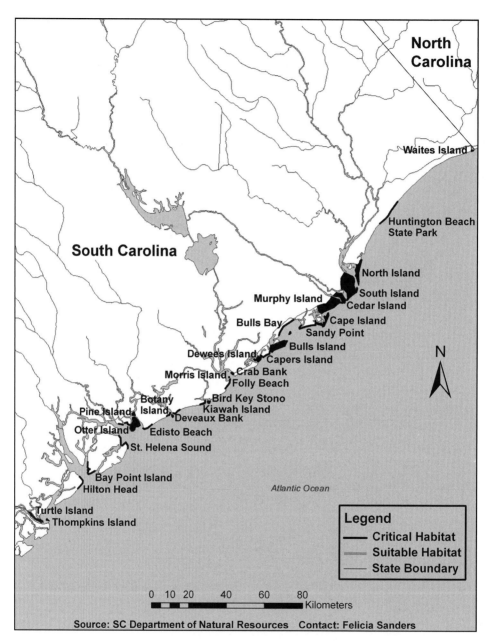

MAP 15. Critical habitat in South Carolina.

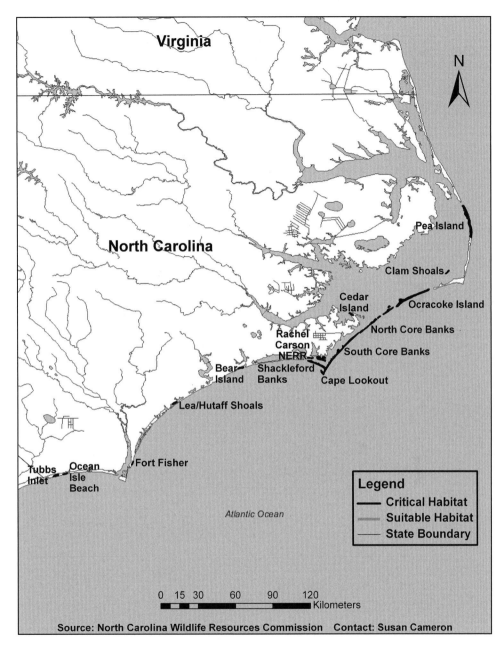

MAP 16. Critical habitat in North Carolina.

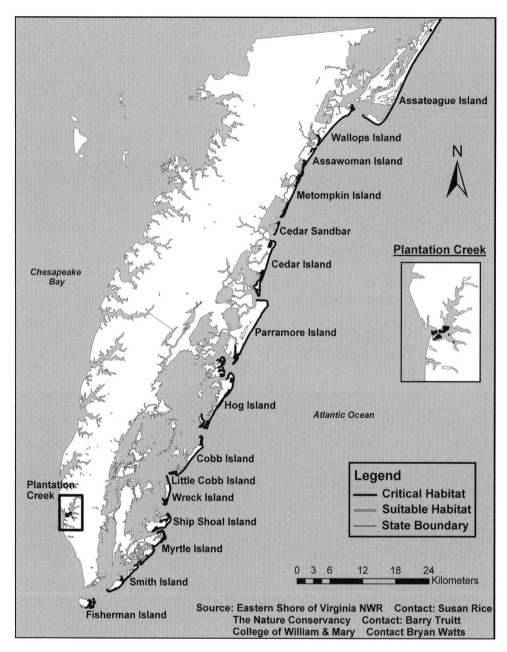

MAP 17. Critical habitat in Virginia.

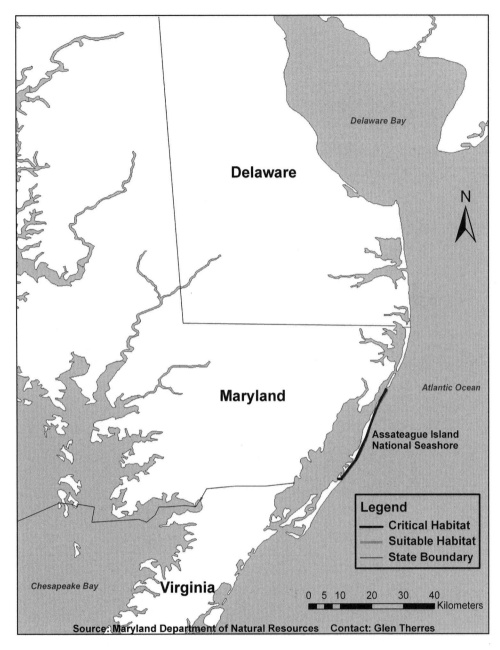

MAP 18. Critical habitat in Maryland.

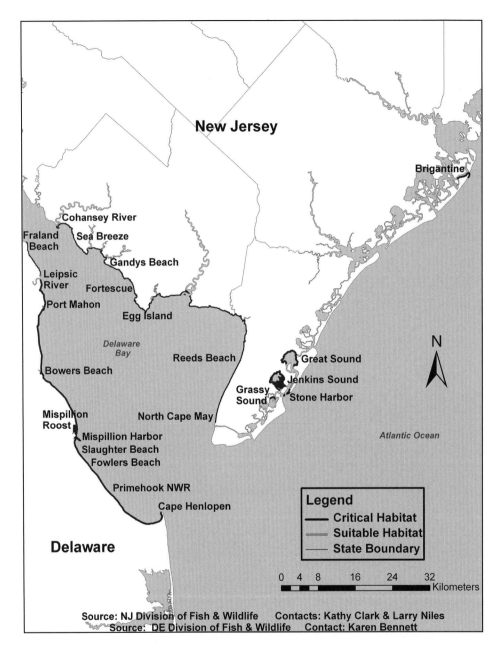

MAP 19. Critical habitat in Delaware Bay in spring.

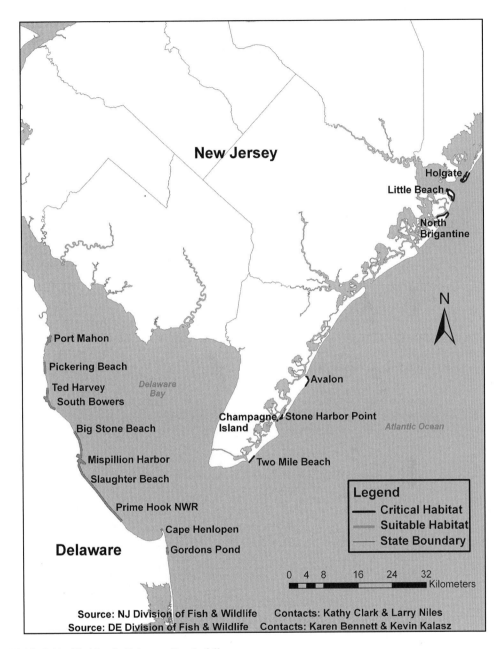

MAP 20. Critical habitat in Delaware Bay in fall.

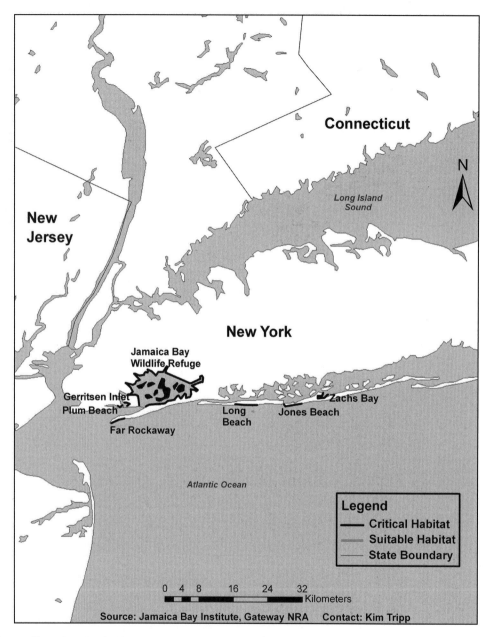

MAP. 21. Critical habitat in New York.

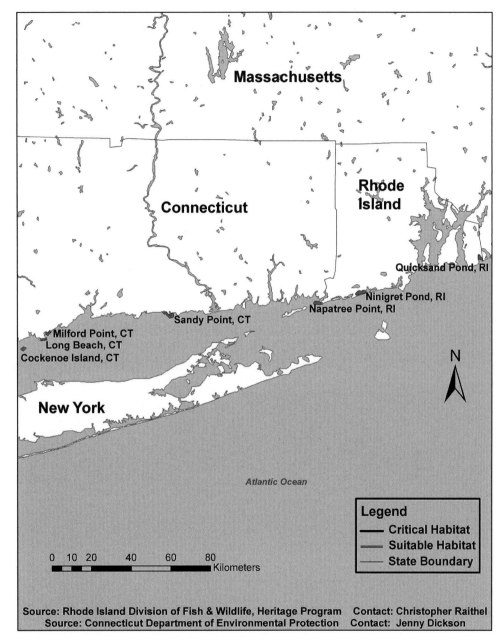

MAP 22. Critical habitat in Connecticut and Rhode Island.

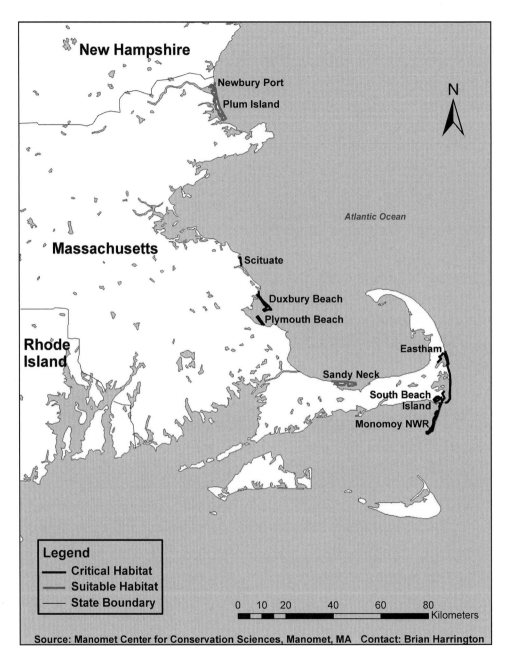

MAP 23. Critical habitat in Massachusetts.

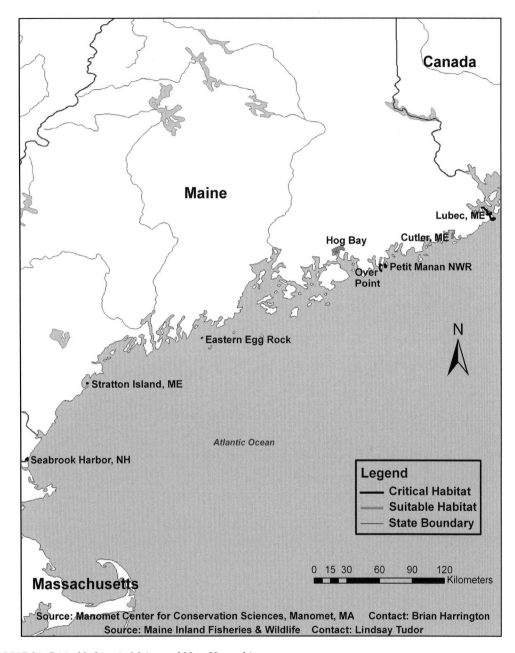

MAP 24. Critical habitat in Maine and New Hampshire.

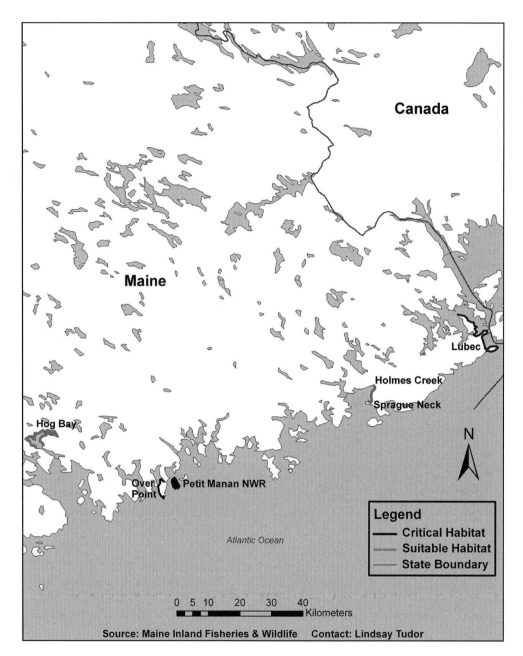

MAP. 25. Critical habitat in northern Maine.

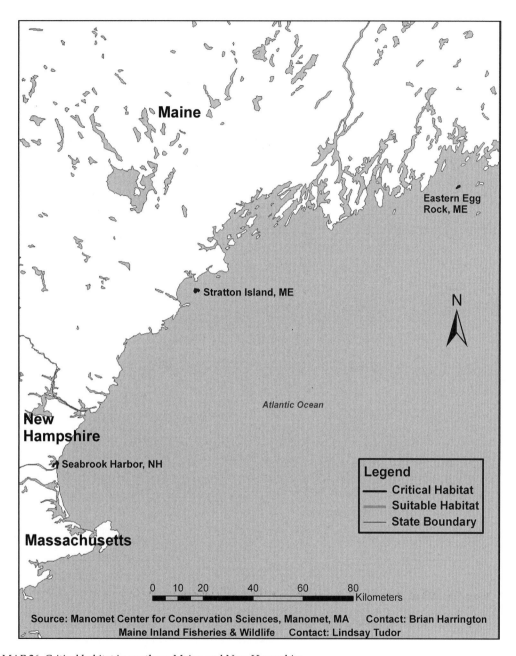

MAP 26. Critical habitat in southern Maine and New Hampshire.

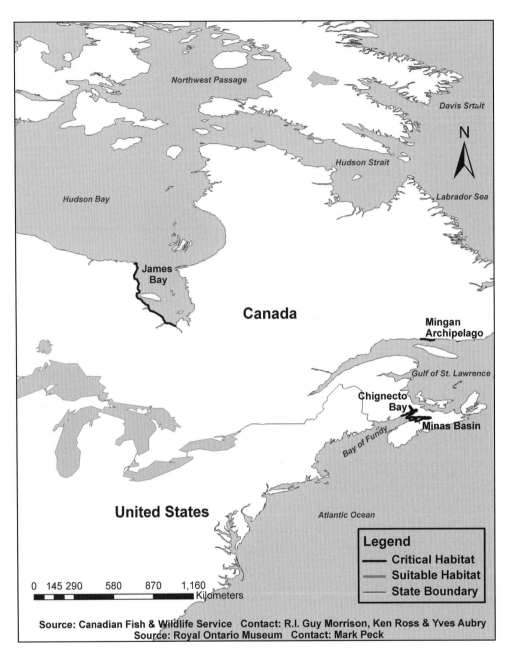

MAP 27. Critical habitat in Canada.

APPENDIX 2. PEAK COUNTS OF RED KNOTS DURING SPRING AND FALL MIGRATION AT VARIOUS SITES IN FLORIDA. INTERSTITIAL PERIODS NOT INCLUDED. ISS = INTERNATIONAL SHOREBIRD SURVEY.

	Fall Migration (1 Jul–31 Oct)				Spring Migration (1 Apr–10 Jun)		
Location	Peak Count	Year	Source	Location	Peak Count	Year	Source
5 Phosphate Mines	1	1992	ISS	5 Phosphate Mines	-	-	-
Alligator Point	132	1988	ISS	Alligator Point	-	-	-
Anclote Key	-	-	-	Anclote Key	-	-	-
Bald Point	10	1975	ISS	Bald Point	1	1981	ISS
	1	1977	ISS		4	1982	ISS
	6	1979	ISS		15	1983	ISS
	2	1981	ISS		11	1993	ISS
	5	1993	ISS		49	1993	ISS
	1	1994	ISS		87	1994	ISS
					15	1995	ISS
Bayway and	2	1975	ISS	Bayway and	-	-	-
Ft. Desoto	9	1976	ISS	Ft. Desoto			
Bell Glade	1	1977	ISS	Bell Glade	-	-	-
Farm	2	1980	ISS	Farm			
Caladesi Island	-	-	-	Caladesi Island	-	-	-
Cape Romano	15	1980	ISS	Cape Romano	25	1981	ISS
	95	1981	ISS		55	1982	ISS
	1,375	1982	ISS		1,050	1983	ISS
	1,300	1983	ISS		414	1984	ISS
	1,530	1984	ISS		300	1985	ISS
	1,250	1985	ISS		690	1986	ISS
	1,250	1986	ISS		1,205	1987	ISS
	915	1987	ISS		420	1988	ISS
	1,348	1988	ISS		1,000	1989	ISS
Cape San Blas	6	1981	ISS	Cape San Blas	16	1999	ISS
	8	1988	ISS				
Capri Pass	-	-	-	Capri Pass	-	-	-
Carl Ross Key	-	-	-	Carl Ross Key	-	-	-
Carrabelle	160	1988	ISS	Carrabelle	109	1993	ISS
Beach (CB)	98	1992	ISS	Beach	6	1994	ISS
	102	1993	ISS		90	1995	ISS
	6	1994	ISS				
	50	1995	ISS				
CB Lighthouse	64	1995	ISS				
CB W picnic	45	1993	ISS				
Casey Key	72	1977	ISS	Casey Key	5	1978	ISS
Beach	41	1978	ISS	Beach	21	1980	ISS
	460	1979	ISS		168	1981	ISS
	31	1981	ISS		7	1982	ISS
	13	1983	ISS		34	1983	ISS
CC Causeway	7	1977	ISS	CC Causeway	-	-	-
Clear Springs	-	-	-	Clear Springs	1	1981	ISS
Crooked Island	-	-	-	Crooked Island	-	-	-
Ding Darling NWR	28	1999	ISS	Ding Darling NWR	14	2003	ISS
Dunedin	-	-	-	Dunedin	-	-	-
East of Bay North	-	-	-	East of Bay North	-	-	-
Englewood	-	-	-	Englewood	-	-	-
FSU Marine Lab	-	-	-	FSU Marine Lab	27	1993	ISS
					4	1994	ISS
Ft. Desoto	800	1999	B. A.Harrington, (unpubl. data)	Ft. Desoto	-	-	-
	330	2004	B. A. Harrington, (unpubl. data)				
Ft. George Inlet	500	2003	B. A. Harrington, (unpubl. data)	Ft. George Inlet	1,500	2004	B. A. Harrington, (unpubl. data)

APPENDIX 2. CONTINUED.

Fall Migration (1 Jul–31 Oct)				Spring Migration (1 Apr–10 Jun)			
Location	Peak Count	Year	Source	Location	Peak Count	Year	Source
Ft. Myers	351	1999	B. A. Harrington, (unpubl. data)	F.t Myers Beach	-	-	-
	400	2003	B. A. Harrington, (unpubl. data)				
Ft. Myers North	800	1999	B. A. Harrington, (unpubl. data)				
Ft. Pierce Inlet	2	1978	ISS	Ft. Pierce Inlet	-	-	-
	2	1979	ISS				
	5	1982	ISS				
Georgestone State Park	20	1979	ISS	Georgestone State Park	-	-	-
Hickory Mound Impound	-	-	-	Hickory Mound Impound	-	-	-
Honeymoon Island	4	1986	ISS	Honeymoon Island	200	1987	ISS
	8	1987	ISS		500	1988	ISS
	500	1989	ISS		250	1990	ISS
	40	1990	ISS		450	1993	ISS
	800	1992	ISS		500	1994	ISS
	500	1993	ISS		450	1995	ISS
	1,500	1994	ISS		20	1996	ISS
	700	1995	ISS		200	1997	ISS
	400	1996	ISS		350	1998	ISS
	400	1997	ISS		10	1999	ISS
	550	1998	ISS		180	2000	ISS
	1,100	1999	ISS		240	2001	ISS
	1,750	2000	ISS		146	2002	ISS
	360	2001	ISS		250	2003	ISS
	162	2002	ISS				
	1,140	2003	ISS				
(Honeymoon Isl. South Beach	12	1992	ISS				
Hooker's Point	200	1979	ISS	Hooker's Point	300	1980	ISS
	10	1980	ISS				
Hugenot State Park, Ward's Bank	2	1977	ISS	Hugenot State Park, Ward's Bank	35	1980	ISS
	5	1978	ISS				
	400	1979	ISS				
	2,069	1980	ISS				
Island N Bunces Pass	-	-	-	Island N Bunces Pass	-	-	-
Kennedy Space Center	-	-	-	Kennedy Space Center	-	-	-
Lake Ingraham	-	-	-	Lake Ingraham	-	-	-
Lake Woodruff NWR	-	-	-	Lake Woodruff NWR	1	2003	ISS
Lanark Reef	-	-	-	Lanark Reef	-	-	-
Lido Beach	-	-	-	Lido Beach	-	-	-
Little Estero	-	-	-	Little Estero	-	-	-
Longboat Key	1,700	1977	ISS	Longboat Key	39	1981	ISS
	700	1979	ISS		2	1982	ISS
	1,300	1981	ISS		60	1983	ISS
	750	1982	ISS				
	250	1983	ISS				
	400	1999	B. A. Harrington, (unpubl. data)				
Marco Island, Tigertail Beach	-	-	-	Marco Island, Tigertail Beach	-	-	-
Marco River	300	1974	ISS	Marco River	258	1981	ISS
	80	1975	ISS		138	1982	ISS

APPENDIX 2. CONTINUED.

Fall Migration (1 Jul–31 Oct)				Spring Migration (1 Apr–10 Jun)			
Location	Peak Count	Year	Source	Location	Peak Count	Year	Source
Marco River	70	1976	ISS	Marco River	500	1983	ISS
(continued)	120	1977	ISS	(continued)	600	1984	ISS
	410	1978	ISS		474	1985	ISS
	300	1979	ISS		450	1986	ISS
	216	1980	ISS		360	1987	ISS
	298	1981	ISS		353	1988	ISS
	279	1982	ISS		172	1989	ISS
	247	1983	ISS				
	291	1984	ISS				
	1,211	1985	ISS				
	598	1986	ISS				
	301	1987	ISS				
	282	1988	ISS				
Mayport Naval Stn., Jetties Beach	1	2003	ISS	Mayport Naval Stn., Jetties Beach	-	-	-
Mckay Bay, Tampa	-	-	-	Mckay Bay, Tampa	80	1993	ISS
Merritt Island NWR (10D)	-	-	-	Merritt Island NWR (10D)	-	-	-
N. Sarasota Bay	1	1978	ISS	N. Sarasota Bay	-	-	-
Naples	10	1981	ISS	Naples	33	1981	ISS
					1	1982	ISS
Nassau Sound	15	2004	B. A. Harrington, (unpubl. data)	Nassau Sound	-	-	-
Nevarre Beach, Pensacola	7	1977	ISS	Nevarre Beach, Pensacola	-	-	-
New Smyrna Beach	6	1975	ISS	New Smyrna Beach	-	-	-
Palm Island Resort	-	-	-	Palm Island Resort	-	-	-
Palm Key	-	-	-	Palm Key	-	-	-
Passage Key	-	-	-	Passage Key	-	-	-
Phipps Preserve	-	-	-	Phipps Preserve	-	-	-
Port Orange Spoil Islands	-	-	-	Port Orange Spoil Islands	-	-	-
Sanibel Island	292	1975	ISS	Sanibel Island	41	1986	ISS
	198	1979	ISS	Ramada to	10	1988	ISS
	150	2001	B. A. Harrington, (unpubl. data)	Lighthouse	200	1989	ISS
					109	1990	ISS
					200	1992	ISS
Sarasota	550	1981	Harrington and Leddy (1982)	Sarasota	-	-	-
Shell Island Inlet, W	-	-	-	Shell Island Inlet, W	3	1993	ISS
Snake Bight	-	-	-	Snake Bight	-	-	-
S.t Marks NWR	2	1988	ISS	St. Marks NWR	-	-	-
	4	1993	ISS				
St. Petersburg	800	1981	Harrington and Leddy 1982	St. Petersburg	-	-	-
	450	1999	B. A. Harrington, (unpubl. data)				
St. Vincent NWR	75	1988	ISS	St. Vincent NWR	22	1988	ISS
					7	2000	ISS
					120	2001	ISS

APPENDIX 2. CONTINUED.

Fall Migration (1 Jul–31 Oct)				Spring Migration (1 Apr–10 Jun)			
Location	Peak Count	Year	Source	Location	Peak Count	Year	Source
St. George	25	1978	ISS	St. George	7	1981	ISS
Island	11	1979	ISS	Island	4	1983	ISS
	3	1982	ISS				
Three Rooker Bar				Three Rooker Bar			
Turkey Point	-	-	-	Turkey Point	1	1993	ISS
Venice	6	1977	ISS	Venice	-	-	-
	9	1978	ISS				
West Lake				West Lake			
Virginia Key	26	1984	ISS	Virginia Key	10	1985	ISS
mudflats	8	1985	ISS	Mudflats			
	17	1986	ISS				
sewage	12	1984	ISS				
sewage	5	1985	ISS				
sewage	6	1986	ISS				
Yent Bayou	2	1994	Sprandel et al. (1997)	Yent Bayou	22	1994	Sprandel et al. (1997)

APPENDIX 3. PEAK COUNTS OF RED KNOTS DURING WINTER AT VARIOUS SITES IN FLORIDA. INTERSTITIAL PERIODS NOT INCLUDED. ISS = INTERNATIONAL SHOREBIRD SURVEY.

Location	Winter (1 Nov –28 Feb)		
	Peak count	Year	Source
5 Phosphate Mines	1	1990	ISS
Alligator Point	62	1988	ISS
	42	1989	ISS
North Anclote Key	1	1993	Sprandel et al. (1997)
	12	1994	Sprandel et al. (1997)
South Anclote Key	53	1994	Sprandel et al. (1997)
Bald Point	20	1977	ISS
	16	1994	ISS
Bayway and Ft Desoto	-	-	-
Bell Glade Farm	-	-	-
North Caladesi Island	300	1994	Sprandel et al. (1997)
Dunedin Pass	165	1994	Sprandel et al. (1997)
Cape Romano	600	1980	ISS
	902	1981	ISS
	1,025	1982	ISS
	1,625	1983	ISS
	1,800	1984	ISS
	2,000	1985	ISS
	1,410	1987	ISS
	1,170	1988	ISS
	650	1989	ISS
	200	2003	B. A. Harrington (unpubl. data)
Morgan Beach	1,550	1993	ISS
Cape San Blas	37	1988	ISS
	120	1993	ISS
Capri Pass	30	1993	ISS
	286	1994	Sprandel et al. (1997)
Carl Ross Key	4	1993	ISS
Carrabelle Beach	203	1992	ISS
	114	1993	ISS
	69	1994	Sprandel et al. (1997)
	105	1995	ISS
	24	1996	ISS
Casey Key Beach	300	1977	ISS
	195	1978	ISS
	6,500	1979	ISS
	402	1980	ISS
	365	1981	ISS
	200	1983	ISS
	844	1984	ISS
CC Causeway	20	1977	ISS
	39	1994	Sprandel et al. (1997)
	19	1994	ISS
Clear Springs Phosphate Mine	-	-	-
Crooked Island	4	1993	ISS
Ding Darling NWR	1,000	1990	ISS
	30	1994	Sprandel et al. (1997)
	35	2000	ISS
	31	2003	ISS
Dunedin	3,000	2001	B. A. Harrington (unpubl. data)
East of Bay North	1	1993	ISS
	5	1995	ISS
Englewood	1,125	1982	Harrington and Leddy (1982)
FSU Marine Lab	1	1978	ISS
Ft. Desoto	400	2003	B. A. Harrington (unpubl. data)
	125	2004	B. A. Harrington (unpubl. data)
Ft. Desoto East and North	9	1994	Sprandel et al. (1997)

APPENDIX 3. CONTINUED.

	Winter (1 Nov –28 Feb)		
Location	Peak count	Year	Source
Ft. Desoto North	6	1993	ISS
Ft. George Inlet	-	-	-
Ft. Myers Lagoon	30	1993	ISS
Ft. Pierce Inlet	1	1979	ISS
Georgestone State Park	16	1979	ISS
Hickory Mound Impoundment	15	1995	ISS
Honeymoon Island	10	1986	ISS
	30	1988	ISS
	200	1989	ISS
	100	1990	ISS
	1,000	1992	ISS
	1,520	1993	ISS
	1,500	1994	ISS
	2,300	1995	ISS
	1,000	1996	ISS
	300	1997	ISS
	400	1998	ISS
	700	1999	ISS
	550	2000	ISS
	300	2001	ISS
	140	2002	ISS
	191	2003	ISS
	4	2004	ISS
Honeymoon Island north of toll booth	1	1993	ISS
Hooker's Point, Tampa	-	-	-
Hugenot State Park, Ward's Bank	402	1977	ISS
	603	1978	ISS
	156	1979	ISS
	500	1980	ISS
	4	1980	ISS
	2	1981	ISS
Island N Bunces Pass	280	1994	Sprandel et al. (1997)
Kennedy Space Center	2	1994	Sprandel et al. (1997)
Lake Ingraham	10	1993	Sprandel et al. (1997)
	122	1994	Sprandel et al. (1997)
Lake Woodruff NWR	-	-	-
Lanark Reef	212	1993	ISS
	147	1994	Sprandel et al. (1997)
Lido Beach	7	1994	Sprandel et al. (1997)
Little Estero	241	1993	Sprandel et al. (1997)
	164	1994	Sprandel et al. (1997)
Longboat Key	1,400	1982	Harrington and Leddy (1982)
	3,000	2000	B. A. Harrington (unpubl. data)
	2,300	2004	B. A. Harrington (unpubl. data)
North Longboat Key	100	1977	ISS
	2,000	1978	ISS
	1,000	1979	ISS
	700	1980	ISS
	550	1981	ISS
	140	1993	ISS
Beer Can Island	100	1977	ISS
Beer Can Island	100	1978	ISS
Marco Island, Tigertail Beach	25	1993	ISS
Marco River	150	1974	ISS
	20	1975	ISS
	5	1976	ISS
	1	1977	ISS

APPENDIX 3. CONTINUED.

Location	Winter (1 Nov –28 Feb)		
	Peak count	Year	Source
Marco River	100	1978	ISS
(continued)	35	1979	ISS
	60	1980	ISS
	130	1981	ISS
	89	1982	ISS
	70	1983	ISS
	25	1984	ISS
	487	1985	ISS
	490	1986	ISS
	2	1986	ISS
	800	1987	ISS
	275	1988	ISS
	200	1989	ISS
Mayport Naval Station, Jetties Beach	-	-	-
Mckay Bay, Tampa	-	-	-
Merritt Island NWR 10D	9	1999	ISS
	140	2002	ISS
Merritt Island NWR			
Black Point Dr	31	1993	ISS
	164	1994	Sprandel et al. (1997)
Merritt Island NWR			
T10B	53	1999	ISS
	3	2000	ISS
	7	2002	ISS
	47	1999	ISS
N. Sarasota Bay	-	-	-
Naples	19	1981	ISS
	12	1982	ISS
Nassau Sound	-	-	-
Nevarre Beach, Pensacola	-	-	-
New Smyrna Beach	-	-	-
Palm Island Resort	1	1993	Sprandel et al. (1997)
	223	1994	Sprandel et al. (1997)
Palm Key	22	1993	ISS
	65	1994	Sprandel et al. (1997)
Passage Key	300	1994	Sprandel et al. (1997)
Phipps Preserve	42	1993	ISS
Port Orange Spoil Islands	6	1993	ISS
Sanibel Island A	50	1980	ISS
	75	2004	B. A. Harrington (unpubl. data)
Sarasota	900	1981	Harrington and Leddy (1982)
	4,200	1981	Harrington and Leddy (1982)
	200	2004	B. A. Harrington (unpubl. data)
Shell Key	775	1994	Sprandel et al. (1997)
	3,000	2000	B. A. Harrington (unpubl. data)
	3,000	2001	B. A. Harrington (unpubl. data)
Snake Bight	120	1993	ISS
	60	1994	Sprandel et al. (1997)
St Marks NWR	10	1989	ISS
(Lighthouse)	10	1988	ISS
(Lighthouse)	3	1993	ISS
St. Petersburg	325	2004	B. A. Harrington (unpubl. data)
St. Vincent Island - Indian Pass	15	1994	ISS
St.George Island	80	1978	ISS
	1	1982	ISS
	3	1983	ISS
Three Rooker Bar (North)	59	1994	Sprandel et al. (1997)
(Southeast)	20	1994	Sprandel et al. (1997)
Turkey Point	-	-	-

APPENDIX 3. CONTINUED.

Location	Winter (1 Nov –28 Feb)		
	Peak count	Year	Source
Venice	125	1977	ISS
	11	1978	ISS
	56	1979	ISS
West Lake	1	1994	ISS
Virginia Key Mudflats	-	-	-
Yent Bayou	31	1993	ISS
	116	1994	Sprandel et al. (1997)
	81	1995	ISS
	118	1996	ISS

APPENDIX 4. SUMMARY TABLE OF LAND OWNERSHIP AND EXISTING HABITAT PROTECTION FOR POPULATIONS OF RED KNOTS IN THE WESTERN HEMISPHERE.

Country and province/state	Area	Ownership	Approximate percent of habitat under protection
Chile			
Region XII-Magellanes y la Antártica Chilena	Bahía Lomas	1. Federal—Chilean Navy—Dirección del Territorio Marítimo y Marina Mercante 2. Private	100%
Argentina			
Tierra del Fuego	Río Grande	1. Reserva Costa Atlántica de Tierra del Fuego 2. Private	100%
	Bahía San Sebastián	1. Reserva Costa Atlántica de Tierra del Fuego 2. Private	100%
Santa Cruz	Río Gallegos Estuary	1. Reserva Urbana Costera del Río Chico 2. Reserva Provincial de Río Chico Para Aves Playeras Migratorias	100%
Chubut	Bahía Bustamante	1. Public 2. Private	100%
	Península Valdés	1. Public 2. Private	100%
Río Negro	San Antonio Oeste	Bahía San Antonio Natural Protected Area	100%
Buenos Aires	Bahía Samborombón	1. Provincial Integral Natural Reserve with restricted access 2. Provincial Integral Natural Reserve Rincón de Ajó 3. Campos del Tuyú Private Reserve- Fundación Vida Silvestre Argentina 4. Punta Rasa Biological Station—(Argentinean Navy) and the Fundación Vida Silvestre Argentina 5. Punta Rasa Traveled Municipal Ecological Reserve	100%
Brazil			
Maranhão	Baía de Turiaçu	Protected Environmental Area of Reentrâncias Maranhenses	~50%
	Baía dos Lençóis	Protected environmental area of Reentrâncias Maranhenses	~50%
Río Grande do Sul	Lagoa do Peixe National Park	1. Instituto Brasileiro do Meio Ambiente e dos Recursos Naturais Renováveis 2. Municipal- São José do Norte, Mostardas and Tavare	2,971.44 ha, or 8.6% of total area
United States			
Franklin County Florida	Yent Bayou	Private land—part of the Hidden Beaches and Victorian Village developments	0%
	Carrabelle Beach	State and county land	
	Lanark Reef	State and private land	~50%
Brevard County Florida	Merritt Island NWR-Black Point Drive	USFWS	100%
	Kennedy Space Center	NASA	100%
Pinellas County Florida	Anclote Key	Florida Park Service	100%
	Three Rooker Bar	Florida Park Service	100%
	Honeymoon Island	Florida Park Service	100%
	Caladesi Island-Hurricane Pass	Florida Park Service	100%

APPENDIX 4. CONTINUED.

Country and province/state	Area	Ownership	Approximate percent of habitat under protection
	Caladesi Island-Dunedin Pass	Florida Park Service	100%
	Courtney Campbell Causeway SE	Department of Transportation	0%
	Shell Key	Owned by the state of Florida but leased by Pinellas County	100%
	Island north of Bunces Pass	Owned by the state of Florida but leased by Pinellas County	100%
	Fort Desoto- NW end	Pinellas County	~50%
	Fort Desoto- east end	Pinellas County	~50%
	Passage Key	USFWS	100%
Sarasota County Florida	Lido Beach	Sarasota County	0%
	Palm Island	State and private resort	~50%
Lee County Florida	Ding Darling NWR-Back bay of Sanibel Is.	USFWS	~50%
	Little Estero Island	State	100%
Collier County Florida	Capri Pass (Key Island)	State and federal	~50%
Monroe County Florida	Lake Ingraham- SE end	National Park Service (NPS)	100%
	Snake Bite Channel	NPS	100%
	Area NW of Palm Key	NPS	100%
Chatham County Georgia	Little Tybee Island	State government	~50%
	Wassaw Island	Federal government	100%
	Ogeeche River Bar	State government	100%
Bryan County Georgia	Ossabaw Island	State government	100%
Liberty County Georgia	St. Catherines Island	Private—St. Catherines Island Foundation	100%
	St. Catherines Bar	State	100%
	Grass Island	State	100%
McIntosh County Georgia	Blackbeard Island	Federal government	100%
	Sapelo Island	State government	100%
	Wolf Island	Federal government	100%
	Little Egg Island Bar	State government	100%
Glynn County Georgia	Little St. Simons Island	Private—resort	~50%
	Sea Island	Private	0%
	St. Simons Island-Gould's Inlet	Municipality	0%
	Jekyll Island	State park	~50%
Camden County Georgia	Little Cumberland Island	Private	~50%
	Cumberland Island	Federal government	100%
Horray County South Carolina	Waites Island	State—coastal Carolina University segment	~50%
	Myrtle Beach State Park	State	~50%
Georgetown County South Carolina	Huntington Beach State Park	State	~50%
	North Island	State—Tom Yawkey Wildlife Center South Carolina Department of Natural Resources (SCDNR) Heritage Preserve	100%
	Sand/South Island	State—Tom Yawkey Wildlife Center SCDNR Heritage Preserve	100%
	Cedar Island	State—SCDNR Santee Coastal Reserve	100%

APPENDIX 4. CONTINUED.

Country and province/state	Area	Ownership	Approximate percent of habitat under protection
Charleston County South Carolina	Murphy Island	State—SCDNR Santee Coastal Reserve	100%
	Cape/Lighthouse Islands National	Federal— Cape Romain Wildlife Refuge (NWR)	100%
	Raccoon Key	Federal—Cape Romain NWR	100%
	Bull Island	Federal—Cape Romain NWR	100%
	Capers Island	State—SCDNR Heritage Preserve	100%
	Isle of Palms County Park	County	~50%
	Folly Beach County Park north end	County	~50%
	Folly Beach County Park south end	County	~50%
	Beachwalker County Park at Kiawah Island	County	~50%
	Botany Bay Island	Private—conservation easement held by SC Nature Conservancy	100%
	Botany Bay Plantation (Edisto Island)	State	100%
Colleton County South Carolina	Edisto Beach State Park	State	100%
	Pine Island	State—SCDNR	100%
	Otter Island	State—SCDNR Heritage Preserve	100%
Beaufort County South Carolina	Hunting Island State Park	State	100%
	Pritchards Island	State—University of South Carolina	100%
	St. Phillips Island	Private—conservation easement held by SC Nature Conservancy	100%
Jasper County South Carolina	Turtle Island	State—SCDNR Heritage Preserve	100%
Dare County North Carolina	Pea Island	Federal—NWR	100%
	Clam Shoal	Private—remote due to remote nature	100%
Hyde County North Carolina	Cape Hatteras National Seashore	Federal—NPS	100%
Carteret County North Carolina	Bird Shoals	State—NC National Estuarine Research Reserve	100%
Rachel Carson	State—NC National Estuarine Research Reserve	100%	
	Cape Lookout National Seashore	Federal—NPS	100%
Onslow County North Carolina	Bear Island/Bogue Inlet	State—NC State Parks	100%
Brunswick County North Carolina	Tubbs Inlet	1. Private—not protected 2. State	~50%
Accomack County Virginia	Assateague Island	Chincoteague National Wildlife Refuge (CNWR)	100%
	Wallops Island	NASA	100%
	Assawoman Island	CNWR	100%
	Metompkin Island	1. TNC 2. CNWR	100%
	Cedar Island	1. CNWR 2. TNC	80%
	Parramore Island	1. TNC 2. Virginia Department of Conservation and Recreation (VDCR)	100%
Northampton County, Virginia	Hog Island	TNC	95%
	Cobb Island	TNC	100%

APPENDIX 4. CONTINUED.

Country and province/state	Area	Ownership	Approximate percent of habitat under protection
	Little Cobb Island	TNC	100%
	Wreck Island	VDCR—Division of Natural Heritage	100%
	Ship Shoal Island	TNC	100%
	Myrtle Island	TNC	100%
	Smith Island	TNC	100%
	Fisherman Island	Fisherman's Island NWR	100%
Baltimore County Maryland	Hart-Miller Island	State- Maryland State Park	100%
Talbot County Maryland	Poplar Island	1. U.S. Army Corps of Engineers 2. MD Port Administration	100%
Worcester County Maryland	Assateague Island	1. Assateague Island National Seashore—NPS 2. Chincoteague NWR 3. Assateague State Park—Maryland Department of Natural Resources	100%
Kent County Delaware	Bombay Hook	Federal—NWR	100%
	Port Mahon	State	0%
	Little Creek Wildlife Area	State	100%
	Ted Harvey Wildlife Area	State	100%
	Pickering beach	Private—not protected	0%
	Kitts Hummock	Private—not protected	0%
	North Bowers Beach	Private—not protected	0%
	South Bowers Beach	Private—not protected	0%
	Bennetts Pier	Delaware Wildlands	100%
	Big Stone Beach-Conch Bar	1. TNC 2. State Private—not protected	75%
	Mispillion Inlet	State and private—not protected	~50%
Sussex County Delaware	Slaughter beach	Private—not protected	0%
	Prime Hook	Federal—NWR	100%
	Cape Henlopen	State Park	100%
Cumberland and Cape May Counties New Jersey	Delaware Bay shoreline	1. Dennis Creek Wildlife Management Area (WMA) 2. Heislerville WMA 3. Egg Island WMA 4. USFWS—Cape May NWR	30%
Cape May County New Jersey	Hereford Inlet	Municipal	0%
Atlantic County New Jersey	Brigantine	North Brigantine Natural Area	50%
NewYork City-Jamaica County New York	Jamaica Bay Wildlife Refuge	1. Federal—Gateway National Recreation Area 2. Private	~50%
Middlesex County Connecticut	Sandy Point	Private	0%
New Haven County Connecticut	Milford Point	Stewart McKinney NWR	100%
Fairfield County Connecticut	Long Beach	Private	0%
	Cockenoe Island	Private	0%
Newport County Rhode Island	Quicksand Pond	Goosewing Beach Preserve	100%
Washington County Rhode Island	Ninigret Pond	Ninigret NWR	100%
	Napatree Point	Napatree Point Conservation Area	100%
Essex County Massachusetts	Plum Island	Federal—NWR	75%

APPENDIX 4. CONTINUED.

Country and province/state	Area	Ownership	Approximate percent of habitat under protection
	Newbury Port	Private—municipal (part of Plum Island)	0%
Plymouth County Massachusetts	Scituate	1. Municipal 2. Private	50%
	Duxbury Beach	1. Private—Duxbury Beach Reservation, Inc. 2. Municipal	~50 %
	Plymouth Beach	1. Private—not protected 2. Municipal	0%
Barnstable County Massachusetts	Nauset Coast Guard Beach	National Park Service—Cape Cod National Seashore	100%
	Sandy Neck	1. Private-TNC 2. Municipal—Town of Barnstable	100%
	South beach Island	1. Federal—Monomoy NWR 2. Municipal	100%
	Monomoy NWR	Federal—USFWS	100%
Rockingham County New Hampshire	Seabrook Harbor Flats and Beaches	1. County and Municipal 2. Private	85%
Washington County Maine	Lubec Flats	Maine Department of Inland Fisheries and Wildlife (MDIFW)	100%
	Sprague Neck and Holmes Bay	U.S. Navy Ecological Reserve—Cutler Naval Station	100%
	West River (Indian River)	1. Private 2. MDIFW	25%
	Mash Harbor	Private—not protected	0%
	Flat Bay	1. Private 2. MDIFW	25%
	Petit Manan Island and Petit Manan Point	Federal—Petit Manan NWR	100%
	Over Point	Private—not protected	0%
	Ship Island	Maine Coastal Island NWR	100%
Hancock County Maine	Hog Bay	Private—farmland	0%
Waldo County Maine	Spruce Island	Private—not protected	0%
Lincoln County Maine	Eastern Egg Rock	MDIFW—managed by National Audubon Society	100%
Cumberland County Maine	Scarborough Marsh	MDIFW	100%
York County Maine	Stratton Island	National Audubon Society	100%
	Bluff Island	National Audubon Society	100%
	Biddeford Pool	Private—not protected	0%
Canada Nunavut	King William Island	Inuit-owned lands (Nunavut Land Claims Agreement)—Canadian Wildlife Service (CWS)	100%
	Southampton Island	1. Inuit-owned lands (Nunavut Land Claims Agreement) 2. CWS—East Bay Bird Sanctuary and Harry Gibbons Bird Sanctuary	100%
Ontario	Western James Bay	Unknown	? %
New Brunswick	Northern Bay of Fundy-Chignecto Bay	Fundy National Park	? %
Nova Scotia	Northern Bay of Fundy-Minas Basin	Boot Island National Wildlife Area	? %